W9-BTL-433

This Book Belongs to

THE READER'S DIGEST

Pleasantville, New York

Dear Reader,

It was like a Christmas gift to us to have so many boys and girls enjoy the first Reader's Digest Treasury for Young Readers and ask for more. So here now is our gift in return -- a new Treasury brimful of brand-new stories and games.

Once again we have chosen from The Reader's Digest stories and articles that we feel sure you'll enjoy. Once again you can travel with your book to faraway places -- to the icy Antarctic and the steaming jungles, to the towering Alps and the far reaches of outer space. There are stories of boys who helped make history, and of girls who lived brave, exciting lives; of animals in the wild, and of beloved pets; of mystery and magic and the wonderful world of science.

If you want to know how to track a deer or collect butterflies, how to make a tom-tom, a balsa glider or beautiful paper snow stars, this is the book for you. There are jokes that will make you laugh, and clever tricks to play on your friends.

We have spent many happy hours making this new Treasury. And we hope -- and believe -- that it will give you, too, many a happy hour.

The Editors

READER'S DIGEST

NEW

Treasury for Young Readers

THE READER'S DIGEST ASSOCIATION
PLEASANTVILLE, NEW YORK

CONTENTS

The condensations and adaptations in this book have been created by The Reader's Digest Association, Incorporated, and are used by permission of and special arrangement with the holders of the respective copyrights

© 1963 by The Reader's Digest Association, Incorporated

First Edition

All rights reserved, including the right to reproduce this book or parts thereof in any form

Library of Congress Catalog Card Number: 63-15938

Printed in the United States of America

Answers:

"RUNAWAY ENGINE ON THE

Out of control, with throttle wide open, No. 1706 roared down the track. This is the exciting story of one of the wildest rides in railroad history

AT 10:29 P.M., on November 12, 1959, a warning bell sounded in HY tower overlooking the sprawling terminal yard of the Jersey Central Railroad in Jersey City, New Jersey. Towerman Joe Hilinski looked up, startled. The bell shouldn't have sounded. No trains were supposed to be moving in the yard. Hilinski spun around to his model board — the twelve-foot track diagram on the wall. Not a track on the board was lighted.

Then a tiny white bulb lighted up on Track 9. Something was coming!

Joe Hilinski peered out into the dark and silent yard. There were no lights. Nothing was moving. He felt his flesh start to creep.

Suddenly he spotted a dark mass, moving fast. As it neared, he made out the shape of a diesel-electric locomotive, with all lights out. He judged from the roaring sound that she was being driven at full throttle.

MAIN LINE!"

BY E. D. FALES, JR.

"She's going to hit the derail," he gasped. This is a heavy iron wedge clamped to one rail. Its job is to derail any runaway car before it can hit the main line.

The locomotive came to the derail — and the impossible happened. She went right over it. Each wheel sprang eight inches into the air and landed back on the rail. Then the engine blasted out on Main Line Track 3.

Hilinski was stunned. He shouted an urgent

and seldom-used command into his phone: "Hold on Three!" This was an order to stop all trains on Main Line Track 3 — a drastic step on a busy sixty-mile-an-hour thoroughfare.

Two miles away, Joe's warning cry was heard by his brother, Frank Hilinski. Frank was assistant chief dispatcher, the night boss.

"What's wrong?" demanded Frank.

Joe's voice shook. "You have a runaway engine, traveling fast, all dark."

"Which way is she headed?"

"West — against traffic."

Frank Hilinski jumped up. Six trains were rolling on the four main-line tracks within thirty miles of the terminal. The nearest was the eastbound *New York Clocker,* a crack passenger express. She was on Track 1, coming fast and due to stop in Bayonne in four minutes. The runaway on Track 3, next to Track 1, would slam through Bayonne just as passengers would be swarming over Track 3 to get to and from the stopped *Clocker*. If the engine plowed into the crowd . . .

Frank quickly ordered Bayonne tower to try to stop the *Clocker* before she entered the station. He also phoned the Bayonne yards.

"There's a runaway engine coming your way," he told the startled yardmaster. "Set flares. We don't know what's wrong with the crew."

Perhaps the engineer had fainted, with his foot still heavy on the deadman's pedal. Maybe some prankster had stolen the engine, or a madman was holding the crew at gunpoint.

The phone rang. The Bayonne yardmaster reported back. "Your engine is No. 1706. Went by here at 10:34. Never slowed down. Couldn't see any crew." No. 1706 was a huge, 123-ton diesel-electric workhorse assigned to yard duty.

At 10:35 the runaway, having covered four miles from HY tower in five minutes, charged without warning through Bayonne station. The *Clocker* was now stopped safely outside the station. Passengers waiting to board her heard the ghost train coming and drew back in fright. No one was hurt. The crew of the halted *Clocker* were astonished to see an engine, all dark, roar past on the wrong side and vanish into the night.

In the next ninety seconds, Frank Hilinski did some fast thinking. The chart showed that No. 692, a freight, was rolling east from Bound Brook. The runaway would meet it in a head-on collision in about eighteen minutes. Hilinski *had* to get the engine off Track 3 somewhere.

He turned to a two-track line called the Perth Amboy Branch. It swings away from the main line at a busy junction known as E'port (short

Adapted from Popular Science Monthly, © *1961 by Popular Science Publishing Co., Inc.*

for Elizabethport). But both branch tracks were blocked. A Pennsylvania seashore express was barreling north on Track 1. A freight was plodding south on Track 2. However, it would be thirty minutes before the runaway could overtake the freight. Hilinski decided to play for time. He ordered E'port tower to send the runaway hurtling down the branch on southbound Track 2.

Hilinski now phoned Division Superintendent Joseph Galuppo at home. The call awakened Galuppo. A normally calm man, he became in the next half hour almost a nervous wreck.

Hilinski told him what was happening. Should he, he asked, open the Raritan River Drawbridge and dump the engine into the river?

"No!" roared Galuppo. Barges filled with propane gas used the Raritan. An engine smashing onto one could set off a terrible explosion.

A voice on the speaker broke in. It was E'port tower: "Runaway by here. Passing her from Main Line Track Three to Branch Track Two."

Suddenly Superintendent Galuppo had a daring idea. He was still on the phone with Hilinski. "Get hold of Jeffrey," he said. Ed Jeffrey was trainmaster at Long Branch, New Jersey.

At this moment the big freight on Branch Track 2 was approaching the Raritan Drawbridge, fifteen miles south. In command of her engine was Chet Gudmunson, a small, white-haired man. Also riding the engine were Fireman Harold Johns and Head Brakeman Leo Barry.

At the bridge Gudmunson saw a waving lantern. He braked to a stop.

The bridge captain shouted, "Your engineer is wanted on the phone in a hurry — Jeffrey's calling."

Gudmunson climbed down and ran to the bridge phone. Trainmaster Jeffrey's voice said, "Don't say a word! Just listen. Seconds count."

Jeffrey said that a runaway was coming. "We'd like you to cut off your train and proceed at once to the straight track at South Amboy. We'll switch the runaway from Track Two to Track One to go around your stopped train — then back to Track Two so she's behind you. When you see her coming up behind, match her speed. Then slow down. Let her bump you and force her to stop. We'll stop the seashore express at South Amboy."

Gudmunson knew he was being asked, not ordered, to do this dangerous job. It was beyond the call of duty. He didn't have to risk his life. Neither did Johns or Barry.

Gudmunson talked with them a few seconds. They'd all go.

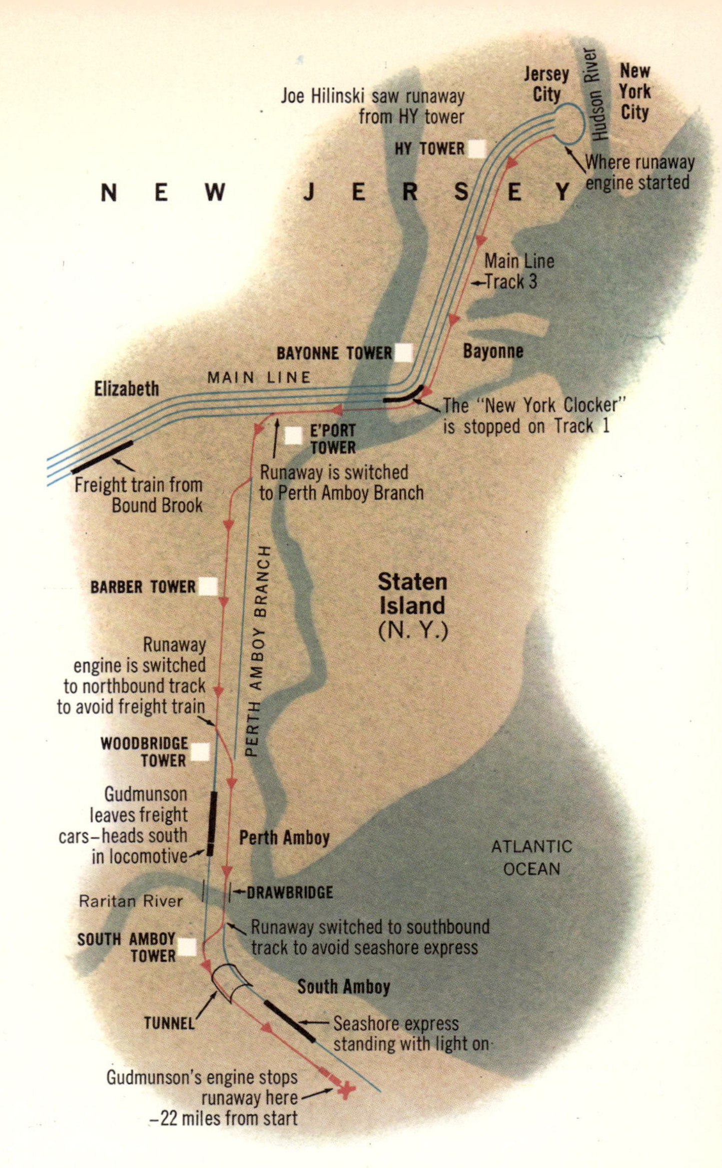

By this time Hilinski had all towers on a single phone circuit. Up and down the line, everyone heard these reports in quick succession:

10:53, from South Amboy tower: "Gudmunson passing southbound at ten miles an hour."

10:54, from Barber tower: "Runaway by here fast on Track Two. Speed is forty-five."

10:55, from Woodbridge tower: "I just switched runaway over to Track One. She nearly dumped, but she made it."

Then, at 10:58, from South Amboy tower, disturbing news: "Gudmunson has stopped!"

At this moment, the runaway was only a mile behind.

Gudmunson was worried. He had proceeded one half mile to the straight track at South Amboy, as suggested. Then, desperate for more information, he had stopped at a trackside telephone. Brakeman Barry went to the track phone for instructions. There had been no time for the voice at the bridge to tell Gudmunson one important fact: The runaway was running dark. So the three crewmen, staring back into the blackness of an empty tunnel through which they had just passed, were watching for something they would never see: a headlight.

At the Raritan Drawbridge, the crew of Gudmunson's train were mystified at being left behind by their engine. Suddenly they heard a roar behind them. At 10:57 the runaway skinned past them on Track 1 and across Raritan Draw.

Ahead of the runaway, a switch slid and locked. The runaway's speed tape later showed that she hit this ten-mile-per-hour switch at forty-six miles per hour. She lurched and leaned over hard. Then she made a slamming turn and settled down on southbound Track 2. The passenger train was now safe. But the runaway was only a half mile behind Gudmunson and his parked engine.

Ahead, to the south, Gudmunson could see the express lying in South Amboy station with her headlight blazing. Normally, it would have been dimmed. Gudmunson didn't know that the engineer had been ordered: "Keep your light on so it will shine on the runaway."

Peering at the darkened tunnel, Gudmunson suddenly saw the faintest glimmer of light — the dim reflection of the express train's headlight on the runaway. The engine was right on them.

Johns shouted for Barry as Gudmunson reached for the throttle. A diesel builds up power slowly — you can't rush it. Gudmunson eased the lever back an inch. Then he gave her quarter throttle and she began to roll. Within ten seconds, he risked half throttle, and the engine shook. When his speedometer said thirty-five, he gave full throttle.

They flew past the express in South Amboy station. Just ahead lay a sharp S curve. "I've got to do it now," Gudmunson decided. With his speed at sixty, he began shutting down and valving air. The runaway was dangerously close. Barry thought Gudmunson slowed too much. He shouted, "Hold on hard — it's going to ram us!" Gudmunson yanked the throttle open — but too late. The collision was deafening. Steel motor-hood doors all along the engine's catwalk burst open. Barry and Johns were slammed into their seats.

The couplers had met and locked. Gudmunson shut off power, but was afraid to apply hard brakes. His engine might cartwheel in front of the heavier runaway.

Johns, holding the handrail, crept back along the rocking catwalk. The heavy steel doors — ten of them — kept slamming in his way. Flashlight in hand, he closed each door. Then he swung to the other engine and into the cab.

There was no one there. He flashed his light on the controls. Everything was perfectly set for running: throttle pulled back full, air brakes set for running. The isolation switch — which can cut generator power from the wheel motors — was on. Johns shut the throttle and heard No. 1706 die. Then he set the brakes and flipped on the cab light. Instantly he felt Gudmunson apply full braking power to wrestle the runaway to a halt.

The two engines slid to a stop in a cloud of hot sand and smoke. Gudmunson proceeded to the nearest phone. He lifted the receiver. And, all along the line, from Jeffrey at Long Branch up to Joe Hilinski at Jersey City, they heard his voice: "This is Gudmunson. We got her."

"How's her crew?" someone asked.

"Crew?" said Gudmunson. "She's got no crew. She's a ghost."

The mystery is still unsolved. The FBI and New Jersey's Public Utilities Commission investigated at once. They found that the runaway had been parked, awaiting a new crew. Her engine had been idling because of the cold weather. The locomotive had taken off within two minutes of the time her crew left her. What happened in those two minutes?

Several theories were considered — and exploded. Had someone tried to steal or wreck the engine? There were no clues, no fingerprints. Besides, it would have taken an expert to know the complicated starting procedure.

Had the throttle vibrated open by itself? This has been known to happen on some engines. But tests showed it couldn't have on No. 1706. Even if it had, who shifted the engine from neutral into gear? Who released the air brakes? Who put the isolation switch on "Run"?

Had the runaway been carelessly parked? All the men on her crew had good records. They said they had carefully gone through the eight-step shutdown routine.

One good thing resulted. Safety locks were put in all Jersey Central engines. Locked in neutral, an engine could be idled, but not moved.

No. 1706 had covered twenty-two miles in a frightening adventure that lasted exactly thirty-six minutes. You can see her today, plodding the yard at Jersey City. She looks like such a good, contented engine — you'd never guess that she once gave one of America's finest railroads a fright it will never forget.

QUIZZLES-ONE

(*Answers and explanations on page 198*)

THE LAZY ARTIST

Perhaps you remember the strange drawings our Lazy Artist did for the first *Reader's Digest Treasury for Young Readers.* Now he has been at work again. The views he takes of his subjects are still very odd, but you will laugh when you turn to page 198 and find out what they are supposed to be.

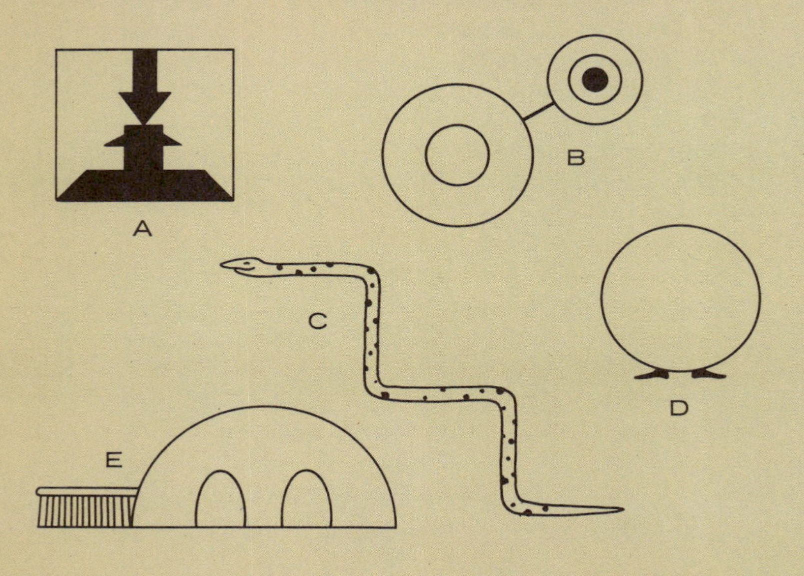

PUZZLING PARAGRAPH

How quickly can you find out what is unusual about *this* paragraph? It looks so ordinary that you would think nothing was wrong with it at all — and, in fact, nothing is. But it is distinctly odd. If you study it you may find out what is missing. Who knows? Go to work and try your skill.

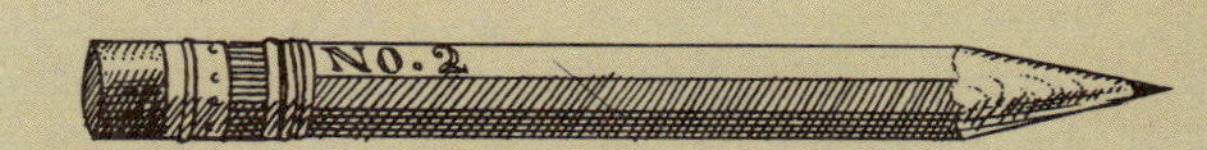

COPY THE DRAWINGS

Try to copy each of these drawings without taking your pencil from the paper, and without going back over the same line.

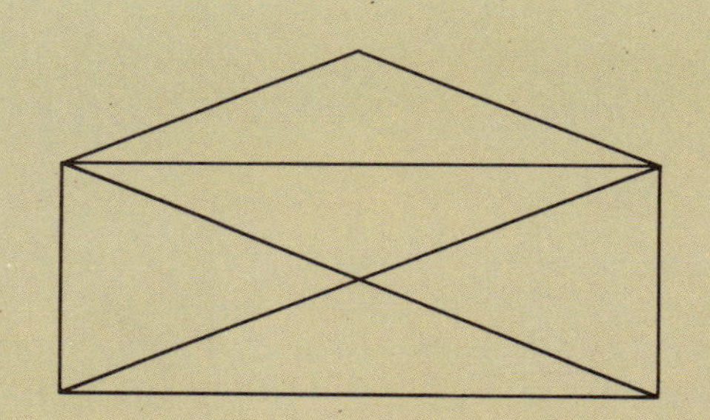

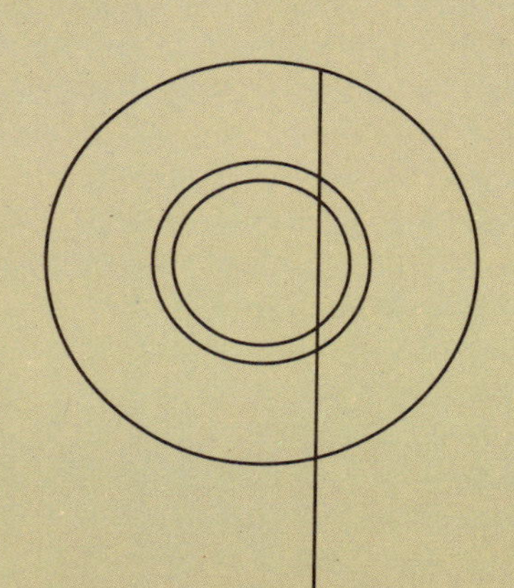

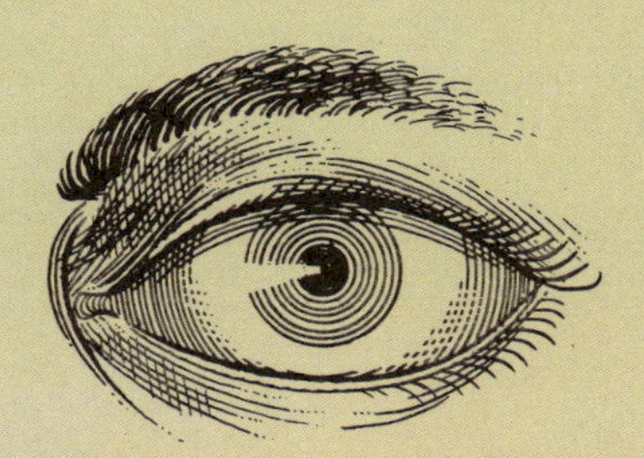

HOW MANY EYES ?

In a deck of ordinary playing cards, two of the jacks are one-eyed. The other jacks have two eyes. What is the total number of eyes on the four jack cards?

HOW IS IT DONE ?

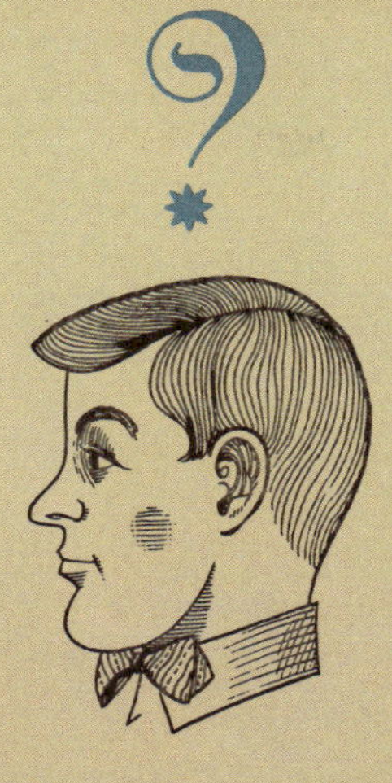

All you need for this trick is a penny. Borrow it from a friend and tell him to look at the date on it. Tell your audience that you are going to rub the penny through the sleeve of your coat. Bend your left arm, and rub the coin against your elbow with the fingers of your right hand. After a moment, carelessly let the penny fall to the floor. Pick it up with your left hand, move it to your right hand, and begin rubbing it against your elbow once again. Drop it a second time, pick it up, and go on rubbing. Now, when you take your right hand away, the penny is gone. Shake down your left sleeve, and the penny reappears in your *left* hand. It is the same penny, and there is no hole in your coat. The secret is on page 198.

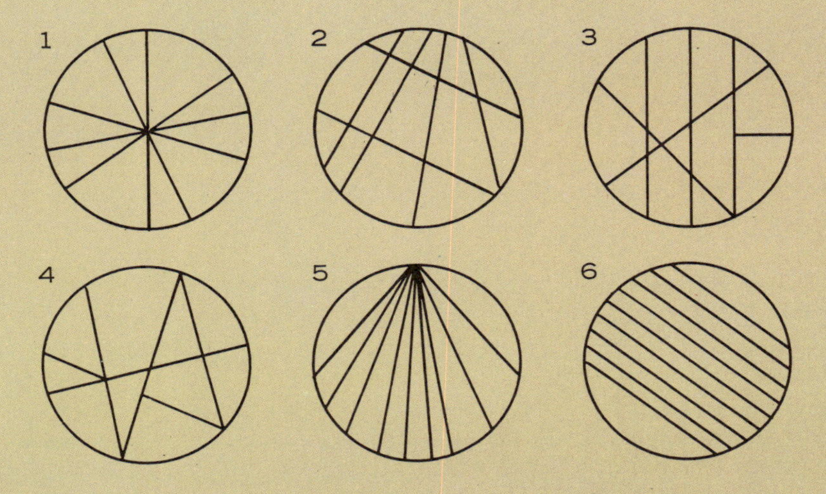

BAFFLING CIRCLES

Put check marks on the two circles that are divided into the greatest number of sections. The time limit is 20 seconds. You won't have time to count the sections, so just make a guess.

"The Lazy Artist" is based on a feature by Charles D. Rice in This Week, *© 1945 by United Newspapers Magazine Corp. "Puzzling Paragraph" was quoted by Cedric Adams in the* Minneapolis Star. *"Baffling Circles" and "How Is It Done?" are adapted from* Test Yourself! *by William Bernard and Jules Leopold, copyright 1947 and published by Hellman, Williams & Co. "How Many Eyes?" is from the radio program Dr. I.Q.*

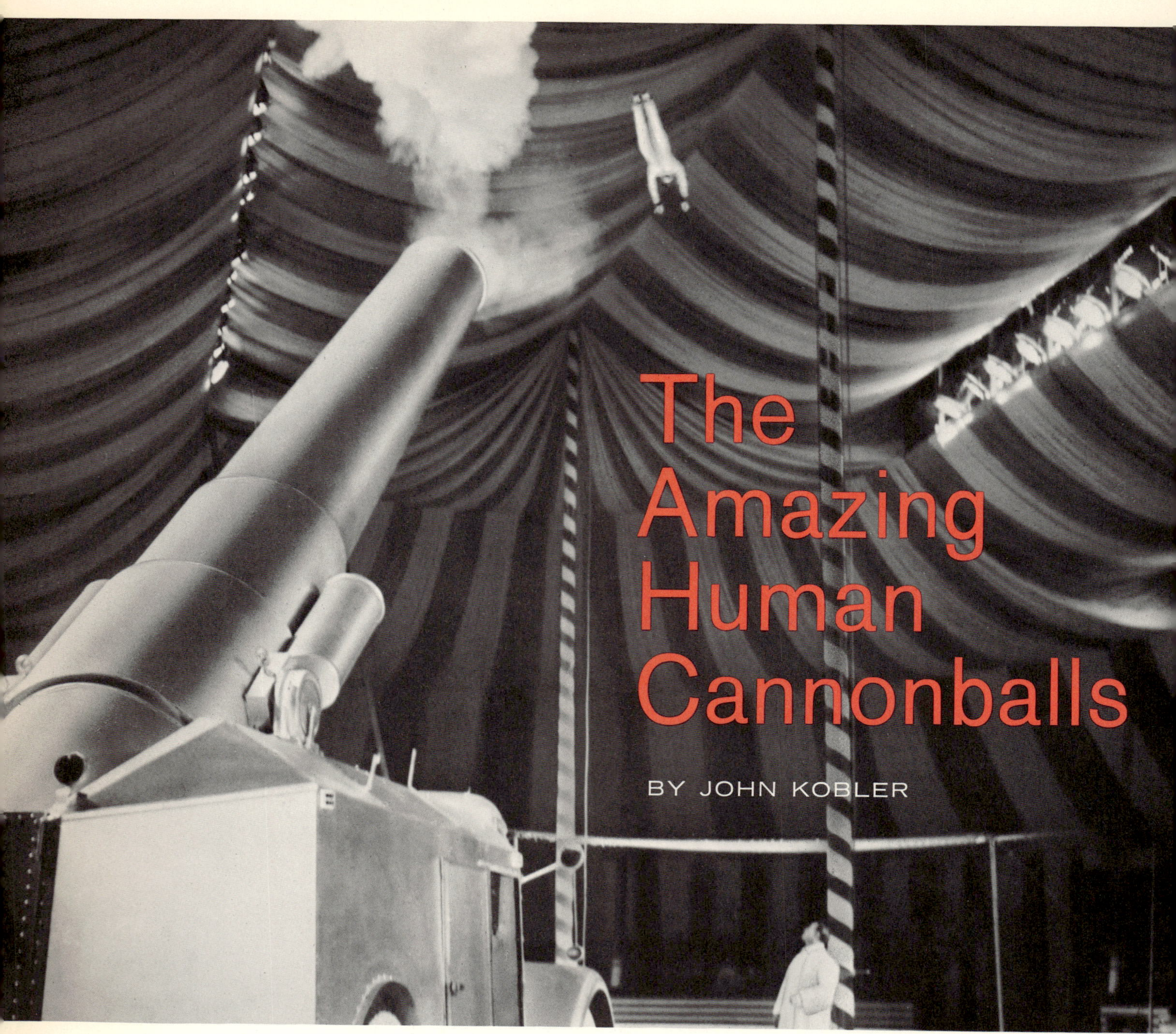

CULVER PICTURES, INC.

The Amazing Human Cannonballs

BY JOHN KOBLER

THE day you are twenty-one, you will probably have a big birthday party. But if your name were Zacchini you would celebrate in a really exciting way. You would be shot from a cannon!

For the Zacchinis are a brave circus family that proudly bears the title of "The Human Cannonballs." Their cannon is a gleaming monster with a barrel twenty-three feet long, and there is always a sudden hush when it is brought into the circus ring. The spectators know they are going to see a feat of daring they will never forget.

At last they hear the long-awaited fanfare from the brass band. Then one of the older Zacchinis limps across the ring to the cannon. He has broken too many bones in the past to be a human

Adapted from Life, *© 1948 by Time Inc., with editorial additions*

cannonball now, but he knows all the secrets of his dangerous trade. He looks the cannon over, makes sure it is quite ready, then sits down at the gunner's control panel.

Now comes a roll of drums, and into the ring struts the human bullet. He (or she) is dressed in a dazzling white space suit, a crash helmet and an asbestos mask. First he steps into a tray beside the cannon and showers himself with talcum powder. This will help him to glide smoothly out of the cannon. Then, with a wave to the crowd, he climbs the steps to the cannon's mouth and lowers himself feet first into the tilting barrel. Slowly he slides out of sight.

The older Zacchini spins the controls, and the great barrel moves as he takes aim. He rises to his feet and holds one arm above his head. *"Sei pronto?"* — Are you ready? — he yells. *"Pronto!"* replies a muffled voice, as if from a tomb. Then the gunner jabs a button.

There is a loud bang, a flash of smoke and flame from the cannon's mouth. And the human missile is seen hurtling skyward at up to two hundred miles per hour. Sometimes he blacks out for an instant because of the terrific pull of gravity on his body as he rockets into space. But he revives quickly to turn a half somersault high in the air. Two seconds later he lands safely on his back in the wide net at the far end of the arena. In their biggest shot, a Zacchini is thrown a hundred feet into the air and lands two hundred feet away.

Secrets of the Cannon

How can a man live through that rapid, shattering journey along the barrel of the cannon? This is the secret: he travels in a hollow piston that slides to the end of the barrel, then stops while the human bullet is shot into the air. The piston measures sixteen inches across — just wide enough to take a man. It is deliberately made a tight fit, so that the man will not be shaken about and battered as he travels along the barrel.

The cannon has a second secret: it is actually fired by compressed air, like a gigantic air gun. The flame and smoke are caused by burning gunpowder, while the loud bang comes from a small bomb at the rear of the cannon. These are "effects" to make a more exciting show for the crowd.

But there are still plenty of dangers, apart from the chance of missing the net. If the piston should jam, for instance, the Zacchini inside could easily be suffocated by the smoke. Although no Zacchini has ever been killed during the act, all of them have been injured at some time or another.

Adventures of a Human Bullet

Edmondo, the eldest brother of the troupe, has many tales to tell of his adventures as a human cannonball. The idea first came to him when he was fighting in the Italian army during the First World War. One day he found himself in a trench, with the enemy less than a hundred yards away. He tried to think of some way of encircling them. "It came to me that maybe soldiers could be shot behind the enemy lines from cannon," he says. Everybody laughed at the idea, but Edmondo did not forget it.

After the war, while touring Malta with his father's circus, Edmondo asked a blacksmith to make him a cannon large enough to shoot a man from its barrel. He gave his first performance in Cairo, Egypt, and broke his leg with the very first shot. In the hospital he had plenty of time to think out what went wrong. He decided that the

Egle Victoria and Duina dressed for their double-cannon act

COURTESY OF RINGLING BROS. AND BARNUM & BAILEY

barrel was too wide and that the piston moved too violently. He designed a second cannon.

With this improved cannon, Edmondo's brother Hugo managed to get through a good many performances without hurting himself. The human cannonballs became a sensation throughout Europe. They were given medals by the king of Norway and the king of Italy. Then, in 1929, the first Zacchini team came to America. In a few years the whole family had settled in Florida — some in Tampa and some in Sarasota.

Wonderful as the original cannon act was, John Ringling asked Edmondo to liven it up for his famous Ringling Brothers and Barnum & Bailey Circus. Edmondo's reply was to invent a cannon with two pistons, which could fire two human bullets, one after the other. To try it out, the Zacchinis all gathered one morning behind Edmondo's house. The family doctor stood by, prepared for the worst. Edmondo fired two dummy bullets first. Then he beckoned to his brothers Hugo and Vittorio. "Pam — pam!" says Edmondo when he tells the story. "It work perfect."

"The White Heron"

When the Second World War came, all the boys joined up, and Edmondo did not know where to turn for human cannonballs. Was this to be the end of the great Zacchini tradition? "No," said Edmondo's two pretty teen-age daughters, "the show must go on." So Duina and Egle Victoria, who for years had been first-class trapeze artists, now put on the white suits of human cannonballs. Duina was just as good with the cannon as she had been on the trapeze. And Egle Victoria turned out to be the best bullet in the history of the act. She often made the full two-hundred-foot flight, turning her half somersault so gracefully that they called her "The White Heron." Sometimes the two sisters were shot from the double cannon within split seconds of each other.

Today both Duina and Egle Victoria are married and have children of their own. But the double-cannon act still closes The Greatest Show on Earth. For what could follow it?

The home life of the human cannonballs is gay and exciting. Friends and relations drop in unexpectedly from all over the world. Some never leave. Among them, the Zacchinis speak eleven languages, including Czech and Arabic. They often switch from one to another in the same sentence! On the exercise ground behind Edmondo's house they practice tirelessly on trapezes, trampolines, high wires and tumbling mats. And of course they often go soaring over the treetops, singly and in pairs — a sight the neighbors have never quite gotten used to!

Pin Money for Marylin

A GROUP of children were excitedly planning to stage a circus of their own. But they were having trouble getting any parent to allow use of their back yard for this show. At last one father agreed to let the children use his yard, but only on one condition — that pins, not money, be used for admission.

This dampened the youngsters' spirits considerably, but not for long. Soon they were marching up and down the block beating on old pans and carrying a sign which read:

BIG CIRCUS IN MARYLIN'S BACK YARD
Admission
3 PINS PLUS 3 CENTS TAX

—Charles Davison

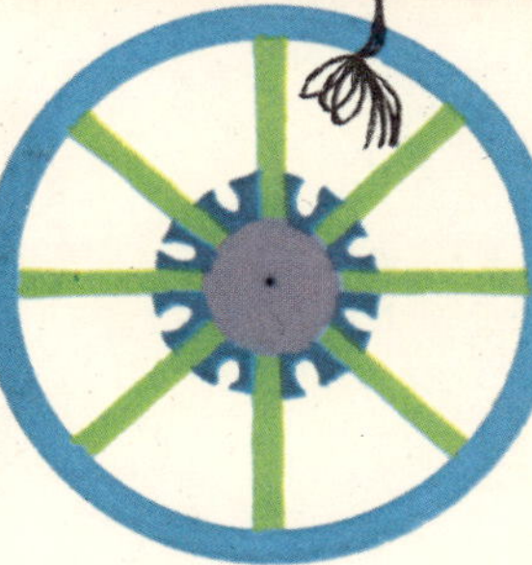

CIRCUS CROSSWORD

Many of the answer words in this crossword are taken from the story of "The Human Cannonballs." See how many you can get right. (The solution is on page 128.)

ACROSS

1. Noise the cannon makes.
4. Every Zacchini wears one for the cannon act.
7. What you have at the circus.
8. Monster.
11. Insect.
13. Doubles over.
15. Musical note.
16. You eat ice cream with this.
18. The whole of.
19. Form of verb "to be."
20. You put this in the lake to see how cold the water is.
21. Magicians keep rabbits up these.
24. Twelve inches.
26. You'll find these at playgrounds ("teeter- ____").
27. Not here.
28. Registered Nurse.
30. Bird for which Egle Victoria was nicknamed.
32. Tie or pin together.
35. A big fuss.
36. Slang for mother.
37. Consumed food.
38. What popcorn is in at the circus.
39. What the Zacchinis are.
40. Cows say this.
42. American Indian tribe.
43. Pronoun.
44. Exist.
45. Fate.
47. It flies through the air.
50. A piece of earth.
52. What your eye does.
54. Three feet.
55. Toy on a string.
56. He takes you to the circus.

DOWN

1. Every Zacchini is a human one.
2. Conjunction.
3. Leave.
4. Not you.
5. Juice of a tree.
6. Full of knots.
7. Game ("____ the Leader").
9. What windows are made of.
10. Male sheep.
12. Also.
13. Quick.
14. Rescue.
16. You can make forts and balls and men with this.
17. Not old.
22. A gas that puts you to sleep.
23. Mistake.
24. The brass band greets the Zacchinis with this.
25. What circus horses eat.
29. What the human cannonballs fall into.
30. A Zacchini brother.
31. Steal.
33. Running game.
34. Birds' home.
35. Their act has brought the Zacchinis much of this.
36. The Zacchinis practice tumbling on one.
39. Kind of bullets Edmondo first shot from his double cannon.
41. Smell.
43. What came to Edmondo when he was in the Italian army.
44. Beside.
46. Queer.
48. Exists.
49. Bright color.
50. Abbreviation for South America.
51. Belonging to me.
53. South Dakota.

Jerry's Prize Lamb

BY STERLING NORTH

Jerry Kincaid, an orphan, lived with his crotchety grandmother. Then along came Danny, the little black lamb, and things began to happen ...

IT WAS a night of wild storm, and Granny Kincaid knew without looking at her calendar that the time for lambing had come.

"It's usually a raw, blustery night like this," said Granny, as she and Jerry beat their way toward the barn. They both had to pull with all their strength to open the door against the wind. Then suddenly they were safe in the warm stable.

In the four sheep pens the miracle had already happened. Beside each mother ewe lay a newborn, wet, tightly curled lamb. The ewes spoke softly, and with small voices the lambs answered.

"Four new lambs," Jerry said.

"All joyous and pert," said Granny.

Then Jerry shouted happily, "Oh, Granny, look! Jezebel's got twins. One of them's black!"

"Black as Satan and as ugly," Granny said.

"I think he's pretty," Jerry said, drying the lamb gently with a clean flour sack. "Look, Granny. He's not a bit afraid."

But Granny was not surprised to see that the lamb was already an outcast. Huddled in a far corner of the pen, he had found the world surprisingly cold and unfriendly. Unlike his twin, he was jet black with cinnamon-brown leggings and a wicked and wonderful little face. Jerry thought he had never seen anything so beautiful as that little black buck lamb.

"Jezebel won't have him," said Granny.

"I'm going to try again," Jerry said.

He lifted the lamb in his arms and crossed to the ewe. She hooked the boy sharply with her small horns. Then she turned and butted the lamb halfway across the pen.

"He'll die, Granny, if he has nothing to eat and nobody to love him. Couldn't we . . ."

"No, we can't," said Granny. "You and I have got a farm to run, Jerry. There's no room on Cat Hollow for a pet sheep."

Jerry knew that Granny could be as hard as flint when she had a mind to say no. While she was putting more straw in the other pens he began saying softly, "You're a fine little black lamb and I've got a name all picked out for you. It's Danny. You like that name, little fellow?"

Granny didn't see him tiptoeing out of the pen and toward the door.

"Jerry."

No answer.

"Jerry, bring the lantern. You heard me. . . ."

But the boy took no notice. He and the lamb slipped out into the night.

At the corner of the springhouse Granny tore a switch from the willow tree and stripped its leaves. Then she went into the kitchen of the cabin. On the wide hearth Jerry had made a bed for his lamb. He had lined a basket with warm flour sacks and dishcloths.

"Jerry," she said, "you disobeyed me, and it's my duty to punish you. Bend over."

"I'm ready for my licking, Granny. But please can I warm and feed this little fellow first?"

"Oh, all right. Suppose I'll have to lend a hand." Granny put the switch within reach on the table. From the copper kettle singing on the range she poured a pan of hot water and cooled it with water from a pail. Then she rummaged in the cupboard for a baby's milk bottle.

"I won't have the little devil around the place. Eating his head off. Busting through fences," she muttered.

"Look, Granny, he's sucking my finger."

"Here, dip him in this warm water."

"Oh, thank you, Granny. . . . Look, he likes it. . . . I'll feed him on clover. He'll get so big and fat and strong."

"And mean and spiteful," Granny added. "Dry him with this flour sack, Jerry. His bottle's ready."

She made sure the milk was not too hot, then offered the eager lamb the bottle. The cloven-hoofed baby pulled on it with joy, his tail whirling like a windmill.

"Where do you think you're going to keep him?"

"Here in the kitchen. Oh, Granny, can I keep him, please?"

Adapted from So Dear to My Heart, *copyright 1947 by Sterling North and published by Doubleday & Co., Inc.*

"Well, yes — at least, until he's big enough to roast."

"Oh, Granny. You're the best Granny," Jerry said, kissing her wrinkled cheek. "Give me my licking now, because I'll hardly feel it I'm so happy."

"Bother," said Granny, breaking the willow switch and throwing it into the fireplace. "I'm getting too soft." She wiped her eyes on the corner of her apron.

Danny Gets in Trouble

In less than a week the lamb had learned to tip over his basket, and to race around the cabin leaving a shambles behind him. Before long Danny was tipping over milk pails, and running riot through the flowers. One Monday morning he tipped over the clothesbasket, spilling all the newly washed clothes.

"Black scalawag," Granny cried, chasing him through the garden. "If he ruins my Monday wash again, I'll roast him."

Several days later Danny and Jerry were in even deeper trouble. Danny had been banished, first from the house and next from the front yard (where he had tipped over a pot of crimson dye which Granny used to color the bedcovers she wove). And now Granny said that the next time the lamb gave trouble he would be sold to the butcher.

There seemed to be only one way to keep Danny out of mischief — a new, strong pen. But where was Jerry to get it? He had only thirteen cents saved up. He decided to ask Uncle Hiram, the blacksmith, what he should do.

Uncle Hiram was making a new treadle for Granny Kincaid's loom when the boy and the lamb came into his blacksmith shop.

"Uncle Hiram, I'm so miserable."

"Tell me all about it."

So Jerry poured his heart out about his lamb, and the fence he needed but could never buy.

"If you'll give me a few days," said Uncle Hiram, "I'll help you build a pen out of locust poles stout enough to hold an elephant. Then I'll try to argue your Granny out of selling the lamb. But it's not going to be easy."

Jerry thanked him, then looked thoughtful for a moment. "Uncle Hiram, horses win races and get to be champions. Then people have to admit they're wonderful. How about animals that don't race? How do they get to be champions?"

"Well, you take them to the county fair, like that lamb of yours, for instance. Now, suppose I'm the judge." Putting his imaginary glasses straight, he stroked an imaginary beard and put on the pompous air of a livestock judge at the county fair. In a commanding voice he said: "Keep a tight hold of that animal, Mr. Kincaid. Looks real ferocious."

"I've got him, Judge," Jerry said.

"Mr. Kincaid, this here's quite an animal. Eyes like shooting stars. Broad as a timber wagon across the back. Can probably outjump, outshoot, outrun, outfight and outbrag any lamb in the county."

"No fooling, Uncle Hiram. What makes a lamb a champion?"

"Well, first it's good breeding. But people will just have to take Danny's breeding on faith. Then it's care and feeding. Just the right mixture of ground feed and lots of clover."

"But all the best clover is way down by the stream, and the pasture fence won't hold him."

"You'll just have to lead him on a rope, Jerry, into green pastures and beside the still waters."

"Oh, I'll lead him into green pastures," Jerry promised. "Anything else I should give him?"

"Well," Uncle Hiram said, "he needs a lot of love and affection. You can hardly ever raise young champions unless you love them."

He helped Jerry put a new length of rope around the lamb's neck and watched him lead it away. And Jerry, as he walked home, dreamed of his plan to take Danny to the county fair. Even Granny couldn't have it in her heart to slaughter a blue-ribbon, prizewinning young ram.

Asleep in the Stable

That night, after Jerry had gone to bed, he lay in the loft listening to Granny talking to him from the room below. She had warped up her loom and started to weave a new cover.

"It's no use arguing, Jerry. I heard about all the things that lamb of yours broke in Mr. Grundy's shop today. Pen or no pen, I'm going to sell him to the butcher in the morning. It'll be the best thing for the animal and a blessing for Cat Hollow Farm. You hear me, Jerry?"

No answer.

"Must have fallen asleep," said Granny to herself. "It's hard for a young 'un to understand."

But Jerry was not asleep. While Granny went on talking to herself, he dressed quickly and slipped out of the loft window. He dropped to the ground as easily as a cat, then padded down the path to the stable. He needed no light to find Danny. The lamb bleated a soft welcome and nuzzled Jerry's hand.

"They'll never slaughter you, Danny," he whispered, "unless they slaughter me first."

Jerry had meant to stay only a few minutes, then climb back to his room. But as he lay there in the deep, clean straw, he fell asleep with his arm around the lamb.

And there, after a wild search with her lantern, Granny found them. She held up the light and looked down on the pair with tears in her eyes. Shaking her head slowly, she said, "What's a woman to do?"

Uncle Hiram's Scheme

A few days later, Jerry jumped out of bed at sunrise to greet Uncle Hiram as he drove up in his wagon. Granny had said that Jerry could keep the lamb until autumn. Today was the day to build Danny's pen.

As he helped Uncle Hiram saw posts down in the locust grove, Jerry was trying to work out how he could keep his lamb not only until next autumn but for the rest of Danny's life. There seemed only one way out. If Danny could win a blue ribbon at the county fair he would never be sold to the butcher.

When they were resting for a moment, Jerry asked: "When will you ask Granny about going to the fair?"

"Suppertime's soon enough. I've schemed me a scheme. But your Granny's going to squirm like a weasel in a sack."

All through supper Uncle Hiram waited for his chance like a cat watching a mousehole. After the table had been cleared, Granny sat contentedly in her rocking chair. Uncle Hiram played a few notes on his guitar, sang a few words of "Billy Boy." He played gay ballads and church hymns, and all the while Granny's rocking chair kept the time. Out of the corner of his eye, Uncle Hiram was watching her every move.

Imitating a steam calliope with his mouth, he began to hum "Over the Waves."

"Remember that song?" he asked.

"I do not."

"They play it on merry-go-rounds — at county fairs."

Granny brought her chair to a stop. Then she started rocking again, her foot striking the floor angrily. "No," she said, "no, we're not going."

"Not going where?" Uncle Hiram asked, pretending not to know."

"To the fair, that's where."

"Oh, Granny," Jerry protested, "everybody goes to county fairs."

"Not everybody," said Granny, tapping her foot sharply, "not old Granny Kincaid who lives at Cat Hollow."

"But, Granny, suppose my lamb won the blue ribbon and the cash prize?"

"Supposing it rained lemonade," said Granny.

"Danny's the best lamb in the county, isn't he, Uncle Hiram?"

"Well," said Uncle Hiram, giving Jerry a long, slow wink, "that lamb's tolerable, just tolerable. But if you want blue ribbons, how about those quilts and counterpanes?"

"Mercy," said Granny, "it never entered my

head to show my weaving at the county fair."

She began to rock with slow, dreamy strokes, imagining her handsome patterns all hung out on show. She would finish her new counterpane — the one that was going to have a picture of a wedding at Cat Hollow. There wouldn't be another counterpane like it in all creation.

"Well," said Granny, weakening slightly.

"Oh, we're going, we're going," Jerry cried, dancing in circles.

But then Granny shook her head sadly. "Now hold your horses, Jerry. I didn't promise."

The room was suddenly so quiet you could hear the clock ticking.

"What are we going to use for money for this fair-going jaunt? Buttons?"

"I can get a job somewhere," Jerry said proudly. "I'm the man of the family."

The Bee Tree

In the days that followed, Jerry struggled to make enough money to take them to the fair. He tramped the roads of the township hunting for work. A man up a cherry tree wouldn't give him a job because he said boys always ate more than they put in the pail. The station agent said there was scarcely ever a telegram to deliver.

Jerry went to Mr. Grundy's store. "No, son, I don't need an errand boy just now," said Mr. Grundy, and went back to the game of checkers he was playing with Grandpa Meeker. Then he looked sharply at Jerry. "You want to get rich quick? Go out and find a wild-bee tree. I'll pay you ten cents a pound for the honey."

Jerry's eyes brightened. "How do I find a wild-bee tree, Mr. Grundy?"

Mr. Grundy was already thinking about his next move at checkers. "Oh . . . why . . . just find a bee and follow it home."

"Sounds real easy," Jerry said. "Gee, thanks, Mr. Grundy." He almost ran from the shop.

"Don't care how much you waste that boy's time, do you?" Grandpa Meeker said.

"What's time to a boy?" said Mr. Grundy.

Meanwhile, Jerry had gone to look for his cousin Tildy. He found her at their usual meeting place between two ancient sycamore trees. He enjoyed his secret silently for a few moments, then plucked a tickle brush of wild barley and began teasing a honeybee.

"What are you doing that for?" Tildy asked.

"Bees, honey, a bee tree, money," Jerry chanted.

"Oh, Jerry, what a wonderful idea!"

"Of course, we haven't found the bee tree yet."

"We will," Tildy cried. "There's nothing on earth can stop us."

"There she goes, straight as a beeline."

Their eyes were glued to the shimmering bee as it sped homeward with its golden load. Careless of scratchy briers and brambles, they started on their treasure hunt. "There's another, and another!" Tildy cried.

Scrambling up a rocky hill, they came at last to a dome of rock overlooking miles of woods and fields. For a few minutes they forgot all about the bees, pointing out the wonders spread before them. Then suddenly the spell was broken. "Tildy, the bees!"

Shading their eyes from the sun, they scanned the countryside until Jerry's gaze found a bee buzzing in the trumpet of a wild columbine. Urged gently from the flower, the bee flew over the ridge and down through long-abandoned fields of cockleburs and corn. Presently the children found themselves on the edge of a vast, gloomy swamp into which a line of bees sped like silver bullets.

"I'm afraid," Tildy said.

"Can't go back now," Jerry said. "Step right where I step. I don't trust those bogholes."

As the swamp closed in around them, darker and even more unfriendly, they again lost track of the bees. Tired and downhearted, they found a mossy log on which to rest. They were far from home, deep in a tangle of gnarled trees, with miles of hazel thickets and briers around them.

Above them on the branch of a high tree they saw a bee-martin that some folks call a kingbird. "See that little gray bird?" Jerry said.

"I've seen lots of them — they're bee-martins."

"And it's catching a bee. And there's another and another. . . . And, Tildy . . . it's the bee tree!" Jerry leaped to his feet, pointing with wild excitement to an enormous old cottonwood. "See where the bees go in?"

Sure enough, high on the dying tree trunk was a hole no larger than a silver dollar into which a ribbon of laden bees was disappearing.

"We've found it, Tildy. We've found it."

"You're wonderful!" Tildy cried. She felt like laughing and crying at the same time.

Before sunrise the next morning, Jerry and Uncle Hiram loaded axe and saws into the wagon and drove along an old logging track into the swamp. At the bee tree Uncle Hiram went to work. When at last the old cottonwood came crashing to the ground, the bees poured angrily from their holes. But Uncle Hiram was ready to light oil-soaked rags on the end of a long pole and "whop 'em with smoke." A few moments' chopping with the axe opened up the hollow trunk. Inside gleamed hundreds of pounds of dark honeycomb. There was enough honey to fill four washtubs.

As they drove up to the hitching rail at Mr. Grundy's store, people poured from every house to see Jerry's treasure. They put their fingers into the tubs and licked them, shaking their heads with amazement. One by one the tubs were weighed on the platform scale, and Uncle Hiram wrote down the weights. "Let's see," said Mr. Grundy, "two hundred and twenty pounds of honey at ten cents a pound . . . Oh dear, I'm afraid it comes to twenty-two dollars. You're going to ruin me, Jerry." He peeled the dollars from a roll of bills in his pocket.

"What are you going to do with all that cash, Jerry?" asked one of the bystanders.

"I'm taking my prize lamb to the county fair."

Then, with the money in his pocket, Jerry walked proudly to the wagon.

At the County Fair

At last the sunny autumn day arrived when Tildy, Uncle Hiram and the Kincaids set off for the county fair. They were all dressed in their brand-new Sunday best. Granny wore a black straw hat covered with purple grapes.

At first, Jerry and Tildy were shy as wood mice in that elegant day coach, where the plush seats were green as moss and only prickled a little under your knees. But before long they were chattering gaily about Danny, who was riding in the baggage car.

With Uncle Hiram's help they had scrubbed him clean in the stream, and combed and brushed his wool until it shimmered in the sunlight. His hooves and horns had been sandpapered till they were smooth as satin, then burnished with an oiled cloth. Even Granny had to admit he was a handsome little devil.

When they got to the fair, Granny said she had never in her life seen such a grand spectacle. She told the sideshow man a thing or two when "The World's Smallest Baby" turned out to be a chattering little monkey. But she loved riding on the Ferris wheel. And later she won a prize for threading three needles in less than a minute.

Uncle Hiram and the children were fresh as daisies, so Granny let them go exploring while she rested her weary bones. She sat beside her display of woven covers with her ear cocked for compliments. She had brought along samples of her dyes and some of the flowers and roots and berries from which she made the dyes. In more than a dozen little jam pots were the gentle reds she used, the mellow yellows and the soft blues. Nobody could pass by such an exhibit without stopping to look. It excited the judges even before they looked at Granny's coverlets.

"That's a real nice cover," one judge said.

"Thank you kindly," Granny murmured.

"What do you call the one with a story picture?"

" 'Wedding at Cat Hollow.' "

The judges whispered to each other, looked at the coverlet once more, wrote in their notebooks, then moved on to other contestants. But in a few minutes they were back, and before Granny's wondering eyes they pinned the blue ribbon to her counterpane.

After the judges had congratulated her, a stout lady said she would give her fifty dollars for her prizewinning coverlet.

"Lady, my covers are not for sale," said Granny.

"But, my good woman, why not?"

"My covers are my pleasure, that's why not," said Granny firmly. "And money isn't everything."

Prize Lambs

But Granny Kincaid would have given anything she had to save Jerry from being disappointed in the lamb-judging contest. She was certain Danny would lose. She was helping the children to snip stray wisps of wool from Danny's back when they heard the call: "All spring rams in the arena at once, please."

Now Jerry was on his own. He knew now how the Christian martyrs felt when they went forth into the Roman arena to face the lions. He needed the aid of someone stronger than himself. He knew he had the love of Granny and Uncle Hiram and Tildy, but it was somehow not enough.

"Suppose he doesn't win?" he whispered to Granny as they parted.

"If he doesn't, I want you to come out of that ring like a Kincaid — walking proudly."

Jerry walked slowly into the ring, and the lamb followed meekly on his tether. Jerry found himself saying the opening words of the Twenty-third Psalm, his lips barely moving: *"The Lord is my shepherd; I shall not want. . . ."*

Jerry's heart sank as he led his lamb along. His beloved Danny was just a common crossbred sheep. What chance did he have against these handsome purebreds?

The judging ring was dotted with lambs, each with its owner kneeling beside it. Jerry kneeled too, his heart beating wildly. He took some comfort when he saw the judges. They were big men with just but kindly faces.

As the three judges moved from lamb to lamb, each owner's name was called, and the owner gave the name and pedigree of his lamb.

"Holloway!" said the leading judge, looking at the list in his hand.

The answer came: "Holloway's Hampshire. Number six nine two. Out of Midas the Second's Butter Cup Belle, by Crenshaw, Duke of Manchester."

There was a ripple of applause. Jerry's heart plummeted down. How could Danny hope to match a lamb with such an aristocratic pedigree?

Next, a boy named Marshall announced: "Shropshire Lad. Number seven eight seven four. Out of Lassie Queen, by National Grand Champion, Hiram of Troy's Golden Thorn."

Again the burst of clapping for the boy and his Shropshire with its beautiful woolly fleece. Down the line came the judges, calling out the names, hearing the proud answers. Jerry looked around him in panic.

"Kincaid!"

No answer.

"Come, come, boy, what's your ram's name?"

"Danny."

"What breed?"

Every eye in the great circle of faces was upon him. Jerry rose from his knees and stood very straight beside his lamb. "This black lamb of mine isn't one of those fancy purebreds," he said in a proud, clear voice. "He's just a Cat Hollow Kincaid, same as me and Granny."

The crowd was so quiet that you could hear the faraway music of the merry-go-round.

"His mam's name was Jezebel. And we're not quite sure who his pap was."

The crowd burst out laughing.

"Go ahead, laugh," Jerry shouted, fighting back the tears. "But he's the best lamb in the world. He's not afraid of anything. And he could lick all of these fancy rams any day of the week — the way David licked Goliath."

The crowd howled with laughter. The tall judge held up his hand for silence. He said very clearly so that all could hear: "Nice pair of shoulders on your lamb, my boy. Good quality wool, too."

The judges were talking among themselves now, looking at their notebooks. Jerry's lips were dry and he felt lightheaded and a little sick — waiting — waiting.

At last, nodding solemnly, the judges turned to award the prizes. They took two steps, three steps — they were passing Jerry by. He watched the tall chief judge walk toward the handsome Shropshire.

"The judging committee hereby unanimously confers the blue ribbon and cash award upon Mr. Marshall's Shropshire Lad."

The crowd clapped and shouted. Marshall beamed and shook hands with the judges. Jerry stood dazed and bewildered as Marshall came past with his lamb proudly wearing the blue ribbon.

"It's all right, Danny," Jerry whispered. "It's all right, boy."

Fighting back his tears, Jerry saw the blurred figures beyond the rail: Tildy openly weeping, Granny dabbing her eyes, while Uncle Hiram bit hard on his cigar. Jerry straightened his shoulders and began to lead his lamb from the ring.

"Just a moment, folks!" the leading judge shouted. "Wait a minute, young man."

"I guess we can take our licking," Jerry said. "We lost fair and square."

"I like your spirit, boy," the judge said, "and I like your lamb. Only trouble is he's black. Sort of puts him in a class by himself."

The crowd laughed lazily, but the judge raised his hand for silence. "This lamb *is* in a class by himself. Raised on a hill farm with no special breeding behind him, he shows what love and care can do for livestock. He has good lines and a deep, fine fleece. No lamb has ever come into this ring better groomed than Kincaid's Danny. This young ram is a champion in every sense of the word. Therefore, we wish to give Mr. Kincaid and his lamb an award we have not made for three years — the Special Award of Merit."

Possibly the crowd was more kindly than Jerry had thought, for they now clapped and shouted louder than they had for any other prizewinner. The judge took a rosette of royal-purple silk from a small box and pinned it on Danny.

A Party for Danny

Traveling home from the fair, they were tired but deeply contented. Suddenly, as the train went around a curve, Jerry caught sight of the little church, Mr. Grundy's store and all the rest of the little town.

"Granny, Tildy, Uncle Hiram! We're home!"

"Mercy!" said Granny as the train pulled up at the station. "What's all the ruckus?"

They didn't know that Uncle Hiram had sent a telegram to Mr. Grundy telling the good news.

"Band and everything," Tildy cried. "Everybody's waving."

"Hmmm," said Uncle Hiram. "A committee of welcome."

It was the way Jerry always wanted to remember it: folks pouring out of every door as tin pans, banjos, mouth organs and fiddles took up the welcome. Everyone wanted to help the stationmaster lift out Danny's crate and the box of Granny's covers. "Stand back, folks. We don't want to scare this prize lamb."

"Well, what do you know!" "The Special Award." "Always did say that boy and lamb would make their mark." "Can I touch him, Jerry?"

"How did you like the train ride, Granny?"

"It's better than walking," Granny said.

"Now this is on me," Mr. Grundy shouted. "I've got two cases of soda pop on ice; I've got six watermelons and plenty of ice cream."

More cheers.

"But what'll I do with Danny?" Jerry asked.

"Why, bring him along," said Mr. Grundy. "It's his party."

Hours later, driving out to Cat Hollow in Uncle Hiram's wagon, Jerry sat dreamily on the box. There was a whole world of joy ahead for them all.

It's fun finding out

WHAT CAN YOU SEE WITH YOUR MIND'S EYE?

BY BRUCE BLIVEN

WHICH weighs more, a pound of feathers or a pound of lead? Everybody knows the answer: they both weigh the same. But what sort of picture popped into your head when you read those words?

You might have seen, clearly, a pair of scales with a lump of lead on one side, balancing a big mound of feathers on the other. Or you might have had no picture at all, but simply thought of the question in terms of words.

There is a great difference in people's power to "make pictures in their heads." Years ago a scientist asked a group of friends to try to picture the breakfast table as they had sat down to it that morning. Some of them saw the table in sharp detail and in color. Others saw it only in black and white. Still others saw a blurred outline, as if through a badly adjusted slide projector. Many could get no picture at all.

Scientists believe that most people are born with the ability to summon up in the mind's eye exact pictures of things that happened in the past. But they say that many of us lose this power as we grow up, simply because we don't practice enough. Yet it can be quite useful to remember things in this way.

Children usually have far better picture memories than grownups. A boy was once shown a picture of a crocodile with its mouth open. A year later he was asked how many teeth the crocodile had. He recalled the picture from his memory, and gave exactly the right number! Could you do this?

Some grownups, too, have good picture memories. The great chess players can play fifteen or twenty games at a time, while blindfolded! Such a player sees, one by one, each board in his mind, with every chessman in the place where it was after the last move.

Mathematicians usually have strong picture memories. They can imagine complicated problems as though set out on a blackboard in their minds. And they "see" the answer written down, so that all they have to do is "read it off." Next time you have to do a simple example in addition or subtraction, put the figures on an imaginary blackboard and try to get the answer without using paper and pencil.

Try to improve your mind's eye. If you find it difficult to remember names and faces, look hard at the next stranger you meet. When he has left the room, summon up his face in your mind — in full color. Or try covering up the bottom two thirds of any line on this page — the tops of the words should be enough for you to visualize the rest.

Rudyard Kipling, in his famous book *Kim*, tells how an Indian secret-service agent trained Kim and another small boy. He put before them a tray on which various jewels were spread out. The boys were allowed to look at the tray for only a few seconds. Then it was covered, and the boys recited what they had seen. The first time Kim tried it he was unable to list all the jewels. But the other boy — who had had several months' training — recited them perfectly.

Why don't you try Kim's game with your friends? You don't need to use jewels! Collect about a dozen small objects from around the house, and put them on a tray. Make your friends look at the tray for thirty seconds. Then cover it with a cloth. The winner is the one who lists the most objects correctly.

On the facing page is a picture of a breakfast scene to test your *powers of observation. You and each of your friends should study it for thirty seconds, then close the book. See who can write down the most objects he has seen in the picture, and describe them correctly.* *Turn to page 108 to see some of the things you should have remembered.*

Adapted from The Diplomat, *© 1957 by Diplomat Publishing Co., Inc.*

UPI

The Girl Who Wouldn't Give Up

BY ALEX HALEY

How a crippled child's courage led her to unexpected triumphs

WILMA RUDOLPH was the seventeenth child in a Negro family in Clarksville, Tennessee. She weighed only four and a half pounds when she was born. And she was four years old before she could even toddle. Then this poor child came down with scarlet fever and double pneumonia. She lay near death for weeks. Finally she pulled through, but her left leg was paralyzed.

The Rudolph family had very little money, but Wilma's mother believed that her little girl had a right to be healthy. She wrapped her in a blanket, and she took her forty-five miles by bus to a medical clinic in Nashville. There, doctors gave Wilma many tests. They said she *might* be able to use her leg again — but only if it were massaged every day for years.

Mrs. Rudolph had a job as a maid, but she had one free day every week. For the next two years she used this day to make the long trip to Nashville with Wilma. The other six days she came home, tired from work, and fixed supper for her large family. Then she massaged the thin little leg until long after Wilma had fallen asleep. At the end of the first year, the doctors found the leg only a little better. So Mrs. Rudolph taught three older children how to massage it too. After that Wilma's leg was rubbed four times a day.

"She's going to walk," said Mrs. Rudolph.

Adapted from The Rotarian, *© 1961 by Rotary International*

Making Up for Lost Play

By the time she was six years old Wilma could hop for short distances. Then her leg would buckle. At eight, she was able to walk with a leg brace. Later that year the doctors gave her a high-top shoe instead of the brace. And Wilma limped happily off to school.

One of Wilma's brothers, Westley, got a basketball. He put a peach basket up on a pole in the back yard. To the family's surprise, Wilma was soon playing basketball. In spite of her heavy shoe, she would swivel and pivot the ball away from Westley. Then she would dribble, and swing to make a shot. When others stopped to rest, she would go on playing alone.

"She's making up for all the playing she's missed," said her mother.

One day Mrs. Rudolph came home to find Wilma bounding around under the peach basket, barefoot! She no longer needed the special shoe.

At thirteen, Wilma entered high school and went out for basketball. Once she was playing so hard she bumped right into the referee, Coach Clinton G. Gray.

"You're buzzing around like a skeeter wherever I turn," he said. And from then on Wilma's nickname was "Skeeter."

Not long afterward, Coach Gray started a girls' track team. He saw Skeeter run, and timed her. Then he stared at his stopwatch in amazement. When the girls' high-school meet was held, she won the 50-, 75- and 100-yard dashes.

Edward Stanley Temple, coach of women's track at Tennessee State University, was watching. With his crack team of "Tigerbelles" he was trying to win fame for this Negro university. And he saw a future champion in the young girl with the perfect sprinter's body, the long powerful legs, and the drive to win.

Never Give Up

Each summer Mr. Temple tried out ten high-school-girl track stars. Those who did well enough were given scholarships to the university. "Be glad to try you out," he told Wilma.

The news thrilled the Rudolph family. They had all helped Skeeter grow strong enough to run. "You're the first one in this house that ever had a chance to go to college," her mother told her. "If running's going to do that, I want you to set your mind to be the best. Never give up!"

With nine other speed stars from Negro high schools, Wilma arrived at Tennessee State that summer. Mr. Temple's first order was for a cross-country jog, some five miles across rough pastures. Halfway, many of the girls were sick and worn out. Wilma, too, stumbled and fell. But somehow they all dragged themselves back.

Mr. Temple greeted them bluntly: "If you want to run here, you have to be in good condition."

Next morning the girls were up at five. Each of them was paired with a Tigerbelle to do fifty-yard sprints. Every high-school runner finished five or ten yards behind, and Wilma did worse than most. When she got back to her room, she cried. She felt ashamed that she had come. But she thought of her mother's saying, "Never give up."

Mr. Temple knew just how to make the girls want to win. He kept telling Wilma what was wrong with her style. "Stretch out those long legs — *stride!*" he told her. "Your elbows look like a windmill. Pump the arms straight. No clenched fists — you run more relaxed with open palms."

He also knew when Wilma had had enough. "Look, Skeeter," he said, with kindness in his voice, "right now you are a fair runner. But I want great runners. My Tigerbelles make you look bad because they're better trained than you. Now you can go home if you want to. Or you can stay, and I'll teach you how to win races." He paused, and then he added, "I think you can be a champion if you want to."

But Something Was Wrong

Three days later Wilma was included among the four Junior Tigerbelles Mr. Temple was taking with his college stars to Ponca City, Oklahoma. There they were to take part in the National A.A.U. (Amateur Athletic Union) meets. These four girls won the Junior Division's 440-yard relay. Their sister Tigerbelles swept all the Senior Division sprints and the relay. Tennessee State had its first A.A.U. championship.

Wilma returned to her family and schoolmates a heroine — to everyone but herself. She still felt she could never run as well as Coach Temple's college girls. Her mother put her finger on the trouble. "It *looks* like you can't," she said. "But you mustn't *think* you can't. You just got to forget everything but trying."

Through the rest of her high-school summers, Wilma drilled in all the details of Tigerbelle style. By the time she entered the university, Mr. Temple was telling the other girls, "Watch Wilma!"

Over and over she would race a hundred yards. Then she would walk back to the starting line and race again. She had heard so many starting pistols and counted her early strides so often that, by now, instinct set her in motion. It told her the exact instant to begin straightening up and "floating" — and, seconds later, when to start leaning to meet the tape.

Everywhere they raced, the Tigerbelles were winners. With the three other members of the relay team — Martha Hudson, Barbara Jones and Lucinda Williams — Wilma ranked as one of the four fastest Tigerbelles. Yet, in intrasquad races, the other three always beat her.

"What's wrong?" Mr. Temple often asked.

"I don't know, Coach," she said. For she was trying with all she had.

Then, in November 1959, Wilma began suffering from sore throat. Mr. Temple took her to a doctor, who took out her tonsils. "Those infected tonsils have been sapping her strength for years," the doctor said.

A Great Race

Three weeks later, Wilma returned to the track. She was in full health for the first time in her life. At the Chicago Indoor A.A.U. Nationals she blazed to first place in three races. In Corpus Christi, Texas, she shaved three tenths of a second off the Olympic and world 200-meter record. Tryouts for the 1960 Olympic games were held at Abilene, Texas. There Wilma took the 100 and 200 meters. She anchored the winning Tigerbelle relay team.

"Somebody will have to set a new world record to beat her!" Mr. Temple exclaimed.

Seven Tigerbelles were among the three hundred and ten United States athletes who flew to Rome to take part in the Olympic games in August 1960. There, in the 100-meter sprint, Wilma set a new Olympic record of eleven seconds flat. In the 200-meter finals she won a breathtaking victory over Germany's great star Jutta Heine.

Now it was time for the women's 400-meter relay! The people packing the huge stadium fell silent. Six teams were taking their places on the track. But all eyes were on one girl — Wilma Rudolph. If the United States team won this final, she would be the first American woman ever to win three gold medals in track.

A starting pistol cracked. The first runners shot from their starting blocks and raced the batons to the second. The second runners raced to the third. And now Lucinda Williams was in the lead. She flashed toward Wilma, who had already started her forward motion.

Then a gasp went up from the crowd. The baton was fumbled, and Wilma had to stop to grasp it! Germany's Jutta Heine was flying two strides ahead. But now Wilma's long scissorlike strides began to burn up the track. She came abreast of Jutta Heine . . . pulled slightly ahead . . . and burst the tape in first place.

Queen of Track

The Tigerbelles had won the relay, and the lean brown girl from Tennessee was a three-time gold-medal winner! The noise in the stadium was deafening. "Wilma!" the crowd roared. "Skeeter!" Hats, newspapers, programs and autograph books rained down on the field as she half circled and jogged toward the sidelines.

"Coach Temple! Coach Temple!" Wilma was crying, as athletes and photographers crowded around her. She was the world's Queen of Track. And she was weeping tears of thanks for her coach's patient training and for her mother's determination that a crippled child would walk.

When Wilma came home, every school and business in Clarksville was closed for "Welcome Wilma Day." The whole town lined the streets to cheer her. American sports writers voted her "Woman Athlete of the Year." A year later she was given the James E. Sullivan award for being America's outstanding athlete, male or female. In 1962 she went on to break more world records as a sprinter, both at home and in Europe, to prove that she is still the fastest woman in the world.

But the girl from Clarksville is always modest and good-natured. Life means more to her than medals and meets. Her desire is to be a schoolteacher and to pass on to other children the important lesson she has learned — that those who really want to can win.

Nonstop Speller

Asked if she could spell "banana," a little girl said, "I know how to spell 'banana' but I never know when to stop."

— *Quoted by Charles Poore in* The New York Times

The Scotty Who Knew Too Much

BY JAMES THURBER

SEVERAL summers ago there was a Scotty who went to the country for a visit. He decided that all the farm dogs were cowards, because they were afraid of a certain animal that had a white stripe down its back.

"You are a pussycat and I can lick you," the Scotty said to the farm dog who lived in the house where the Scotty was visiting. "I can lick the little animal with the white stripe, too. Show him to me."

"Don't you want to ask any questions about him?" said the farm dog.

"Naw," said the Scotty. "*You* ask the questions."

So the farm dog took the Scotty into the woods and showed him the white-striped animal and the Scotty closed in on him, growling and slashing. It was all over in a moment and the Scotty lay on his back. When he came to, the farm dog said, "What happened?"

"He threw vitriol," said the Scotty, "but he never laid a glove on me."

A few days later the farm dog told the Scotty there was another animal all the farm dogs were afraid of.

"Lead me to him," said the Scotty. "I can lick anything that doesn't wear horseshoes."

"Don't you want to ask any questions about him?" said the farm dog.

"Naw," said the Scotty. "Just show me where he hangs out." So the farm dog led him to a place in the woods and pointed out the little animal when he came along.

"A clown," said the Scotty, "a pushover," and he closed in, leading with his left and exhibiting some mighty fancy footwork.

In less than a second the Scotty was flat on his back, and when he woke up the farm dog was pulling quills out of him.

"What happened?" said the farm dog.

"He pulled a knife on me," said the Scotty, "but at least I have learned how you fight out here in the country, and now I am going to beat *you* up."

So he closed in on the farm dog, holding his nose with one front paw to ward off the vitriol and covering his eyes with the other front paw to keep out the knives.

The Scotty couldn't see his opponent and he couldn't smell his opponent and he was so badly beaten that he had to be taken back to the city and put in a nursing home.

Moral: *It is better to ask some of the questions than to know all the answers.*

Condensed from The Thurber Carnival, *copyright © 1940 by James Thurber and published by Harper & Row*

Male rose-breasted grosbeak feeding its young

PAINTING REPRODUCED COURTESY OF JOHN MORRELL & CO., © 1958, CHICAGO, ILL.

Birdman to the World

BY PETER FARB

With his remarkable guidebooks, Roger Tory Peterson has opened the eyes of millions to the wonderful world of birds

A REBEL, always in trouble at school. That was Roger Tory Peterson when he was a boy in Jamestown, a factory town in western New York State. He was a daydreamer, and rules rubbed him the wrong way.

But when he was eleven, and in seventh grade, his teacher started a Junior Audubon Club. Class members paid a dime, and each of them got a set of Audubon bird leaflets. Young Roger was amazed at the sheer beauty of the birds — the brilliant crimson of the cardinal and the rainbow colors of the hummingbird. He was thrilled, too, by their freedom to soar into the sky.

Roger soon started a list of birds he saw. He combed the woods and fields around Jamestown. He even rose before daybreak to get in some bird-watching before school opened. He planned his newspaper route to take in the best bird haunts. And he bought his first camera with his newspaper earnings.

When Roger saw a strange bird, he usually scrawled a picture of it. Then he would trudge to the library to read books on bird identification. For hours he pored over the scientific descriptions, trying to puzzle out the names of birds he had seen. That was when he first felt

Adapted from Audubon Magazine, © *1961 by National Audubon Society*

the need for books that would tell how to identify quickly and easily the various species of wildlife.

In high school Roger was still a daydreamer, and he did poorly in most of his subjects. But he got the highest marks in art in the history of the school. After graduating, he worked in a furniture factory, painting designs on cabinets. But always the world of birds was in his thoughts.

By 1925 — when he was just seventeen — he had saved enough money to make a bus trip to New York City. He took with him two of his watercolor paintings: one of a darting hummingbird and one of a large black-and-white kingbird. When an artist at the American Museum of Natural History saw these pictures, he had them shown at an important meeting of ornithologists.

One of the museum's ornithologists took Roger on a field trip to Long Island. This was Ludlow Griscom, who was known for his ability to identify birds on the wing. Roger found that Griscom could name a bird in a split second because he had noticed special markings, shapes or patterns of color that were easy to recognize. He used these "field marks," as he called them, as keys to quick identification.

Peterson got the idea that it might someday be possible to identify *all* birds by their field marks alone. He began jotting down the telltale field marks of every new bird he saw — a crest, a patch of white on the body, anything. Soon his private list of birds had grown to more than three hundred — or three quarters of all the species found in the eastern United States.

From 1927 to 1931 Peterson attended art schools in New York City, and in 1931 he began teaching art at Rivers School near Boston. Evenings, he completed his list of field marks, and made paintings to show the key points of difference between birds. In 1934 his first book, *A Field Guide to the Birds,* was published. It was a success right away.

The Peterson system makes bird identification simple. If you see a bird that looks like a small gull, but has a forked tail and narrow wings, it is a tern. The only all-red bird with a crest is a cardinal. How can you tell the little chipping sparrow from the many similar sparrows? Peterson points to its reddish cap and the black line running through its eye with the white line over it. This system worked so well that the armed services copied it for aircraft identification during World War II.

When *A Field Guide to the Birds* appeared, Peterson was asked to become educational director of the National Audubon Society. His first job was to rewrite more than one hundred Junior Audubon Club leaflets — the very leaflets that had so inspired him when he was a boy! The Peterson leaflets are still in use. By now they have been read by millions of young people.

Peterson also did much to interest boys and girls in conservation. He helped to start new bird and nature clubs. And he made whirlwind speaking tours, sometimes visiting as many as eleven groups in one day. Largely through his efforts, membership in Junior Audubon Clubs more than doubled in five years. There are now a quarter of a million members. Peterson still spends about five months of each year away from his wife and his own two boys, talking at Audubon Society meetings and making field trips. And there is a whole series of books based on his system — books on identifying trees, flowers, shells, insects, mammals and rocks. His guide to birdsongs is on two long-playing records.

Roger Tory Peterson has seen many more species of birds than were ever seen by John James Audubon, the great artist-naturalist of the nineteenth century. There are said to be six hundred and fifty species in the United States and Canada, and he has seen all but six of them — more than anyone else in history. He has photographed and sketched almost all the European species west of the Iron Curtain. And he has focused his field glasses on birds of every continent except Australia. His fourteen field guides have opened the wonders of the living world to people everywhere. In 1961 alone he made expeditions to Japan, Hawaii and other Pacific islands, to Mexico's wild Gulf of California, and to many wilderness areas of the United States.

PHOTOGRAPH BY CHARLES E. MOHR, NATIONAL AUDUBON SOCIETY

Roger Tory Peterson with the camera gun he uses to photograph birds in flight. The gun-sight arrangement permits smooth following of the flying bird.

His present project is to photograph and sketch the seabirds of the world.

Thus a dreamy and rebellious schoolboy with a talent for art has given the world a precious gift. Millions of young people have learned from him to know and to love nature. Millions of city people have discovered the joys of a weekend in the country, identifying birds and animals and flowers. Many of these bird watchers have become so skilled that they are able to help the ornithologists. Some keep the dates that the migratory birds arrive in spring, and track migration routes. Some help take the yearly bird census. Others work with the U.S. Fish and Wildlife Service in banding birds.

Roger Tory Peterson has done marvelous things for American wildlife. But — in the words of one famous American naturalist — "he has done even more for people. He has opened their eyes to the wonders that surround us."

If you, too, would like to become a bird watcher, you can find out about the bird clubs nearest you by writing to the National Audubon Society, 1130 Fifth Avenue, New York 28, New York; or, in Canada, to the Canadian Audubon Society, 46 St. Clair Avenue, East, Toronto 7.

Bird-watching in Your Own Back Yard

WOULD you like to start a list of birds *you* know — and help the birds at the same time? You can have fun doing both by setting up a "restaurant" in your own back yard.

First, pick a sheltered spot, perhaps near a bush or a tangle of vine. Then put out a shallow basin of water. Bits of mirror in the bottom will reflect the sun and attract the birds. In winter, add a drop or two of glycerine to keep the water from freezing. In winter, too, you should scratch up the frozen earth around the basin and sprinkle it with sand or ashes. This will give your "customers" the grit they use instead of teeth to grind up their food.

Now, what to feed these customers? Sparrows will eat bread crumbs. But other birds prefer cracked wheat, cracked corn, chick feed, millet or hemp. Just scatter these on the ground along with peanuts for the jays, and sunflower seed for the cardinals and chickadees. Hang a piece of suet from a nearby tree limb to provide fat — and a doughnut swinging by a string to be both treat and trapeze for the little birds. Bones with shreds of meat on them will please the woodpeckers. And many birds like popcorn, or crackers spread with peanut butter.

It is important not to frighten the birds while they are eating. Most are shy. But in time some, like the chickadees, may fly to greet you — and even eat from your hand! If you watch quietly and use Peterson's identification system, you will soon know the names of all your customers.

Based on Pageant in the Sky *by Raymond S. Deck, copyright 1941 and published by Dodd, Mead & Co., Inc., and on several articles published in The Reader's Digest*

Can you name these birds?

*Here are some common birds that may come to feed at a back-yard restaurant. You should be able to name two of them quickly from having read the story "Bird-man to the World." There are hints in the story on bird feeding to help you name some of the others. For the names and field marks of all of them—as given in Peterson's famous "A Field Guide to the Birds"—**turn to page 128*

The bird paintings reproduced here are by Dr. Roger Tory Peterson, from his A Field Guide to the Birds,*copyright 1934, 1939, 1947, 1962 by Roger Tory Peterson and published by Houghton Mifflin Co. The answers on page 128 are based on the same book.*

The story of a challenging—and terrifying —day in the life of a fifteen-year-old boy who grew up to be an associate justice of the United States Supreme Court

Two Boys on a Mountain

BY WILLIAM O. DOUGLAS

I WAS not quite fifteen and my friend Douglas Corpron was nineteen when the two of us climbed Kloochman Rock in the Cascade Mountains of Washington State. It is an oval-shaped lava rock, rising two thousand feet above Tieton Basin. A third of the way up there are gentle slopes of pine and fir. Then a twelve-hundred-foot cliff rises to the sky — straight as the Washington Monument and twice as high.

We were on a camping trip with another boy named Walter Kohagen, and we had spent the night in the Tieton Basin. It was bitter cold, and we rose at dawn to cook frying-pan bread and trout for breakfast. Doug and I had not planned to climb Kloochman. But somehow the challenge came to us as the sun touched her crest. Walter decided to wait for us at the base of the cliff. If we did not return by night, he could summon help.

There were fairly easy routes up the rock, but we chose the southeast face — the one that, I believe, never has been conquered. Doug led. The beginning was easy. For a hundred feet or so we found ledges six to twelve inches wide. But then the ledges became narrower and the footwork dangerous. We took off our shoes and tied them behind us on our belts. Then we wormed up the wall in stocking feet. We tested each toehold and fingerhold for loose rock before putting our weight on it. At times we had to inch along sidewise, pressed tightly against the rock, in order to reach the ledge above us.

Doug Takes a Chance

Often we could not climb easily from one ledge to another. The one above might be only a foot or so high. Then we would have to reach it with one knee and slowly bring the other knee up. Delicately balancing on both knees on the upper edge, we would come slowly to our feet by pressing close to the wall and getting such hold with our fingers as the lava rock permitted.

In that tortuous way we made perhaps six hundred feet in two hours. It was late morning when we found we were in serious trouble. The three-inch ledge on which we stood ended in a cul-de-sac. There seemed nothing above us within reach.

Just out of reach above Doug, however, was a fairly large crevice which would make a good handhold. How could he get up to it? I could not boost him, for my own balance was unsteady. Clearly, he would have to jump to it — and he would have but one jump. He was standing on a ledge only a few inches wide; so he could not expect to jump for his handhold, miss it and land safely. A slip meant he would hurtle down six hundred feet onto the rocks. After much discussion, Doug decided to take the chance. Closing my eyes, I asked God to help Doug up the wall.

In a second Doug said in a cheery voice, "Well, here goes."

He placed both palms against the wall, and bent his knees slowly. Then he paused a second, and jumped straight up. It was not much of a jump — only six inches or so. But it was a daredevil jump for one pressed against a cliff six hundred feet in the air. The suspense was over at once — there was Doug hanging from a strong, wide ledge. But there was no toehold. He would have to hoist himself by his arms alone. His body went slowly up as if pulled by some unseen winch. A moment later he was on the ledge.

"Nothing to it," he chuckled.

But a great disappointment followed. There was no higher ledge Doug could reach. We would have to go down the sheer rock wall.

Near the Breaking Point

First Doug had to leave the ledge he was on. He dared not slide blindly to the skimpy ledge he had left. I must help him. I could not hold his weight, so I must exert enough pressure to slow up his descent and to direct his toe onto the ledge.

Doug lowered himself and hung full length, his feet about six inches above the ledge. It was now up to me. I placed my right hand in the small of his back and pressed upward with all my might.

He let go gently, and the full length of his body came against my arm. I trembled under the tension. My left hand hung onto a crack in the rock, like a grappling hook. My stomach pressed against the wall as if it were glued there.

Down Doug came — a full inch. I couldn't help glancing down and seeing the rocks far below.

Down Doug moved another inch, then a third. My left hand seemed paralyzed. My toes were aching. My right arm shook. I could not hold much longer. "Steady, Doug," I said. "The ledge is a foot to your right." He pawed the wall with his foot, searching.

"I can't find it," he said. "Don't let go. The only hold I have is with my left hand, and it's not much."

The crisis was upon us. In a few seconds I would reach the physical breaking point and Doug would go hurtling off the cliff.

I will never know how I did it. But somehow I stood for a moment on my left foot alone. I used my right leg as a rod to guide his foot to the ledge. His toes grabbed it as if they were the talons of a bird. "Are you okay?" I asked.

"Yes," said Doug. "Good work."

My right arm fell from him, paralyzed. I shook from exhaustion. My face was wet with perspiration. We stood against the rock for several minutes, relaxing and regaining our calm.

Doug said: "Let's throw our shoes down. It will be easier going." So we untied them from our belts and dropped them to Walter, who was waiting at the rock field below us.

A Ledge Gives Way

Our descent was painfully slow, but uneventful. By midafternoon we reached the bottom. We got our shoes from Walter, and started around the other side of the rock. We left the southeast wall unconquered.

But we were still determined to climb the rock. We chose the northwest wall. Here, too, is a cliff, rising a thousand feet, but it has many toeholds and fingerholds that make the start fairly easy. So we set out with our shoes on.

When we were partway up, I worked along a ledge to the south. This was easier going, and soon I was twenty-five feet above Doug and fifty feet to his right. Suddenly the thin ledge on which I was standing gave way. As I felt it crumble, I grabbed for a hold above me. The crevice I seized

Adapted from Of Men and Mountains, *copyright 1950 by William O. Douglas and published by Harper & Row*

was solid. But there I was, hanging by my hands two hundred feet in the air. I yelled for help.

Doug at once started toward me, shouting, "Hang on! I'll be there."

Hang on I did. My fingers, then my wrists and arms ached terribly. Every second seemed a minute, every minute an hour. I would slip, I thought, slip to sure death. In my mind's eye I saw the jagged rocks below that seemed to pull me toward them. My fingers began to give way.

Fright grew in me. The idea of hanging helpless two hundred feet above the abyss brought panic. I cried out to Doug, but the words caught in my dry throat. I was like someone in a nightmare who struggles to shout, but cannot.

Suddenly I realized how much I wanted to live. But I would need the help of One more powerful than Doug and I. And so again that day I prayed. I asked God to give me guts, to give me power to do the impossible. Oh, God, help me hang on!

I felt someone pushing my left foot upward. As if through a dream, Doug's voice was saying, "Your feet are eighteen inches below your toehold." Doug found those toeholds for my feet.

I pulled myself up. I rested on my elbows on the ledge to which my hands had been glued. Then I flexed my fingers and bent my wrists to bring life back.

It was shortly above the point where Doug saved my life that we discovered a path up Kloochman. It was a three-sided chimney chute a few feet wide, that led almost to the top. And it was filled with loose rock that had to be cleared away. Once again we tied our shoes on our belts. Then we climbed the chute in stocking feet, pressing our hands and feet against the opposing walls.

The sun was setting when we reached the top. We were gay and excited. We talked about the glories of the scene in front of us. We shouted and hallooed to the empty meadows far below us. It was wonderful to be alive, breathing, using our muscles, seeing.

On that July afternoon Doug and I found life especially good because death had passed so close.

We stayed only a short while at the top. Then we went down the way we had come up. We were racing the darkness, as we did not want to spend the night on Kloochman's treacherous wall.

Walter was waiting for us, and it was dark when we reached our camp. That night I knelt on a bed of fir boughs beside the embers of a campfire and thanked God for giving Doug and me the strength to save each other's lives.

Since that day I have climbed many mountains, but none more challenging — or more thrilling — than Kloochman Rock.

UPI

When Justice Douglas is not serving in Washington, he roams the world — exploring its wilderness areas from Alaska to Afghanistan and climbing its snow-capped mountains. He has left his bootprints on the Sierras of the West and the White Mountains of New England; on India's giant Himalayas; on the jagged peaks of Australia, Indonesia and Iran. Here he is shown vacationing in the Wallowa Mountains of Oregon. His companion's name is Frosty.

The Lone Ranger

POSTED on a fence outside a hamlet in Montana's badlands is this sign: "Powderville, Mont., population 1. Mayor, Joe Hodges. Chief of Police, Joe Hodges. Fire Chief, Joe Hodges. Drive carefully—the life you save may be Joe's."

—UPI

It's dangerous to make a magician mad!

The Sleeve Trick

BY STEPHEN LEACOCK

"LADIES and gentlemen," said the conjurer, "I have shown you that the cloth is absolutely empty. Now I will proceed to take from it a bowl of goldfish. Presto!"

All around the hall people were saying, "Oh, how wonderful! How does he do it?"

But the Quick Man on the front seat was nobody's fool. He said in a big whisper to the people near him, "He—had—it—up—his—sleeve."

The people nodded brightly and said, "Oh, of course." And everybody whispered around the hall, "He—had—it—up—his—sleeve."

"My next trick," said the conjurer, "is the famous Hindu Rings. You will notice that the rings appear to be separate. At a blow they all join *(clang, clang, clang)*. Presto!"

There was a buzz of amazement. Then the Quick Man was heard to whisper, "He must have had another lot—up his sleeve."

Again everybody nodded and whispered, "The rings were—up his sleeve."

The conjurer frowned.

"I will now," he went on, "show you a most amusing trick, by taking any number of eggs from a hat. Will some gentleman kindly lend me his hat? Ah, thank you. Presto!"

He took seventeen eggs from the hat. For thirty-five seconds the audience began to think he was wonderful. Then the Quick Man whispered along the front bench, "He has a hen—*up his sleeve.*"

The egg trick was ruined.

The Quick Man went on whispering as the conjurer performed more tricks. According to him, the conjurer must have concealed up his sleeve a loaf of bread, a doll's cradle, a live guinea pig and a rocking chair — in addition to the fishbowl, the rings and the hen.

The conjurer could tell that everybody was losing faith in his tricks. So he rallied for a last try.

"Ladies and gentlemen," he said, "I will now present to you the famous Japanese Trick recently invented by the natives of Ireland." He turned toward the Quick Man. "Will you, sir, kindly lend me your watch?"

It was passed to him.

"Have I your permission to put it into this mortar and pound it to pieces?" he asked savagely.

The Quick Man nodded and smiled.

The conjurer threw the watch into the mortar and grasped a sledgehammer from the table. There was a sound of violent smashing.

"He's slipped it *up his sleeve,*" whispered the Quick Man.

"Now, sir," said the conjurer, "will you kindly pass me your derby hat and allow me to dance on it? Thank you."

The conjurer made a few quick passes with his feet and showed the hat completely crushed. The Quick Man beamed. This time the real mystery of the thing fascinated him.

"And will you now, sir," said the conjurer, "take off your tie and permit me to burn it with a match? Thank you, sir. And will you allow me to smash your glasses with my hammer? Thank you."

By this time the Quick Man was beginning to look puzzled. "This thing beats me," he whispered. "I don't see through it a bit."

There was a great hush upon the audience. The conjurer gave the Quick Man a withering look. Then he said, "Ladies and gentlemen, you can see that I have — with this gentleman's permission — broken his watch, burned his tie, danced on his hat and smashed his glasses. If he will give me the further permission to paint green stripes on his overcoat, I shall be delighted to entertain you. If not, the show is at an end."

Amid a burst of music from the orchestra, the curtain fell. And the audience went home knowing there are *some* tricks, at any rate, that are not done up the conjurer's sleeve.

Adapted from Literary Lapses *by Stephen Leacock, and reprinted by permission of Dodd, Mead & Co.*

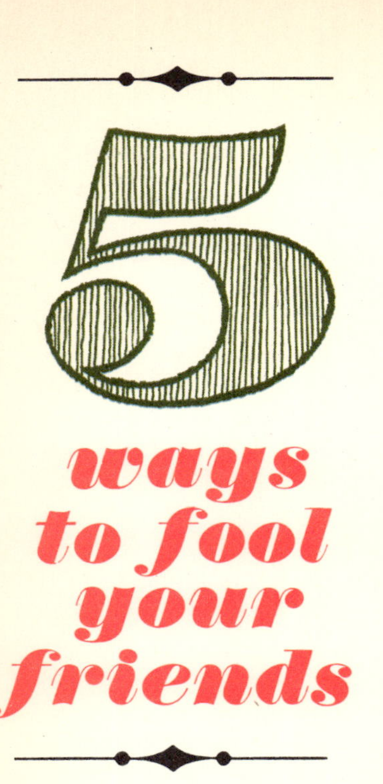

5 ways to fool your friends

BY GUY FREDERICK

Here are some clever tricks you can perform for your friends. Or you can use them in putting on a magic show for a little brother's or sister's birthday party. Let's hope there is no one in your audience as rude as the "Quick Man"!

famous names

For this trick, you will need ten small cards or pieces of paper, a slate and a hat.

With everything at hand, ask someone in your audience to call out the name of a famous person. Write this down on one of the cards and drop the card into the hat. Ask for another name. This time do not write the name that is called, but write the first name again. As different names are called you continue writing the original name on each card until the ten cards are in the hat, all with the same name on them. Now write this name on the slate so that the audience does not see it.

Place the slate where it can be seen, but with the writing away from the audience. Invite a spectator to assist you. Shake the hat to mix the cards. Ask the spectator to reach into the hat and select one of the slips, and read the name written on it, aloud. When he has done so, turn the slate around to show that the name selected was the same as the one that you predicted on the slate. Be sure to destroy the slips after your performance, so that no one will see them.

Adapted from Magic Tricks, *copyright © 1958 by Sterling Publishing Co., Inc., with editorial additions*

the same as you

This is a gag which you can use to get a laugh.

Hand a spectator a slip of paper and tell him to go to the other side of the room and write a short sentence on the paper, fold it and hand it to another spectator. Appear to concentrate very deeply, and say, "I will write the same as you on my slip," which you do. Hand your slip to the spectator who is holding the other slip. Ask him to open the other slip and read it aloud. Now you say, "That's right. I wrote the same as you." And that's exactly what you **have** written—just the four words, "The same as you"!

a simple reverse

Before you start this card trick, turn the bottom card in the deck over so that it faces the rest of the cards. Fan the deck slightly, so as not to expose the turned-over card.

Have someone select a card and, while the spectator is looking at it, secretly turn over the deck so that the bottom, or reversed, card is at the top. The deck will still appear to be the same way up. Have the spectator replace the card in the deck, but hold the deck firmly so that he cannot see the other cards in it.

Turn around and go to a table and, as you do so, turn the bottom card over so that it will be facing the same way as the rest of the cards. Spread the cards face up on the table. One card will be reversed. Ask the spectator to name his card. He does so, and you then turn over the face-down card, which proves to be the card he selected.

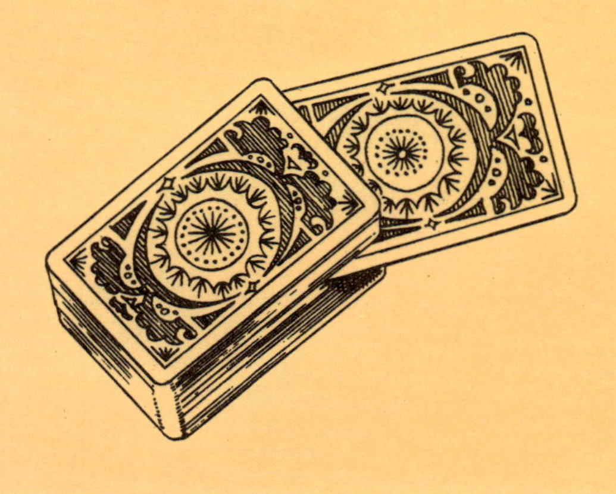

the disappearing coin

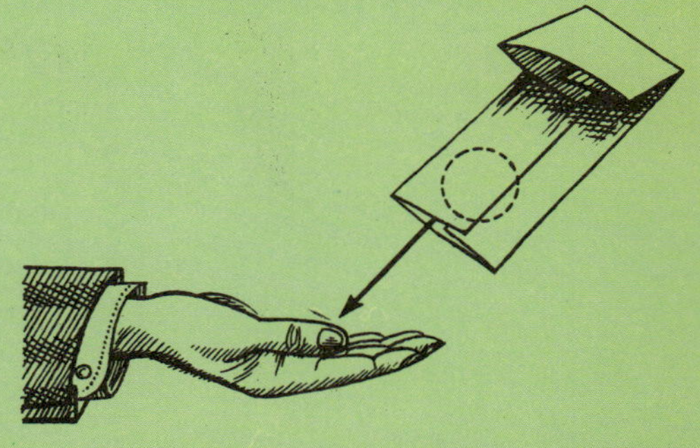

Take a piece of stiff paper, about 3 by 5 inches in size. Lay a penny in its center, and fold the paper lengthwise over the penny so that the sides overlap. In other words, you roll the penny in the paper, but not too tightly, as it must be able to slide through the "tube" of paper.

Let someone feel the paper to prove that the penny is actually there. Hold the packet vertically in your left hand, and fold the top part down over the penny. Release the pressure on the penny and let it slip down into your hand. Now fold the bottom part of the paper up and over the spot where the penny should be.

Take the packet in your right hand, and drop your left hand to your side, where you slip the coin into your pocket. Now, with both hands, tear the paper in half, showing the penny is gone.

the banana sliced inside its skin

Shortly before you want to do this trick, take a very slender needle with some fine but strong thread. Stick the needle into a banana at A and draw it out again at B (see top diagram). Stick it in again at B, and draw it out at C. Keep on in this way until the needle comes back out at A, after having gone all the way around (lower diagram). Gently, and at the same time, pull out the two ends of the thread. The banana will have been sliced on the inside without leaving any noticeable marks on its skin. Repeat the process at several places along the length of the banana, and you are ready to fool your friends with it.

Offer the banana to one of them, saying, "Please eat this banana. It is not a fake and it won't do you any harm. It has even been sliced for you already. . . ."

When your friend peels the skin off the banana, he will be amazed to discover that, although the peel was intact, the banana inside is already sliced into several pieces.

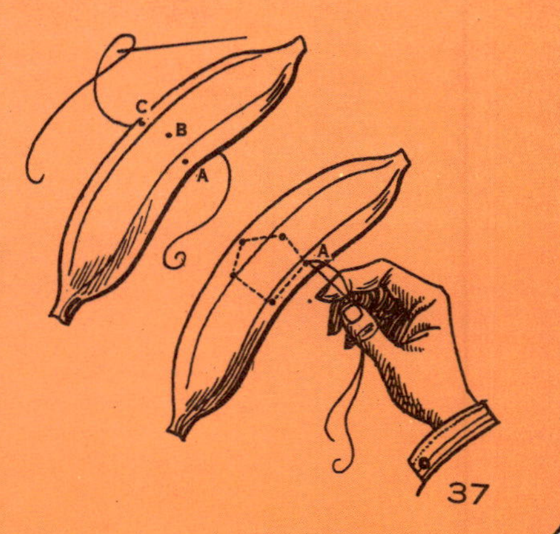

COURTESY OF NASA

John Glenn
and His Day in Space

With skill, with daring and with faith, John Glenn became the first American to orbit the earth. Others have followed him. Still others will venture even farther into space. But none will dim the memory of his thrilling and historic flight

THIS was the moment. He had worked toward it for three years. Now he was alone, flat on his back on a form-fit couch inside the capsule *Friendship 7*. Calmly, Lieutenant Colonel John Herschel Glenn, Jr., began to count: "Ten, nine, eight, seven, six . . ." A great yellow-white gush of flame spewed out from the Atlas-D missile. For nearly four seconds, it seemed rooted to its pad.

Then it headed into the brilliant blue sky. "We're under way," he said. The next four hours and fifty-six minutes were like none John Glenn had ever known. There was beauty. "I don't know what you can say about a day in which you have seen four beautiful sunsets —" Glenn said later "— three in orbit, and one after I was back." There was the wonder of weightlessness. And there was danger: "This," he said, "could have been a bad day all the way around."

After lift-off, rocket and capsule would have to separate at the proper angle to put Glenn into orbit. When he got word from Cape Canaveral that he was indeed in orbit, Glenn radioed back joyfully: "Capsule is turning around. Oh, that view is tremendous! I can see the booster doing turnarounds just a couple of hundred yards behind. Cape is go and I am go."

Adapted from Time, © *1962 by Time Inc.*

Eerie World

As he began to cross Africa, Glenn tested his reactions to the eerie world of weightlessness. He carefully squeezed a tube of applesauce into his mouth. Swallowing was no problem. "Your tongue forces it back in the throat," he reported. "And you swallow normally."

He shook his head violently to see if the motion would give him space sickness. Nothing happened. "I have had no ill effects at all from zero G," he reported. "It's very pleasant, as a matter of fact."

Glenn had with him a small hand camera to take pictures through his window. "It seemed perfectly natural. Rather than put the camera away, I just put it out in midair and let go of it." With the camera suspended as though on an invisible shelf, he went on with other work. Then he reached back and plucked the camera out of the air.

Only once was there any trouble. Glenn was getting ready to change film when he let the roll slip out of his fingers. He grabbed for it. But "instead of clamping onto it, I batted it and it went sailing off around behind the instrument panel. That was the last I saw of it."

Soaring over the Indian Ocean, Glenn began his first night in space. The stars were bright diamonds on black velvet.

As he approached Australia, he radioed Astronaut Gordon Cooper in the tracking station at Muchea: "That was about the shortest day I've ever run into. Just to my right, I can see a big pattern of light, apparently right on the coast."

The glow was the city of Perth, which had prepared a welcome for Glenn that was also a test of his night vision. Streetlights were ablaze. People turned on their porch lights, and spread sheets in the yard as reflectors. When the lights were explained to him, Glenn radioed Cooper: "Thank everybody for turning them on, will you?"

Then, in the first moments of dawn, Glenn saw a fantastic sight. At first he thought that "the capsule had gone up while I wasn't looking, and that I was looking into a new star field. There were thousands of little particles outside the cabin. They were a bright yellowish green, about the size and intensity of a firefly on a real dark night. As far as I could look off to each side, I could see them."

Glenn soon decided that his own capsule was probably giving off electrically charged particles

COURTESY OF NASA

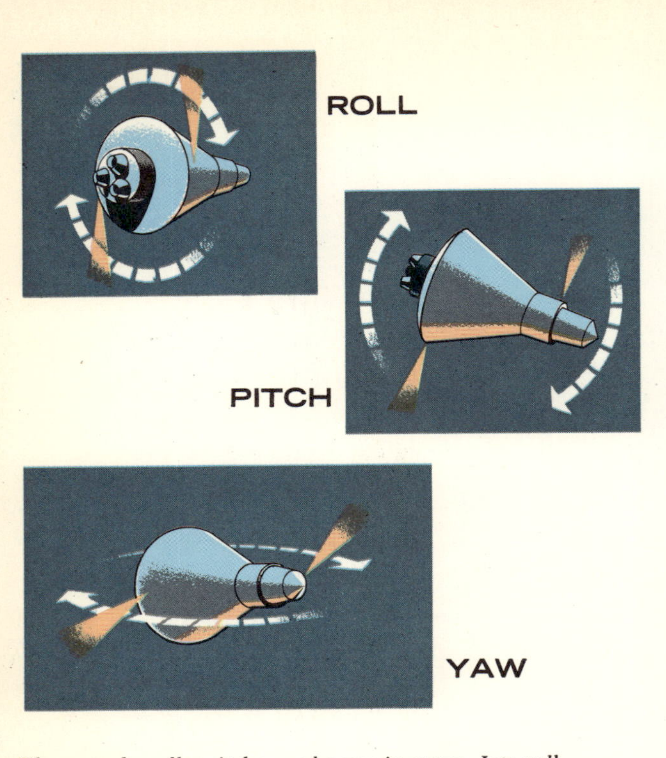

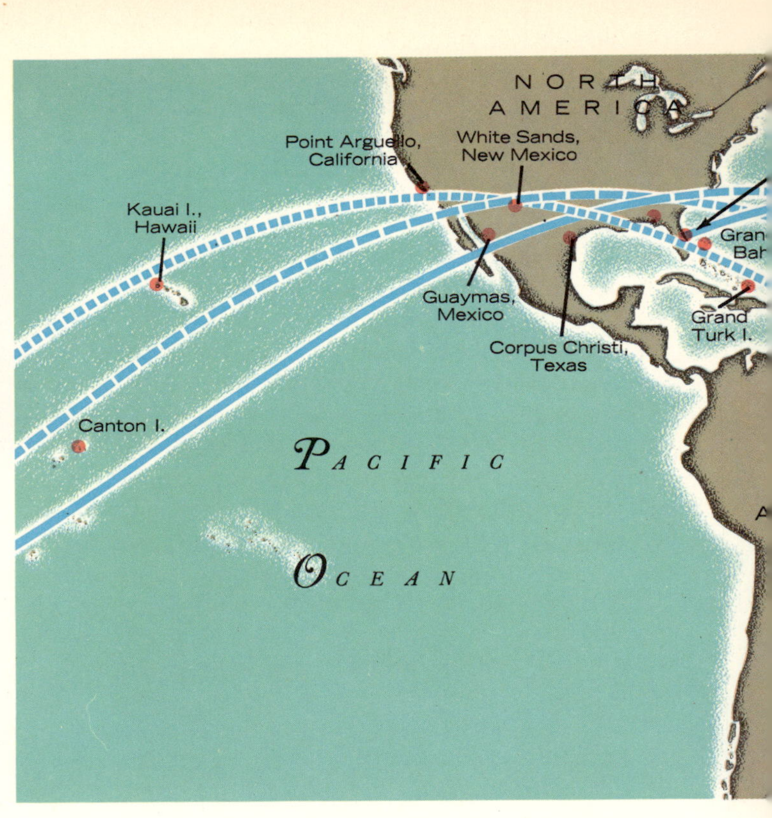

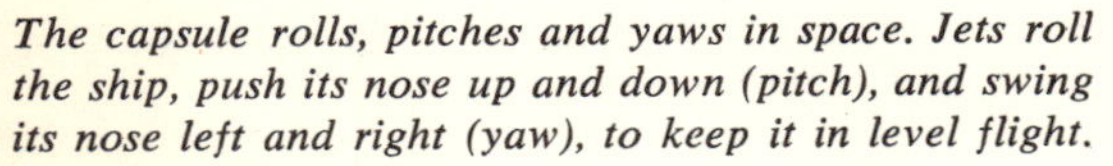

The capsule rolls, pitches and yaws in space. Jets roll the ship, push its nose up and down (pitch), and swing its nose left and right (yaw), to keep it in level flight.

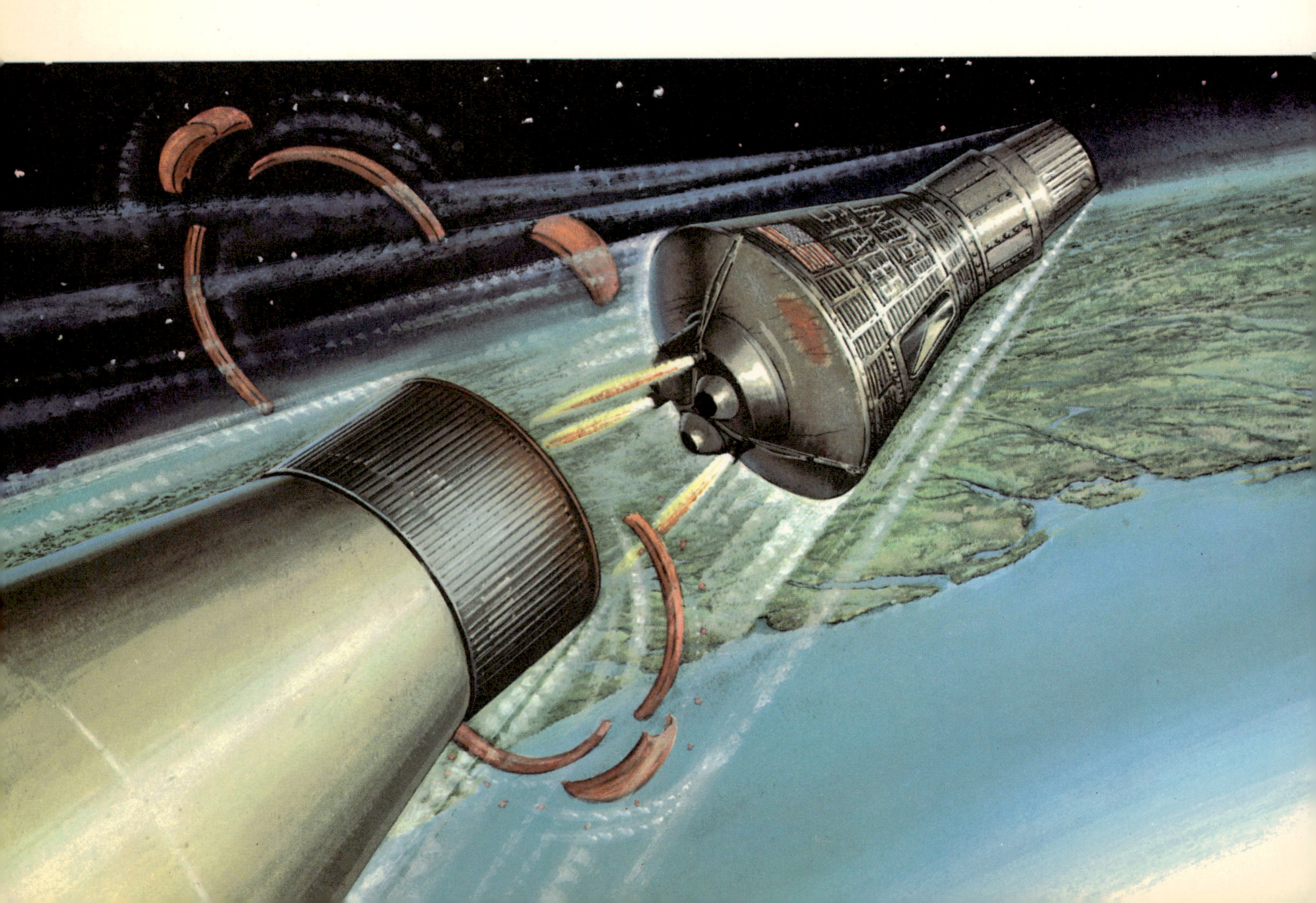

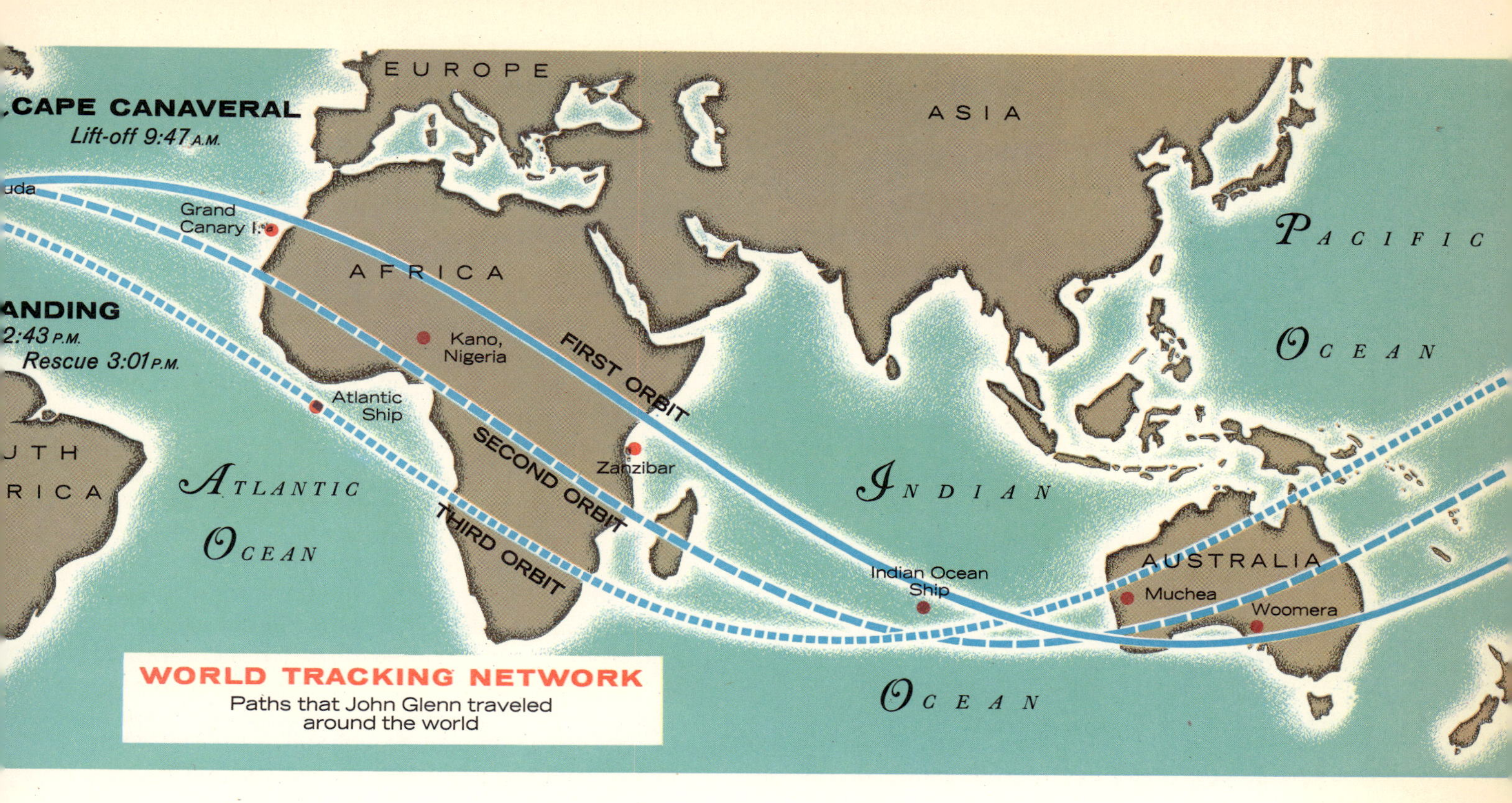

of water or gas vapor. These, he knew, would be attracted to each other, and could have built up the specks that he saw.

Nightmare of Suspense

Throughout his thrilling day, John Glenn recorded what it felt like to be the United States' first tourist in orbital space. He had little sensation of speed. It was, he said, "about the same as flying in an airliner at, say thirty thousand feet, and looking down at clouds at ten thousand feet."

Over California, he spotted part of the Imperial Valley to his left, and the Salton Sea. He could even pick out the irrigated acres around El Centro, where he once lived. Looking down on the Atlantic, he saw the Gulf Stream as a river of blue. Cabin temperature at one point went up to 108 degrees. But Glenn was comfortable inside his separately cooled space suit. During periods of darkness, he flicked on the tiny flashlights that were attached to the fingers of his gloves. These little beams of light helped him to read his maps.

But Astronaut Glenn's adventure soon turned into a nightmare of suspense. Over Guaymas, Mexico, on his first orbit, the capsule's attitude-control system began to act up. A small jet, designed to release hydrogen-peroxide steam to keep the capsule in a stable position, was not working properly. Glenn reported that the capsule "drifts off in yaw to the right at about one degree per second. It will go to twenty degrees and hold at that."

To return the capsule to its normal position, Glenn took over the controls himself. He put other jets into action. For most of the rest of the flight, he had to "fly" the capsule by hand — or by using a semi-automatic "fly-by-wire" system something like power steering on an automobile.

As he crossed the Pacific a second time, the troublesome jets made the capsule "roll" (turn on its horizontal axis). Chimpanzee Enos's capsule had been brought down after two orbits because of a similar roll. But John Glenn was able to overcome the trouble by hand.

This problem was worrisome. But it was nothing as compared with the next threat. It came as Glenn was beginning his second orbit. At Cape Canaveral an instrument panel in the Project Mercury Control Center picked up a warning that the Fiberglas heat shield on *Friendship 7* had come ajar. If the shield were to separate before or during the capsule's re-entry into the earth's atmosphere, John Glenn would perish in a flash of flame.

One by one, other tracking stations picked up the ominous signal. Project Mercury officials huddled tensely, trying to decide what to do. The answer might mean life or searing death to John Glenn. The final decision was made by Operations Director Walter Williams. An attempt would be made to hold the heat shield in place by changing the re-entry procedure.

The retro-rocket packet was supposed to be jettisoned after the rockets themselves had been fired. But the packet itself was bound to the capsule by three thin metal bands. Williams figured that the bands might be strong enough to hold the shield to the capsule during the descent. He knew that, in time, the heat would burn away the bands. But he hoped that by then the air resistance would be dense enough to hold the shield in place.

Life or Death

Glenn took the news of the deadly threat with his usual calmness. He made the adjustments necessary to keep the retro-rocket packet in place. Then he hand-flew his capsule into proper attitude for descent — and braced himself. Timed by a pre-set mechanism in the capsule, the braking rockets fired in sequence. *Friendship 7* shuddered.

"It feels like I'm going clear back to Hawaii," Glenn radioed. He could feel his body beginning to be squeezed by the buildup of G forces.

Outside the window, he could see a fiery glow. "Something was tearing up the heat-shield end of the capsule," Glenn said later. "There were large pieces anywhere from as big as the end of your finger to seven or eight inches in diameter coming past the window. You could see the fire and the glow from them — big flaming chunks."*

Astronaut Alan Shepard, the capsule communicator at Cape Canaveral, lost radio contact with Glenn at this time. Other instruments tracking the capsule stopped registering. The blackout was no surprise, however. It was caused by ionization from the heat of re-entry. It lasted for seven minutes and fifteen seconds.

Then came John Glenn's happy voice. "Boy!" he cried. "That was a real fireball!"

Glenn had made it. He had successfully reentered the earth's atmosphere. It later turned out that the heat shield had been in place all along. A monitor in the capsule had been flashing a misleading signal to the ground. But John Glenn could not be certain even yet that he was safe. He could only know this when the parachute which would lower his capsule gently into the Atlantic had opened. The next day he said, "That's probably the prettiest ol' sight you ever saw in your life."

*The "chunks" were found to be disintegrating fragments of the retro-rocket packet.

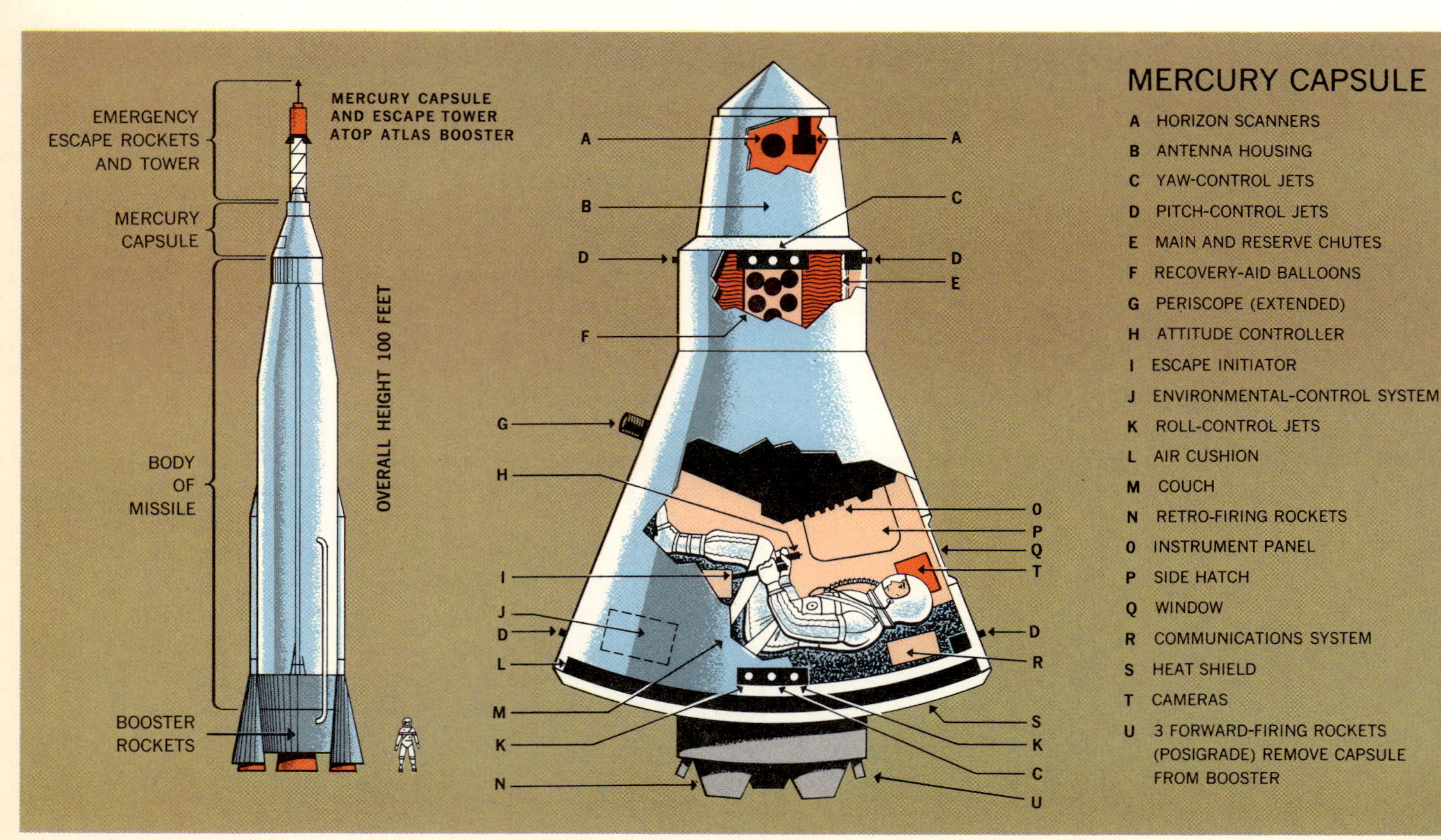

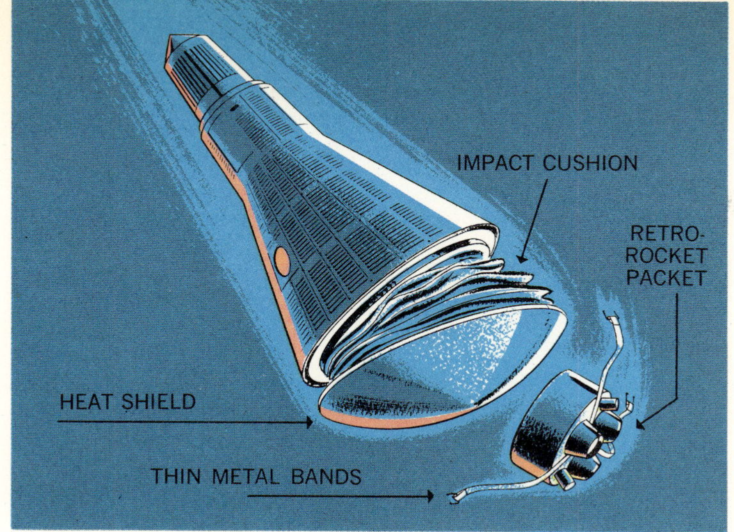

Between the Mercury's detachable heat shield and the capsule itself is a compressed (folded, accordion-pleated) rubber landing bag. When the capsule's parachute opens for landing, the shield is automatically detached. The landing bag unfolds and drops down to cushion the shock of impact. Trouble signals relayed to the Mercury controllers by tracking stations made the controllers think that the heat shield had come unlatched while Glenn was in orbit. They advised him not to jettison the retro-rocket packet; they hoped its stays (made of thin metal bands) would hold the heat shield in place. As it turned out, however, there was actually nothing wrong except an out-of-order warning signal.

John Glenn had been rocketed from the Cape Canaveral launching pad at 9:47 a.m. on February 20, 1962. At 2:43 p.m. *Friendship 7* splashed into the Atlantic with a sizzle as the red-hot shield turned the seawater to steam. The destroyer *Noa* began to race helicopters from the carrier *Randolph* to the scene. The *Noa* won, and plucked the capsule out of the ocean at 3:01. Across the United States, millions of television watchers sighed with relief.

Inside the capsule it was stifling hot from the friction of re-entry. Glenn struggled for a moment to get out via the narrow upper exit. Then he gave that up and opened the side hatch by pulling a release lever. "I'd been sweating for a long time," Glenn recalled, "and it seemed like the thing to do was to get on out of there." He stepped out onto the deck of the *Noa* into the afternoon sun and was given a glass of iced tea. "It was hot in there," said John Glenn.

His historic flight was over.

John Glenn was raised in the little Ohio town of New Concord. As a boy he hunted rabbits, played football and basketball, and blew a trumpet in the town band. He always wanted to fly. And, as soon as he could, he joined the Marine Corps and won his gold wings. "Johnny would fly up alongside you," one fellow officer says, "and slip his wing right under yours, then tap it gently against your wing tip. I've never seen such a smooth pilot." He flew many a dangerous mission in World War II and the Korean War; later became a test pilot for high-speed high-altitude airplanes. No one who knew his bravery and determination was surprised when, in 1959, he was chosen as one of America's first astronauts.

"SONG FROM HEAVEN"

BY HERTHA PAULI

How four Austrian children, quite by accident, gave us one of our most beloved Christmas carols

It was the twenty-fourth day of December, 1818, in Hallein, an age-old village in the Austrian Alps. Father Joseph Mohr sat alone in his study, reading the Bible.

All through the valley the children were filled with excitement. For it was Holy Eve, and they could stay up for Midnight Mass. Soon they would be on their way down the open, frozen paths carrying the rush lights that made the valley look like a huge Christmas tree with a hundred moving candles.

With open Bible, the young priest sat at his oaken table working on a sermon for the midnight service. He read again the story of the shepherds in the fields to whom the angel said: "For unto you is born this day in the City of David a Saviour . . ."

A Christmas Miracle

Just as Father Mohr read these words a knock sounded at his door. He opened it to find a peasant woman wrapped in a coarse shawl. The woman told him of a child born earlier that day to a charcoal maker's wife living on one of the highest Alps in his parish. The parents had sent her to ask the priest to come. They wanted him to bless the infant that it might live and prosper.

When he entered the poorly lighted hut Father Mohr was strangely moved. The young mother lay on a crude bed smiling happily. Her baby was asleep in her arms. The scene certainly did not resemble the manger in the City of David. Yet the last words Father Mohr had read in his Bible suddenly seemed to be meant for him. Returning to the valley, he saw that the dark slopes were alight with the torches of the mountaineers. They were on their way to church. And, from all the villages far and near, bells began to ring.

For Father Mohr the Christmas miracle had come to pass. After the midnight service he tried to write down what had happened to him. The words kept turning into verse. And when dawn broke Father Mohr had written a poem. On Christmas Day his friend Franz Xavier Gruber, music teacher at the village school, composed some music to fit the verses.

Village children heard the priest and the teacher singing. The church organ was out of order, so the pair were using what they had — two voices, and a guitar played by Franz Gruber.

"After all," they said, "the Lord can hear us without an organ."

They did not know that this anniversary of

Adapted from Silent Night, *copyright 1943 and published by Alfred A. Knopf, Inc.*

Christ's birthday was also the birthday of a great Christian hymn — one that would be known in all lands where there is a Christmas. Nor did they dream that four children would one day start it on its way to fame.

They Sang Like the Nightingales

Of all the youngsters in the Zillertal (the valley of the Zill) in the Austrian Tyrol, the ones with the most beautiful voices were the Strasser children: Caroline, Joseph, Andreas and Amalie, who was called Maly. Maly was so young that, although she could sing, she couldn't pronounce the words of songs correctly.

"Those Strassers," people used to say. "They sing just like the nightingales."

Like the nightingales, too, every spring the children traveled northward to Leipzig, in the kingdom of Saxony. For this was the site of the great annual trade fair. Their parents were glove makers, and it was the children's job to display and sell the soft chamois gloves that were sought far and wide.

Leipzig, at fair-time, was an exciting city. Often the youngsters from the Zillertal felt lost in the bright and curious crowd. But they did just what they did at home when their spirits needed lifting — they sang together. The song they sang most, because it was their favorite, was "Song from Heaven."

Karl Mauracher, the famous Zillertal organ builder, had taught the children the song. Once he had been called to a neighboring village to repair an organ and, when his work was done, he had asked the organist to try it out. The organist was none other than Franz Gruber, and somehow he slipped into the Christmas melody he had composed for Father Mohr.

"I never heard that song before," the organ builder said, with awe in his voice. "Would you mind if I took it with me? The people where I live would like to hear it."

Gruber offered to write it down, but Mauracher

told him not to bother. He had so many songs in his head that one more would not matter.

The song quickly became popular in his valley, and it was called "Song from Heaven." The organ builder didn't realize that he had brought back a precious gift from two unknown composers to the whole world.

The children found the song's charm worked in the busy city. Passers-by stopped to listen and were enchanted by the beautiful melody.

A Treat for a King

One day the children received a visit from the director general of music in the kingdom of Saxony. He gave them tickets to a concert that he was to conduct in Leipzig. The youngsters were delighted.

When they entered the brilliantly lighted auditorium filled with silk-hatted gentlemen and ladies in rustling gowns, they felt timid. They were glad to be led to seats beneath the platform where they would not be noticed.

They were still rapt and glowing at the concert's end when the shock came. For the conductor rose to announce that there were four children present, with the finest voices he had heard for years. Perhaps they would treat their Royal Majesties, the King and Queen of Saxony, to some of their lovely Tyrolean airs.

The announcement took the youngsters' breath away. And their faces flamed as people began to applaud.

"Let's just shut our eyes and pretend we're singing at home," Maly whispered to the others.

Their first song was "Song from Heaven." When they had finished it, there was a moment of almost reverent silence before applause broke loose. They sang all the songs they knew. And when they knew no more, they sang "Song from Heaven" again. The audience was still shouting for more when a gentleman in uniform came up on the platform. He said that their Majesties desired to receive the singers.

"That was very pretty indeed," the king said after the children had been introduced. "We've never heard that Christmas song before. What is it?"

"It is a Tyrolean folk song, your Majesty," said Joseph.

"Won't you come to the castle and sing it at Christmas?" the queen asked. "Our children will love it."

So it happened that on Holy Eve of the year

CULVER PICTURES, INC.

Franz Gruber (1787-1863), composer of "Silent Night"

1832, in the chapel in Pleissenburg Castle, the Strasser children sang at the end of the Christmas services:

"Silent night, holy night!
All is calm, all is bright
Round yon Virgin Mother and Child.
Holy Infant, so tender and mild,
Sleep in heavenly peace,
Sleep in heavenly peace."

And on that Christmas Eve the song bade the Strasser children farewell, to spread quietly around the world.

For years on each Holy Eve the song, now known as "Silent Night," was sung in the village of Hallein, in the house where Gruber lived and died. It was sung by a choir accompanied by Gruber's grandson playing his grandfather's original guitar.

Later this yearly performance was carried around the world by radio. And today the "Song from Heaven," like the Christmas story itself, still rings for all men of good will.

What Would You Have Done?

1 One day a boy rode his bicycle up a country lane, leaned it against a hedge, and walked up to a house to visit a friend. Suddenly a fierce dog rushed at him. Fortunately, it was chained to a tree nearby, and the boy was able to get out of its reach. Finding no one at home, he walked back to get his bicycle. The dog growled and rushed at him again. The chain was long, and the bicycle in such a position that the dog could get the boy before the boy got the bicycle. Can you guess how the boy was able to take his bike without being touched by the animal? *– Lawrence Bolz*

2 A large trailer truck was trying to go through a railroad underpass. It almost made it – but not quite. With a grinding crash, the truck wedged itself tightly between the road and the steel girders overhead.

Traffic jams formed on both sides of the bridge as experts from the state highway department tugged and hauled in vain. When someone suggested cutting away part of the bridge, the railroad officials objected. And the driver refused to let anyone take his truck to pieces.

Then a little boy, who had been watching with interest, tugged at the sleeve of one of the truckmen. "Mister," he said, "I know how to get that truck out."

The man looked down at him impatiently. "All right, how would you do it?"

The boy told him, and in a few minutes the truck was on its way. How did the boy solve the problem?

– Harry W. Henderson

3 A camp cook wanted to measure four ounces of syrup out of a jug. He had only one five-ounce and one three-ounce bottle. How did he do it?

– Andrew G. Ross

4 A girl was riding a frisky pony when the bridle worked loose. The pony quickly shook the bridle off and started to gallop down the road. The girl ordered it to stop, but the pony paid no attention. She stuck on and hoped for the best, until a car came around the corner ahead of her. She *had* to stop the pony. Can you guess how she did it? *– Dorothy Dicks*

5 When a sudden thunderstorm overturned her canoe, a girl managed to swim to a small rocky island. In a deserted hut she found an old kerosene lamp and a few matches. The wood on the island was too wet to build a fire, so the lamp was her only means of signaling for help. But it held only about an inch of kerosene – not enough to reach its short wick. Can you guess how she got the lamp burning and summoned help? *– Mrs. H. K. Modery*

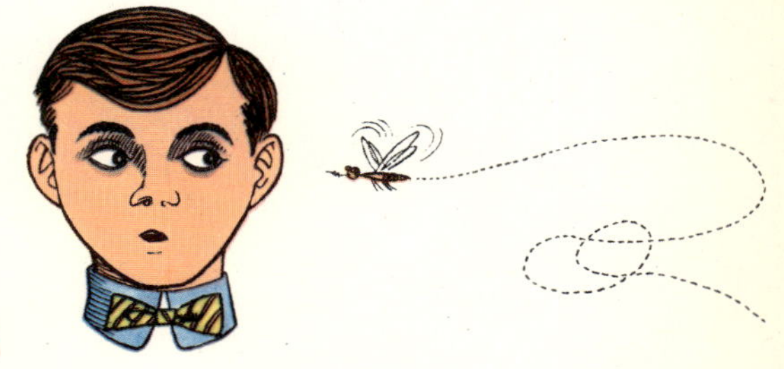

6 What would you have done if an insect had flown into your ear, too deep for you to reach, and started buzzing like all four motors of a giant airplane? The man to whom this happened one evening managed to get it out again on his own. Would you have done the same? *– James H. Corwin*

(Answers are on page 200)

Questions 1, 4, 5 and 6 are adapted from a feature in The Saturday Evening Post. *Question 3 is adapted from* Outdoor Life.

Man-Eater!

BY JIM CORBETT

Time after time Colonel Jim Corbett risked his life stalking man-eating tigers and leopards in the foothills of the Himalayas. When a man-eater was at large in some part of the jungle, the villagers would send for Colonel Corbett, wherever he might be. But this famous hunter would usually shoot the animal only if he was sure that it had taken human life. Here he tells one of his most exciting hunting stories

IN THE north-central part of India, near the border of Nepal, is an eight-thousand-foot hill, twelve to fifteen miles long. The western end of the hill rises steeply, and near this end is the small village of Muktesar. From it, you get one of the best views of the snowy Himalayan range.

A tigress had come to live in the great forests surrounding the village. Here she lived very happily on deer, such as sambhar and kakar, until she had the bad luck to quarrel with a porcupine. In this meeting she lost an eye, and got some fifty quills stuck in her right foreleg.

While she was lying up in a thick patch of grass, starving and licking her wounds, a woman chose this very patch of grass to cut as fodder for her cattle. The tigress struck once, killing the woman with the blow. Leaving the woman where she had fallen, the tigress limped off and took refuge in a little hollow under a fallen tree. Two days later a man came to chip firewood off this tree, and the tigress killed him also. A day later she killed her third victim, and after that she became a regular man-eater.

The Danger Spreads

I heard of the tigress shortly after she started killing human beings. But there were already a number of sportsmen at Muktesar, all of whom were keen on bagging her, and I did not consider it would be sporting of an outsider to meddle in the matter. When the number of human beings killed by the tigress had risen to twenty-four, however, the government asked for my help. By now the lives of all the people in the area were in danger. Even in daylight no one cared to move about alone, and after dusk everyone stayed behind locked doors.

My task would not be an easy one. Apart from the fact that I had had very few dealings with man-eaters at that time, I did not know the country in which the tigress was lurking. A friend of mine called Badri Sah, who lived near Muktesar, had offered to help me in every way he could to shoot the man-eater. I decided I would call on him and accept his offer.

With a servant and two other men, I left my home at Naini Tal and walked ten miles to a dak bungalow (government inn), where I spent the night. Next morning, leaving my men to pack up and follow me, I took a double-barreled .500 express rifle and climbed the hill to Muktesar.

Putli and Kalwa

It was still early when I arrived. Before calling on Badri, I had time to look at some of the other villages farther along the hill to the east. After visiting two villages, I had retraced my steps for several miles when I overtook a small girl of about eight years old. She was having trouble with a bullock.

The girl, whose name was Putli, wanted the bullock to go toward Muktesar, while the bullock wanted to go the other way. He was a quiet old beast, even though he was stubborn. With Putli in front, holding onto his rope, and me behind to keep him on the move, he gave no further trouble.

After we had gone a short distance, I said:

Adapted from The Temple Tiger and More Man-Eaters of Kumaon, *copyright © 1954 and published by Oxford University Press, Inc.*

"We are not stealing Kalwa, are we?" I had heard her calling the bullock by that name.

"No," she answered indignantly.

"To whom does he belong?" I asked.

"To my father," she said.

"And where are we taking him?"

"To my uncle. To plow his field. He has only one bullock now, but he did have two."

"Where is the other one?" I asked.

"The tiger killed it yesterday," I was told. Here was news indeed. While I was wondering what I could do about it, Putli plucked up courage to ask: "Have you come to shoot the tiger?"

"Yes. I have come to try to shoot the tiger."

"Then why are you going away from the kill?"

"Because we are taking Kalwa to Uncle." My answer seemed to satisfy her, and we plodded on.

Presently I said: "Don't you know the tiger is a man-eater?"

"Oh, yes," she said, "it ate Kunthi's father and lots of other people."

"Then why did your father send you with Kalwa? Why did he not come himself?"

"Because he has *bhabari bokhar* (malaria)."

So this small girl had been given the dangerous job of taking the bullock along a road where even grown men were afraid to walk! On the way back I asked her to show me where the tiger had killed the other bullock, and she eagerly agreed.

"Was the bullock alone when it was killed?" I asked.

"No, it was killed when it was going out to graze with the village cattle."

While talking, I was keeping a sharp lookout all around, for the narrow road was bordered by thick jungle where the tiger could be hiding. We had gone about a mile when we came to a well-used cattle track, leading off into the jungle. Here Putli stopped and said it was on this track that the bullock had been killed.

The Tiger's Kill

After seeing Putli safely to her home, I returned to the cattle track. I had gone along it for about a quarter of a mile when I came to a spot where the cattle had stampeded. A short distance away was a mark made by something being dragged along the ground. After following this drag mark for a few hundred yards, I found the bullock, from which only a small portion had been eaten. It was lying at the foot of a bank about twenty feet high, and some forty feet from the top of a deep ravine.

Between the ravine and the kill was a stunted tree, smothered over by a wild rose. This was the only tree on which I could sit with any hope of bagging the tiger. There would be no moon that night, and I felt sure the tiger would come back after dark. The nearer I was to the kill, the better would be my chance of shooting the beast.

It was now two p.m., and there was just time for me to call on my friend Badri and ask him for a cup of tea. When I arrived, Badri took me up to his guesthouse, which was on a little hill overlooking his orchard. While we sat on the veranda I told him about the kill, and about the tree I was going to sit on that night.

After tea I returned to the kill. Badri came with me, and brought two men carrying materials for making a small machan (shooting platform). When they saw the stunted tree, they begged me not to sit up that night. They thought the tiger would remove the kill, and that I should find a better place to sit up the following night.

This was what I myself would have done if the tiger had not been a man-eater. As it was, I didn't want to miss a chance that might not come again tomorrow—even if it did mean a little risk. There were bears in this forest, and if one of them smelled the kill there would be no hope of my getting a shot at the tiger. Himalayan bears are not afraid of tigers and do not hesitate to steal their kills.

I climbed into the tree, making myself as comfortable as the thorns on the rosebush would allow. Badri handed me my rifle. Then he and his men left, promising to return early next morning.

I was facing the hill, with the ravine behind me. I could be seen easily by any animal coming down from above; but if the tiger came from below, as I expected, it would not see me until it got to the kill. The bullock, which was white, was lying about fifteen feet away from me.

A Night Encounter

I had taken my seat at four p.m. An hour later a kakar (barking deer) started making a noise on the side of the ravine, two hundred yards below. The tiger was on the move, and the kakar, having seen it, was standing still and barking. After a time the kakar started to move away, and its bark grew fainter and fainter. This told me that, after coming within sight of the kill, the tiger had lain down. It would now be lying somewhere close by with its eyes and ears open, to make quite sure that there were no human beings near the kill.

Minute followed long minute. Dusk came, and objects on the hill in front of me began to fade from sight. I could still see the kill as a white blur, when a stick snapped at the head of the ravine. Stealthy steps came toward me, and then stopped immediately below. For a minute or two there was dead silence. Then the tiger lay down on the dry leaves at the foot of the tree in which I sat.

When at last the tiger got up and went to the kill, the night was pitch-black. Strain my eyes as I would, I could see nothing of the white bullock or the tiger. I should have to depend on my ears for aim.

On reaching the kill, the tiger started blowing on it. In the Himalayas, especially in the summer, kills attract hornets. A tiger, not wanting to be stung, blows off the hornets before starting to feed.

The tiger had not moved the bullock before starting to eat, so I knew about where it would be. There was no need for me to hurry over my shot. Close though I was, the tiger would not see me unless I attracted its attention by some movement or sound.

Raising the rifle and resting my elbows on my knees, I took careful aim at the sound the tiger was making. While I held the rifle steady, I carefully turned my right ear to the sound, and then back again. My aim seemed a little too high, so I lowered the muzzle a fraction of an inch. Again I turned my head and listened. After I had done this a few times I was satisfied that I was pointing at the sound. Moving the muzzle a little to the right, where I thought the tiger's body would be, I pressed the trigger.

Sitting Up with a Tiger

In two bounds the tiger was up the twenty-foot bank. At the top there was a small bit of flat ground, beyond which the hill went up steeply. I heard the tiger on the dry leaves as far as the flat ground, and then there was silence. This silence could mean either that the tiger had died on reaching the flat ground, or that it was not wounded.

Keeping the rifle to my shoulder, I listened intently for a few minutes. Then, as there was no further sound, I lowered the rifle. This movement brought a deep growl from the top of the bank. So the tiger was unwounded, and had seen me.

My seat on the tree had originally been about ten feet up. As I had nothing solid to sit on, however, the rosebush had sagged under my weight. I was now no more than eight feet above the ground, with my dangling feet very much lower. And a little above, and some twenty feet from me, a man-eating tiger was growling deep down in its throat.

Many minutes had passed, and the tiger was still there, when it began to rain—a few big drops at first, and then a heavy downpour. I had put on light clothes that morning, and I was soon wet to the skin. The tiger, I knew, would have hurried off to shelter the moment the rain started. The rain came at eleven p.m. At four a.m. it stopped and a wind started to blow. While I had been cold before, I was now frozen.

We Plan a "Beat"

Just as the sun was rising, Badri, good friend that he was, arrived with a man carrying a kettle of hot tea. Taking my rifle from me, the two men caught me as I slid from the tree; for my legs were too cramped to work. Then, as I lay on the ground and drank the tea, they rubbed my legs to get back the circulation. When I was able to stand, we walked back to Badri's guesthouse.

While drying my clothes in front of a roaring

fire, I asked Badri about the jungle into which the tigress had gone. On our way back, we had seen her footprints on a path. Badri told me that this path led to a deep ravine which ran down the side of a very steep hill. He thought the tigress would lie up for the day in the ravine.

It seemed to be an excellent place for a "beat" (the act of scouring the countryside to drive out game), so we decided to try this way of getting a shot at her. Badri called his gardener, Govind Singh, and explained our plan to him. Govind said he could muster a gang of thirty men by midday.

After cleaning my rifle, I joined Badri for breakfast, and at noon Govind produced his gang. He was to give me an hour's start to let me search the ravine for the tigress. If I failed to get a shot, I would take up my position on a patch of open ground near a stream at the bottom of the ravine. He was to divide his men into two parties, and at the end of the hour they would set off, one on each side of the ravine. They would roll rocks down, shout and clap their hands, to drive the tigress out of the cover.

Things Go Wrong

I set off along the path the tigress had taken, only to find that it ended in a great jungle of brushwood. Forcing my way through it for several hundred yards, I came to the edge of the ravine. In front of me was a big drop, at the bottom of which was the stream.

While I was looking down I heard flies buzzing near me, and found the body of a cow that had been killed about a week before. The marks on the animal's throat showed that it had been killed by a tiger. For no particular reason, I sent the body crashing down the steep hill. It landed in a little hollow on the edge of the ravine, about fifty feet above the stream.

Working around to the left, I found the open patch of ground Badri had described, about three hundred yards from this hollow. But the ground was very different from what I had pictured it to be. There was no place from which I could overlook the hillside that was to be beaten, and the tigress might break out anywhere without my seeing her. However, it was then too late to do anything. Away in the distance I could hear men shouting. The beat had started.

At last the beaters came down the hill to my right. When they were on a level with me, I shouted to them to stop the beat and join me. It was no one's fault that the beat had failed, for we had not known the ground.

While the beaters sat in a bunch, removing thorns from their hands and feet, Govind and I stood facing each other, talking. Suddenly, in the middle of a sentence, Govind stopped. I could see that his attention had been caught by something behind me, for a look of astonishment came over his face. Swinging around, I looked where he was facing. There, quietly walking along a field, was the tigress.

The Tigress Is Hungry

The tigress was about four hundred yards away on the far side of the stream, and was coming toward us. She still had three hundred yards to go to reach the stream, and most of that was over open ground on which there was not a single tree or bush. She would see any movement we made, so there was nothing I could do but watch her, and no tigress ever moved more slowly. When at last she entered some bushes, I decided to go forward and try to get a shot at her after she crossed the stream.

Telling the men not to make a sound, I set off at a run. I ran along the hill and came to a large bush, through the middle of which was a low tunnel. As I bent down to run through the tunnel, my hat was knocked off. I went on running until I reached the hollow into which I had rolled the cow from the hill above. Suddenly I heard a bone crack. The tigress had reached the hollow before me and, finding her old kill, was trying to make up for the meal I had robbed her of during the previous night.

The upper end of the hollow, where the tigress was eating, was overgrown with dense brushwood. The lower end, where I stood, was free of bushes. If, after leaving the kill, the tigress came toward me over the open ground, I would get a shot at her. But if she went up the hill I would not see her. I was thinking of driving her onto the open ground by throwing a stone onto the hill above her, when I heard a sound behind me.

Looking around, I saw Govind, standing behind me with my hat in his hand. Having seen my hat fall off in the bush, he had picked it up and brought it to me. Near us there was a hole in the hill. Putting my finger to my lips, I pressed Govind into the hole. Sitting on his hunkers, with his chin resting on his drawn-up knees, he looked very unhappy, for he could hear the tigress crunching bones a few yards away.

I Meet a Charge

As I resumed my position on the edge of the ravine, the tigress stopped eating. For a long minute there was no sound, and then I caught sight of her. She was climbing up the hill at a place where there was a clump of young trees. I could see only her outline as she went through them. Hoping that my bullet would miss the trees and hit the tigress, I took a hurried shot.

At my shot, the tigress whipped around and came down the hill as hard as she could go. She crossed the hollow and then charged down a narrow path that ran between me and the edge of the ravine.

Waiting until she was two yards away, I leaned forward and, with great good luck, managed to put my second bullet into the hollow where her neck joined her shoulder.

The heavy .500 bullet turned her just enough for her to miss my left shoulder, and the force of her charge carried her over the fifty-foot drop into the stream below. There she landed with a great splash. I looked over the edge and saw the tigress lying in the water, dead. I signaled to Govind, who was still sitting in the hole, and he came out and joined me.

On seeing the tigress, Govind turned and shouted to the beaters behind us, "The tiger is dead! The tiger is dead!" The beaters now started shouting too, and Badri heard them from his house. To spread the good news, he fired off ten rounds of his shotgun.

These shots were heard at Muktesar, and in the surrounding villages. Presently, from all sides, men were flocking toward the stream. Willing hands pulled the tigress from the water, lashed her to a branch and carried her in triumph to Badri's orchard. Here she was put down on a bed of straw for all to see, while I went to the guest-house for a cup of tea.

The shooting of a man-eater gives one a feeling of satisfaction. Satisfaction at having done a job that badly needed doing. Satisfaction at having outwitted, on his own ground, a very worthy enemy. And, greatest satisfaction of all, at having made a small portion of the earth safe for a brave little girl to walk upon.

The story of a very unusual punishment

A Scientific Whipping

BY HIRAM PERCY MAXIM

The father in this amusing story was Sir Hiram Stevens Maxim, inventor of the Maxim machine gun. His brother, Hudson Maxim, invented smokeless powder. And his son, Hiram Percy Maxim, who wrote the story, invented the Maxim silencer for guns. Hiram Percy also designed one of the first automobiles—and he was keenly interested in radio and aviation when both were still very new

As a boy, I was sometimes a problem to Mother. I used to tease my sisters and break things in the house. One day I accidentally smashed a full-length mirror in Mother's room.

When Mother beheld her broken glass she sank into a chair and wept. She told me that I had got beyond her control and that she would have to turn me over to Father for a good whipping—something that had never happened before.

That evening Father was shown my latest offense. He sank into a chair and held his head in his hands. He rocked back and forth as if he were completely undone. He said he was too upset to whip me then, but that he would attend to it later.

After a gloomy supper, Father announced that he would read his paper. Then he would take up the whipping matter. Mother had spanked me aplenty, but I did not regard that as a whipping. I wondered what it would be like to be whipped.

Finally Father finished his paper. He arose briskly. "Well, now," he said. "Come along, Percy."

He led me into the back yard and opened his pocketknife to cut a suitable whip. He explained that it was necessary to find a whip that had just the right length and thickness and straightness. If it were too short it would not have enough spring. If it were too long it would have too much. If it were too thick it would bruise, which of course would not do.

We searched and searched without finding anything that just suited. I pointed out several likely-looking sticks. He discussed them with me, examining each one with care. Finally he cut a long thin one, a long thick one and a middle-length one.

He whittled them all down smooth. Then he said, "Now come along up to my room and we will try them."

He led the way to the third floor, took off his coat and rolled up his sleeves. I was worried. For this suggested that a whipping must be something calling for considerable activity.

He laid the three whips on the bed. Then, taking one at a time, he smote the coverlet. The savage whirr and the succeeding whack sounded all over the house. He put real muscle into it and the whip broke. He explained that he expected this to happen, for the stick was too thin for its length. The thick one made a fearful whack when it hit the coverlet. We rejected this one because it probably would bruise.

Later on I heard Mother say she had never felt so nervous in all her life, listening to the savage whirr of the whip and the awful whack

Adapted from A Genius in the Family, *© 1936 and published by Harper & Row*

as it struck. I firmly believe that most of this bed-whacking business was for Mother's benefit, as she sat downstairs trying to read.

Father whacked the coverlet for a long time, testing whips and breaking most of them. But he was still not satisfied.

"What we need," he said, "is something fairly long, very strong, and yet very light and springy. Where can we find such a thing?"

By this time I was as keenly interested in the problem as if someone else were to be whipped. I suggested a baseball bat, but pointed out that it would hit awfully hard.

"Oh, *much* too hard," Father replied. "Why, you could break a man's back with a baseball bat."

"I suppose a broomstick would be too stiff," I ventured.

"Altogether too stiff and too heavy. It would break bones."

There was a long pause while we both thought. Then I had an idea. "Gosh, Papa! I know the very thing. That thin cane of yours."

"By Jove!" he exclaimed. "That's a good idea. Go and fetch it."

Father whacked the coverlet with his cane with all his might. It made a particularly savage noise. But he shook his head and handed the cane to me, asking me to try it. I got the best grip I could on the curved handle, and whacked the bed for all that was in me. It made only a fair noise, and Father feared that Mother downstairs would not hear it. He told me to put more "beef" into it, but the curved handle got in my way.

We discussed the matter again. Finally Father said, "Well, I guess we shall have to give up the whipping, Percy. We can't seem to find the right whip. But, anyway, you understand that you must be more careful about the house and that you must not make so much trouble for Mamma. You *will* be a better boy, won't you, Percy?"

Being deeply impressed by the way he said it, I resolved to make a serious effort. I said, "Yes, Papa, I will."

And time proved that I kept my promise in pretty good shape.

The frailest of all Nature's creations has the power to transform the world

The Wonders of Snow

BY JOHN STEWART COLLIS

IT HAS snowed all night. The evergreens are holding up thick fists of snow like white boxing gloves. On other trees long twigs, thin as wire, make a base for high walls of snow. The laying of the pure white bricks on the black boughs has been so gentle and each brick is so light that there is a perfect balance.

We shall not find a more delicate miracle than the birth of snow. Unlike hail, which is frozen rain, snow is born from the molecules of water vapor which, at normal temperatures, flow freely and invisibly through the air. When the temperature drops to freezing, their motion is slowed down. Then the mutually attractive power which all molecules possess draws them together. It unites them, and they become visible.

In this way, they form solids which we call crystals. And here is another marvelous thing: vapor molecules build themselves into definite and lovely forms. We can see in them the beginning of geometry.

There is something else to notice about the way these crystals are formed. They need a base upon which to grow. They get this from the dust in the air — of which there is a vast amount. There is earth dust consisting of pollen, bacteria, soot, spores, volcanic ash and so on. And there is also stardust from outer space, which is said to fall onto the earth at the rate of two thousand tons a day. We do not usually notice this dust in the air. But we see it distinctly when it is caught in the shaft of a sunbeam.

Upon this base, tiny disks or needles of ice are built. And upon them the finished crystal is displayed. Very often — though not always — its shape is hexagonal (or six-sided), so that each is a little star with six rays crossing at an angle of sixty degrees. If the crystal looks like a cluster of ferns, it will have six leaves pointing out. If it looks like a windmill, it will have six sails — if like a starfish, it will have six ribs. And if it looks like a fir tree, it will have six plumes set in perfect symmetry.

Only within the last seventy-five years, through photomicrography, has the snow crystal been revealed in all its glory. A man named Wilson Bentley spent his life studying the snow. In 1885, when he was twenty years old, he got a photomicrographic camera. And for forty-six years he photographed the snow around his lonely New England mountain home. Then he published his great book, *Snow Crystals*.

Bentley took more than five thousand pictures of snow crystals. Yet he found no two shapes just alike. It is believed that in an average snowstorm something like a thousand billion crystals fall. Boundlessly, Nature rains down these fleeting flowers of aerial ice — each one different! This

Adapted from The Moving Waters *and reprinted by permission of William Sloane Associates, Inc., with editorial additions*

is not really surprising. The wonder of wonders is that the dancing molecules produce these geometrical designs in the first place.

When these billions of crystals alight, falling layer on layer, they become banks of one white substance. Yet snow is not white in itself. It is frozen water, colorless ice. The whiteness we see is produced by the reflection and refraction of light from the myriad tiny surfaces of the crystals.

The crystals fall upon the earth so lightly (though house roofs can be caved in under a massive load of them!) that a great amount of air is present. There have been extreme cases of drifts made of one part ice to eighty-nine parts air. For this reason men who have been buried deep in snow for as long as two days have not been suffocated. And for the same reason snow is an aid to farmers. It keeps heat in the lower ground levels and saves the seeds from freezing.

Think for a moment of our cities and of our roads. Think of people moving from one place to another as quickly as possible. Now see those falling flakes! The little snow stars, the fairy ferns, descend. They stick and stay where they have fallen. Now an inch, now a foot, many feet at last. A hush, a pause, as the feathers fall without a sound. See, the roads and the city streets grow empty. For a while, at least, all is still.

But soon the children rush out with their sleds and their skis. Their voices echo across the silence. And the world becomes their very own — a world transformed by the frailest of all Nature's creations.

NIGHT

By Sara Teasdale

Stars over snow,
And in the west a planet
Swinging below a star—
Look for a lovely thing and
you will find it,
It is not far—
It never will be far.

From Stars To-night, *copyright 1930 by Sara Teasdale Filsinger, copyright renewed 1958 by Guaranty Trust Co. of N.Y., reprinted by permission of The Macmillan Co.*

Paper Stars and Snow Crystals

BY PAULINE JOHNSON

When winter's blustery days and long evenings keep you indoors, why not make your own snow stars—no two just alike—with scissors, pencil and paper? You can hang them as mobiles in your room, use them as tree decorations at Christmas—or make them just for the fun of it.

THE FIVE-POINTED STAR

Take an 8½-by-11-inch sheet of typing paper (or gold or aluminum foil of the same size). Fold it in half (Figs. 1 and 2). Mark center point between corners B and C. Fold corner A down to this point (Fig. 3.)

Fold corner B over at the line EA (see arrow, Fig. 4). This will give you Fig. 5. Extend line EB with light pencil marks, and fold *back* corner F along this line, to get Fig. 6. Mark the line AG, and cut the paper in two along this line. Point G should be a little more than halfway from E (the center of your star) to H. The closer you place line AG to E, the sharper will be the points. You will have a five-pointed star like the one shown above, which you can decorate in any way you wish.

Adapted from Creating with Paper, *with diagrams, by Pauline Johnson, ©1958 and published by The University of Washington Press*

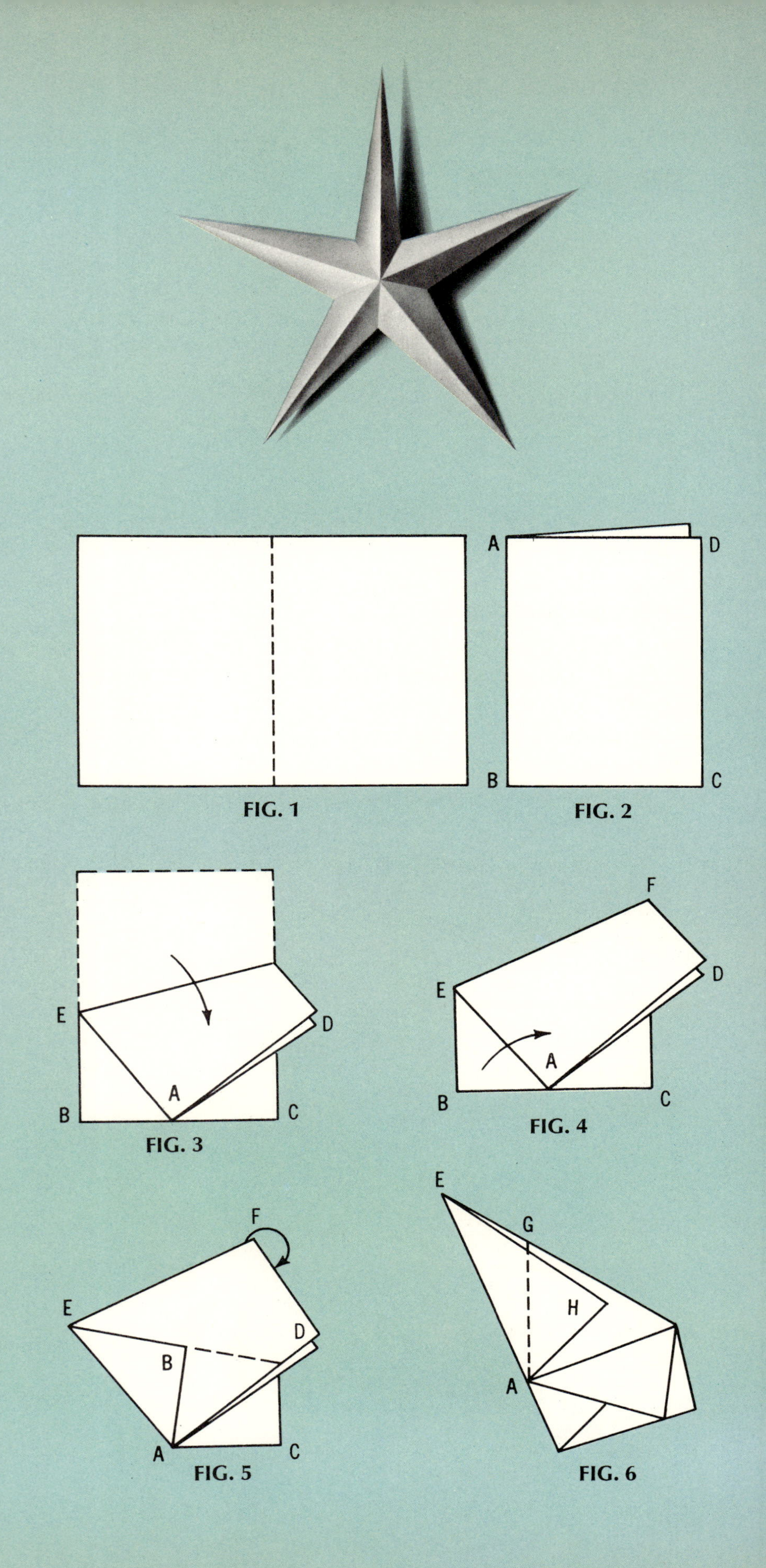

FIG. 1

FIG. 2

FIG. 3

FIG. 4

FIG. 5

FIG. 6

THE SIX-POINTED STAR

Fold a piece of paper as shown in Fig. 7, and cut off the shaded strip to make a triangle. Fold again to make the smaller triangle shown in Fig. 8. With a ruler divide this into thirds, A, B and C (Fig. 8).

Now fold section A up over section B (see Fig. 9). Fold section C back under section B to get Fig. 10; and mark point F halfway between points E and I. Draw a line between points D and F, and cut along it in order to get the star shown above.

If you want to make a star with slender rays, mark point G halfway between F and E on Fig. 10. Cut from D to G instead of from D to F.

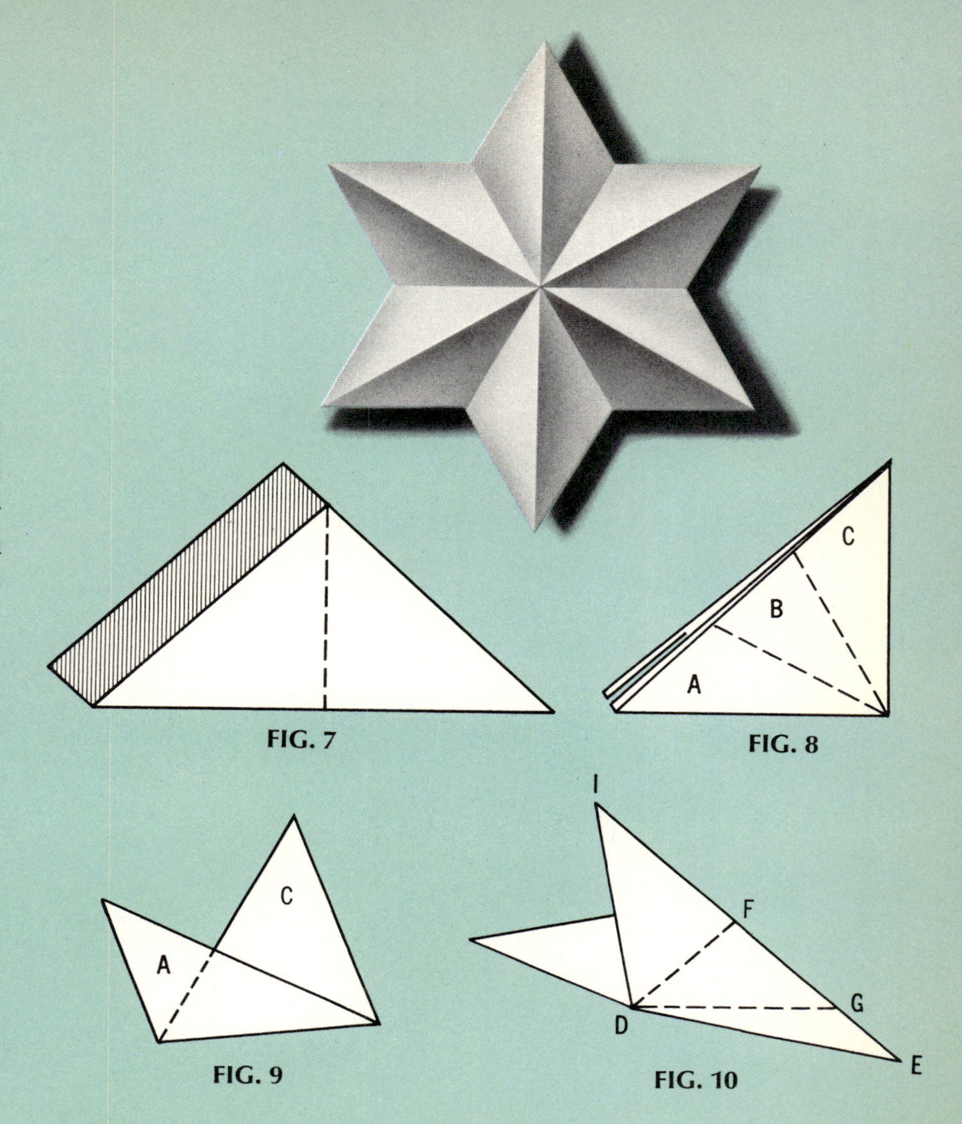

FIG. 7

FIG. 8

FIG. 9

FIG. 10

SNOW CRYSTALS IN MANY DESIGNS

Fold and cut a square of paper or foil as for a six-pointed star (Fig. 10). Before unfolding, copy the penciled design in Fig. 11. Then with small pointed scissors cut out the shaded areas and carefully unfold the paper to get snow crystal (Fig. 12).

You can make many different designs by drawing your own patterns on folded paper and cutting them out.

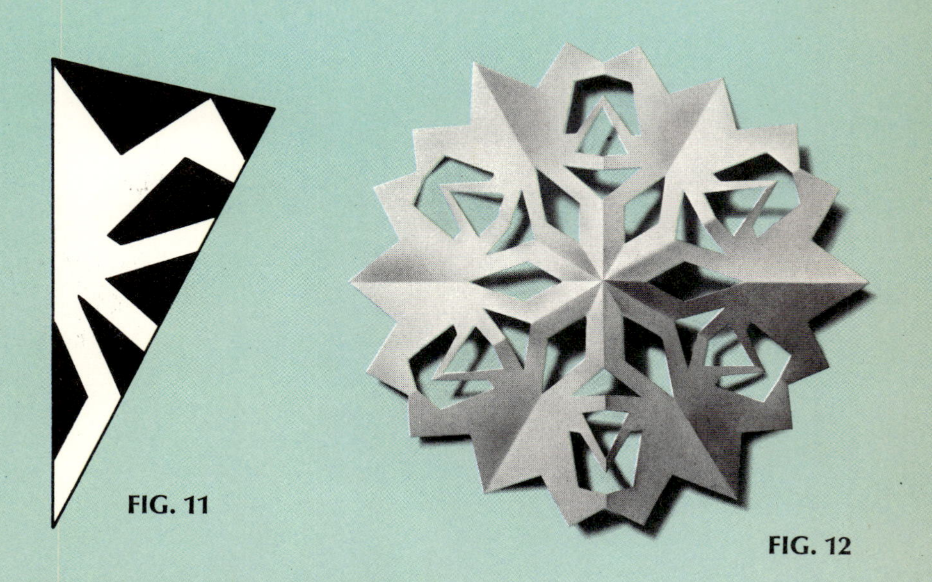

FIG. 11

FIG. 12

The Dragon in the Clock Box

A very short story about a very small boy who had a very secret secret

BY M. JEAN CRAIG

On Tuesday afternoon Joshua's mother bought a new alarm clock. When she unwrapped it, Joshua asked her if he might have the box it came in.

"Of course, Josh. What are you going to do with it?"

"Something," answered Joshua, but politely.

On Wednesday Joshua's mother saw that he had sealed the clock box closed. Every slit and corner was tightly covered with paper tape. And wherever Joshua went and whatever he did, he kept the clock box with him. When he went to bed, he laid it next to his pillow.

Adapted from Ladies' Home Journal, *© 1961 by The Curtis Publishing Co.*

"Can you tell me what you have in the clock box?" asked Joshua's mother, when she was tucking him in.

"It's a dragon's egg," said Joshua.

"Joshua — is it really?"

"Yes, it is," said Joshua, and went to sleep.

On Thursday, at breakfast, Joshua's father asked him, "How is your dragon's egg doing this morning?"

"It isn't *doing*, it's waiting. For it to be time to hatch," said Joshua.

When Joshua's big brother came home from high school, he said, "I hear you have a dragon's egg in that box. How did it get there?" Joshua's big sister giggled.

"The mother dragon laid it there," said Joshua, without smiling even a little bit. "Before."

"Before? Before what?" asked Joshua's big brother.

"Before I sealed it up, of course," Joshua answered him, and he picked up the clock box and went out of the room.

That evening Joshua's father wanted to know how any air could get into the box when it was taped shut.

"It doesn't need air yet," explained Joshua. "Not until it's ready to hatch."

"But how will you know when it's ready to?" Joshua's big sister asked him, not laughing this time.

Joshua looked at her. "*I* don't have to know. *It* will know." And then to himself he added, "Silly."

On Friday morning Joshua came down to breakfast a little late. He put the clock box on the table close to his plate. There was a small, neat hole cut in one corner of it.

"He's a boy dragon," Joshua told his mother as he sat down. "He hatched. Last night. Very late."

Joshua's mother spoke softly: "Did you hear it?"

"*Him*, not *it*. No, he was very quiet. But it was time, and he was ready. So I made a hole. Because now he needs air."

"And now you can peek through the hole to see what he's like," said Joshua's sister.

"I know what he's like. He's like a baby dragon. Just hatched," said Joshua. "And he doesn't want me to look yet. He wants to be alone for a while."

On Saturday it wasn't until nearly bedtime that anyone spoke to Joshua about the baby dragon.

"Have you seen him yet?" asked his brother.

"Yes," said Joshua.

"Say, that's wonderful! What does he look like?"

"He's pink, a little. His wings are still soft. With goldy edges, I think. Because it's dark in there."

"Then make the hole bigger, so you can see him better."

"No, I can't. He wants it dark. While his wings are so soft, it has to be dark."

"How do you know that, Joshua?" his mother asked him.

"It's always that way with dragons," said Joshua. "With baby-boy dragons."

On Sunday morning Joshua told his sister, "His name is Emmeline."

"But, Josh, that's a girl's name!"

"I know, but he's a Chinese dragon. And Chinese boy dragons like to have girls' names. His eyes are purple."

"May I see him?"

"No. He's too shy."

"But *you* look at him, don't you?"

"He's used to me," said Joshua.

Monday evening Joshua's father asked him what he had been feeding the dragon.

"They don't eat when they're little," said Joshua. "Not while their wings are still soft."

"Well, what are you going to feed him when his wings get strong?"

"I won't have to feed him then," answered Joshua, and he laid his hand gently on the clock box.

And then it was Tuesday again, and Joshua came to breakfast without the clock box. But everyone was in a hurry to start the day, and no one noticed. It was later, when Joshua's mother was making his bed, that she saw the clock box on the floor. The tape had been torn off and the box was open wide. It was empty.

"Joshua! Your dragon's gone!"

Joshua was busy taking his marbles out of a bag, and he didn't turn around when he answered her. "He was big enough last night. And his wings were strong. He flew away."

"Did he really? But, Josh, where could he fly to?"

Joshua walked over to the empty clock box, and picked it up.

"Where dragons go," he said. "This is a good box to keep marbles in, I think. I'm going to put my marbles in it now."

And he did.

He lived five hundred years ago, but his "wild" dreams have come true in the air and under the sea

LEONARDO DA VINCI: MASTER OF ALL TRADES

BY DONALD CULROSS PEATTIE

T*he life that is well spent is a long life.* The man who wrote those words lived not only one life, but ten. For Leonardo da Vinci was one of the great painters in the golden age of painting. He was also a many-sided genius of science. He lived in that morning of today which we call the Renaissance. But he foresaw or invented much that scientists have since spent more than four hundred years finding out.

Leonardo's greatest discoveries remained unknown for many years. For after his death his notebooks were lost — some of them forever. Only about eighty years ago were some of them found and published. To read what Leonardo wrote you have to look at it in a mirror. This is because he was left-handed and wrote from right to left. It is symbolic that later he learned to write with either hand.

The son of a lawyer, Leonardo was born at Anchiano, Italy, on April 15, 1452. During his early years he was an only child, and everyone spoiled him. His good looks and quick wit made it easy to forgive his practical jokes, his cockiness and his daydreaming.

The boy grew up on his father's estate near Florence. And he never forgot the parasol pines and winding streams, the crags and wild flowers of that lovely countryside. Later, he brought them all to life in his paintings. He played several musical instruments and liked to write poems. All of life was the young Leonardo's teacher.

When Leonardo's father discovered the boy's first drawings, he placed him as an apprentice in the studio of Andrea del Verrocchio in Florence. Verrocchio was a jack of all the trades at which Leonardo was to become master — painting, sculpture, architecture, music, geometry and natural history. So master and pupil were delighted with each other.

In and out of Verrocchio's studio came other young artists — among them one named Sandro Botticelli. They all became Leonardo's friends. Together they argued about the world, or played pranks, or wrestled, or tamed horses. It is said that Leonardo was so strong he could bend a horseshoe in one hand.

Or you might have found the young Leonardo wandering through the courts and churches of

Adapted from The Catholic World, © *1946 by The Missionary Society of St. Paul the Apostle in the State of New York*

COURTESY OF MUSEE DU LOUVRE REPRODUCTION GIRAUDON

"The Virgin of the Rocks," Louvre Museum, Paris

Florence to study their art treasures. You might have seen him strolling with the leading mathematicians, astronomers and geographers of the day, seeking to learn from them. He loved to talk, too. He would stand cockily in the marketplace, boasting and dreaming aloud of his plans to dig tunnels under mountains and move buildings across the city. The crowd would listen to him, half awed and half laughing.

Leonardo studied mathematics and physics, botany and anatomy, as well as his art. To him there was no real difference between art and science. Both are ways of describing God's universe.

Leonardo's love of life can be seen in the hundreds of pages of his sketchbooks. Here on one sheet are drawings of soldiers killing and dying, there a young woman kneeling in prayer. Now he draws an old pauper or a child at play. It is said he would follow beautiful or hideous people around all day to study them.

Leonardo was fascinated with the beauty of the human body. He spent more time on anatomy than on any other science. He showed that our muscles are levers and that the eye is a lens. He proved that the heart is a hydraulic pump, and that the pulse is synchronized with the heartbeat.

When Leonardo was about thirty, he was sent by Lorenzo de' Medici, ruler of Florence, to Lodovico Sforza, Duke of Milan. Sforza was a treacherous, practical and brutal tyrant. He read the letter Leonardo had written him, and nodded.

"I could use this man," he said to himself. "For this Leonardo da Vinci says that he is the inventor of a light portable bridge useful in pursuit of an enemy. He has devised suction pumps for emptying the moat of a besieged castle. He is an expert in casting enormous guns, and has schemes for a self-propelled armored car!"

In military science Leonardo was way ahea of his time. He could cast a cannon with thirt three barrels, of which eleven could be fired once. He made time fuses and hand grenade He also planned gas masks and gas bombs. H mounted his artillery on wheels. And he invente a breech-loading gun to replace the clum muzzle-loaders of the day.

No Painting Was Perfect

When Leonardo went from Florence to Mil he found that his duties included putting in plu ing for the duchess's bath as well as painting traits. He built a complicated system of c for the city. And he drew up plans for two highways, though these were never used.

He was sent to the Alps to fortify the against an invasion from the north. And saw the waterfalls spilling from hanging the rocks and flowers and ferns that a his famous painting "The Virgin of the

This painting was ordered by a group c in Milan for a mere twenty ducats. But L believed the finished work was worth a When the monks would not pay more t had agreed upon, Leonardo refused to g the picture. He fought with them abo twenty years. Finally the king of Franc the picture and hung it in his palace — today the Louvre Museum in Paris.

and his assistants did a copy for the monks, and that is now in London's National Gallery.

Leonardo painted "The Last Supper" — once one of the world's greatest paintings — on the plaster wall of a convent dining hall. Within twenty years the wall mildewed and flaked, ruining the painting. Later a door was cut right through it. Many attempts have been made to restore the picture. The last and best of these restorations may have brought it back to something like the original. But if it were not for Leonardo's many sketches, and copies made by other artists when the picture was fresh, we would scarcely know how beautiful it once was.

Many "Leonardos" have been lost, and each loss is a tragedy. He actually finished very few paintings, though his sketches and studies run into the thousands. He might paint for days, scarcely taking food. At other times he would sit all day in front of his work and add but three strokes. The next morning he might wash out everything and begin again. It is doubtful if he ever considered any work perfectly finished. Perhaps that is why he signed almost nothing.

Mystery of the "Mona Lisa"

When the French invaded Milan and the Sforzas were driven out, Leonardo had to flee. He escaped to Mantua, wandered to Venice, and stayed unhappily for a while in Rome. From there he returned to Florence. And when it was at last safe he drifted back to Milan. The duke had paid him no money during his last years there. So now he had to accept odd jobs as an engineer and an artist.

One of these jobs was a portrait of Lisa Gherardini, wife of Francesco del Giocondo of Florence. This was Leonardo's last great picture. It is known to us as the "Mona Lisa," or "La Gioconda." The real Mona Lisa was a lady of wealth and fashion. But in the picture she wears severe black and no rings, because her baby had recently died. She was twenty-one when she began to sit for the portrait. But six years passed before Leonardo ceased work on it. The Mona Lisa in the painting is dreamy and mysterious. She seems to smile at something just beyond your right shoulder.

Mysterious too is the fact that the picture was never delivered to Giocondo. There are many theories about what happened. One is that Leonardo took the painting with him as his most prized possession when he went to live in France. King Francis I, who had invited Leonardo, later bought it and hung it in the Louvre.

From the Sea to the Stars

All this time Leonardo was dreaming, as few mortals have dared to dream, of the conquest of the world by science. The sky was no limit to his soaring imagination. Nor was the sea too deep.

Before he tried to conquer the air, Leonardo learned why birds take off into the wind and how

COURTESY OF MUSEE DU LOUVRE REPRODUCTION GIRAUDON

The "Mona Lisa" visited the United States early in 1963. A French ship brought her to New York in an air-conditioned crate. A heavily guarded motor caravan, with permission to speed through all red lights along its route, then took her to Washington, D.C. There President and Mrs. Kennedy were among the first to see this "queen" of paintings when she went on view at the National Gallery of Art. Later she was shown in the Metropolitan Museum of Art in New York City, and people came from all over to glimpse her famous smile. The French government had loaned her to the American people as a gesture of friendship. She is now "at home" again in the Louvre.

the slotted wing helps them mount more steeply. Experimenting with paper models, he foresaw tailspins and falling-leaf spins and nose dives and rolls. He left instructions for coming out of each.

His earliest plans for a flying machine look like a bat. He expected the wings to flap, so he planned a jointed fuselage of stitched leather. He imagined his aviator as lying face down in the frame and "rowing" the air with the wings.

Leonardo was also the first man to hit on the idea of a propeller for locomotion. In his cardboard model the propeller beats horizontally, with the fuselage hanging below it, like a helicopter. He used a tightly wound spring for power. Leonardo wanted the machine to rise straight into the air. But he lacked a light engine, and so he could never see his idea come true.

Yet it seems that he did attempt one flight, in what was probably a glider. This was constructed on a high building. According to a single reference that has come down through the ages, the aircraft was finally launched. Possibly Leonardo himself was at the controls! But the flight was a failure and, as far as we know, he never made another attempt.

Leonardo designed a bulldozer, a spinning machine and a harbor dredge. He was the first man to mount a magnetic needle on a horizontal axis, giving us the compass as we know it today.

He devised a diving bell and a life preserver. He planned large cruising submarines, but destroyed the plans; for he feared that men would use these underwater ships against each other!

Leonardo was the first scientist to understand that fossils are impressions of extinct animals. They had lived, he said, when the rocks in which they are found were but sediment on the bottom of the sea. For the earth, he told men, was not just five thousand years old. He was a pioneer in geology, and believed that it had taken the River Arno (which flows through Florence) two hundred thousand years to build its flood plains.

A century before telescopes, Leonardo claimed that the earth was not the center of the universe but moved around the sun in an elliptical orbit. He said that the earth was but a small planet in the vastness of the solar system; that the stars were distant worlds, much larger than they seemed; and that the sun was but one of their number.

Our deep respect for Leonardo's science was not matched when he was alive. But he was famous as an artist. He had many rivals; for he lived, after all, in the times of Botticelli and Raphael and Michelangelo. But th
people of Renaissance Italy followe
the streets. When he showed one of
they packed and pushed like movi
him. City-states and men of great w
him. Kings asked him to grace their

And yet Leonardo was a lonely m
ably never met another human bein
talk with him of all the things tha
mind.

Leonardo's last years were passed
Amboise, in central France. Thou
were paralyzed, his mind was as bri
He was absorbed in a new plan for
mighty locks, and with the many id
his notebooks. When Leonardo die
1519, his smile was still bright with
understanding.

ABOUT twenty-five years a
Italy, named Roberto
building models from the sketc
da Vinci's notebooks, and w
find that most of them actu
collection of models has now
the International Business M
ration and has been shown
can cities. On the right are
models and a sketch from a
book.

1. Model of a flying ma
of a wooden frame, two hug
of ropes and pulleys, and
flyer was to lie face down i
put his feet into leather sti
by pulleys to the wings. He
wings by moving his feet u
the same time operating th
his arms and guiding the m

2. Model of a rotating bri
nect an island fortress wit
When not in use, the bridge
to the island side so that er
cross it.

3. Model of a hydraulic
nal structure was more than
Erected beside a stream, it
of the stream itself to pum
castle of the duke of Milar

4. Sketch from a Leor
showing the raising of a l
parts that were stored for

THE IBM CORPORATION

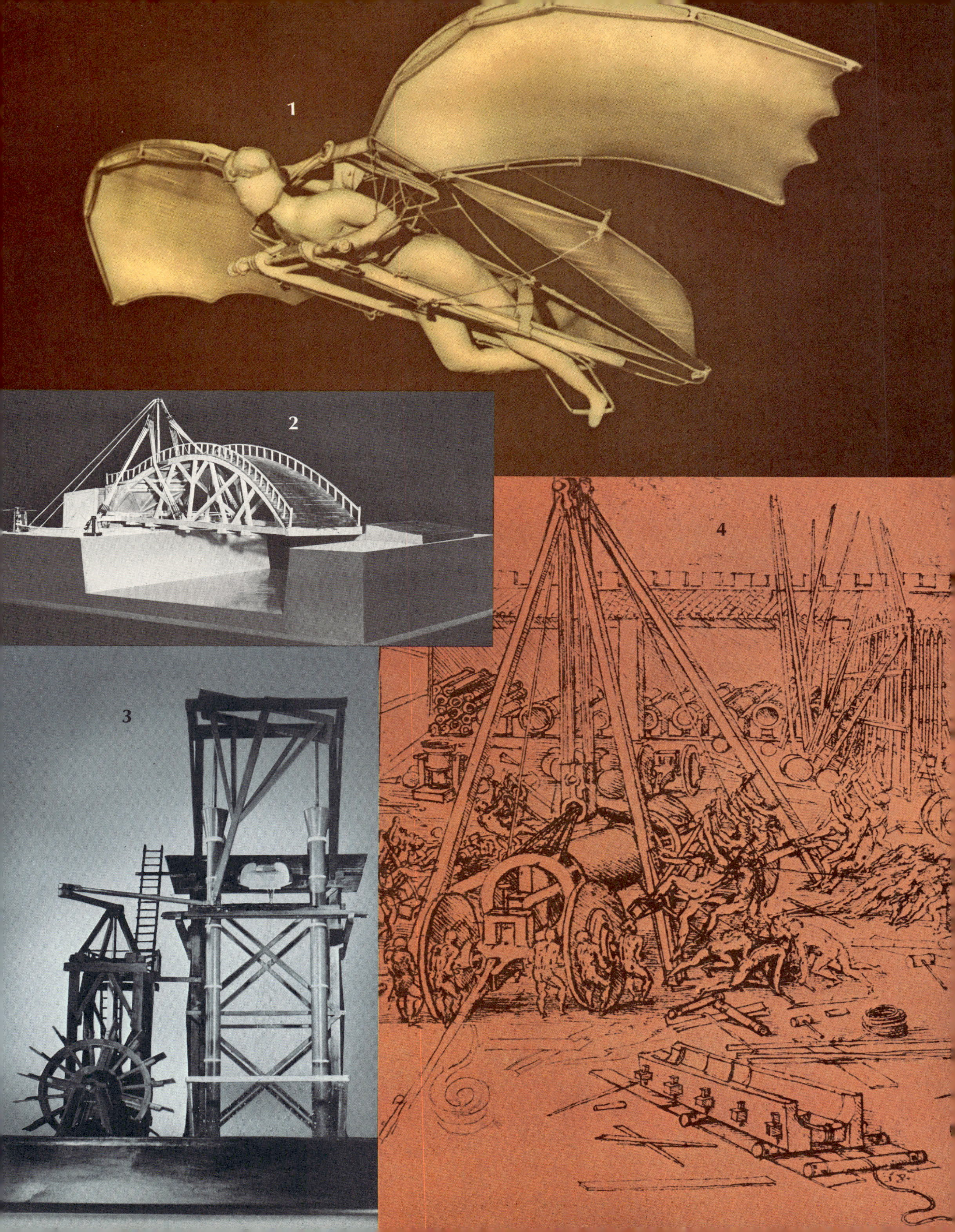
1
2
3
4

Build a Balsa Glider

BY RON WARRING

Balsa modeling is easy and fun. Here is a simple project on which to start. You will need the following tools and materials

MODELING KNIFE with interchangeable blades for general cutting and carving. A short, triangular blade for cutting sheet and strip. A long, parallel blade for carving.

SAW: razor saw to fit modeling-knife handle above, or "junior" hacksaw. Very useful for cutting thicker sheet across the grain, and block.

SANDPAPER for shaping and finishing.

HARDBOARD SHEET for use as a cutting board. Any convenient size.

METAL RULER for measuring and u
straightedge for cutting.

METAL SQUARE for marking out and
assemblies for squareness.

BALSA CEMENT for all glued joints

WOOD: a 13-inch length of 1/2 by
hard balsa, for the fuselage. A shee
balsa, 3 inches wide by 1/16 inch
wings, tail plane and fin.

The model plan shows all the necessary parts to be cut out, actual size. To avoid damage to the plan, trace the outline on tracing paper first, and then transfer it to the wood. This can be done by laying the tracing paper in position over the wood, inserting carbon paper underneath and then drawing around the outline again. Or you can transfer the outline by pricking with a pin, then joining the pinpricks with a pencil line.

Two tips to note in cutting out – tackle the cutting of sharp curves in stages (see diagram). Also, having cut one wing panel you can use it as a pattern for cutting the second, identical panel.

Trace the wing-panel, tail-plane and fin patterns from the plan on the facing page, and transfer them onto your 1/16-inch sheet of balsa by one of the methods described. When these are cut out they will form the main parts for the glider.

Mark and cut out the fuselage, a
tapers toward the tail. Also shape t
the wing position in pencil.

Assembling

The tail plane is cemented directl
of the tapered end of the fuselage.
tail plane is properly centered and s
fuselage, and then hold with a coup
the cement has set. The fin cement
the fuselage, with the bottom edge
tail plane. This gives a larger glu
stronger joint. Again, hold the fin i
rarily with pins and check with you
it is at right angles to the tail plane

The two wing panels are cemer
an angle to give the wings what is c
(necessary to make the model stab

Adapted from Modeling with Balsa, *© by Ron Warring 1958 and published by Sterling Publishing*

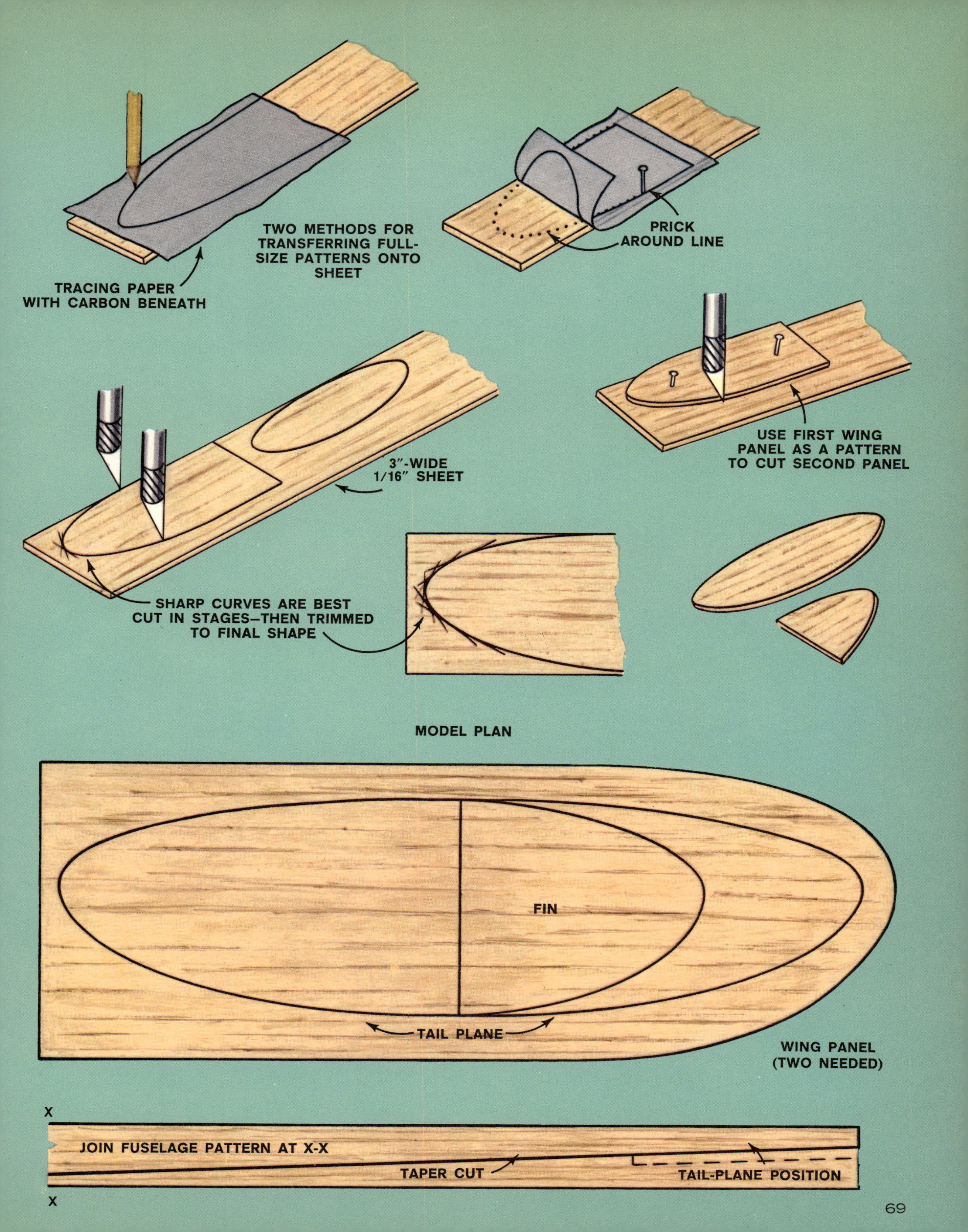
TWO METHODS FOR TRANSFERRING FULL-SIZE PATTERNS ONTO SHEET
TRACING PAPER WITH CARBON BENEATH
PRICK AROUND LINE
USE FIRST WING PANEL AS A PATTERN TO CUT SECOND PANEL
3"-WIDE 1/16" SHEET
SHARP CURVES ARE BEST CUT IN STAGES—THEN TRIMMED TO FINAL SHAPE
MODEL PLAN
FIN
TAIL PLANE
WING PANEL (TWO NEEDED)
X
JOIN FUSELAGE PATTERN AT X-X
TAPER CUT
TAIL-PLANE POSITION
X

one wing down flat on a board, with a strip of waxed paper under the edge to prevent it from sticking to the board when the other wing panel is cemented to it. Put down the second wing panel with the tip raised 3 inches (e.g. with a spare piece of 3-inch-wide sheet supporting the wing tip above the board). The two wings will not meet in a neat joint and the edges must be "bevel" trimmed with a knife until they do. Then you can cement them together, using pins to hold the second wing panel in position. To add extra strength to the wing joint, cover the top joint with a skin of cement.

Allow at least an hour for the wings to set. Then they can be unpinned and tried in position on the fuselage. With your modeling knife, cut a notch in the top of the fuselage to let the wi down properly. The notch should be deep to prevent the wings from rocking, and a inches long to allow easy adjustment of t location. Then slip a rubber band over the stick, bring over the top of the wings and end over the nose, as shown. This arrangen enable you to move the wings fore or aft t any errors in weight distribution.

Sight from the rear to check that the w lined up properly with the tail plane— check that they are square with the fusel model is now ready for flying.

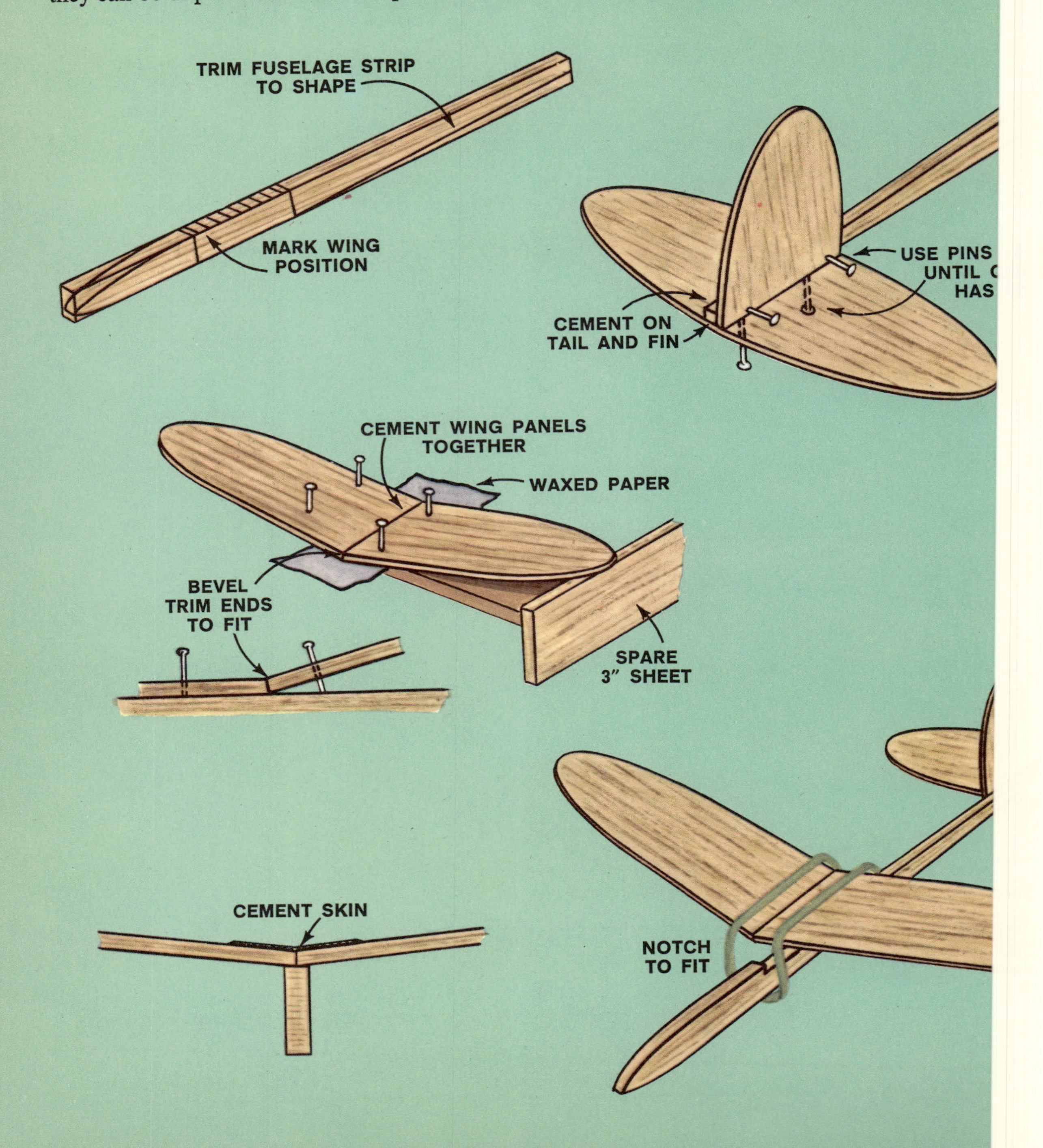

Old Dog

The true story of a little New Mexican boy and his remarkable dog

BY WILLIAM BRANDON

OLD DOG was a neighbor of ours when I was growing up on a ranch in New Mexico. He was a Russian wolfhound. And he belonged to my friend Juan Izquierdo, who lived down the road from us.

Russian wolfhounds, long-nosed and graceful, are the aristocrats of the dog world. But Old Dog was the sorriest Russian wolfhound alive. His coat was ragged and shaggy. He had cauliflower ears. He limped on one leg or another — he didn't care which one. And the only thing he really enjoyed was sleeping.

He would come with Juan to our place and collapse like a dropped rug. There he would sleep until Juan shook him awake to go home. Then he would clamber to his feet and limp away, leaning against Juan so he wouldn't fall over.

Old Dog thought a great deal of Juan. He wouldn't wake up and move for anyone else. If you wanted him out of the way, you just about had to pick him up and carry him. This was a job for a man and a boy, since he weighed close to a hundred pounds.

As for Juan, he loved Old Dog more than anything in the world. Juan had no brothers or sisters, and there was a lot of trouble at his house. Except for Old Dog he felt pretty much alone.

The trouble at home was caused mainly by arguments about how Juan should be brought up. Mrs. Izquierdo's mother, an angry little woman who spoke only Spanish, lived with the family. She and Mr. Izquierdo had furious quarrels over whether Juan should go to Sunday school or church; whether he should be forced to eat something he didn't like; what chores he should do around the place.

One day Mr. Izquierdo said to my mother with tears in his eyes, "I tell her she raised her kids, now let us raise ours!"

As a result, Juan didn't get much raising. Mrs. Izquierdo pitched into the fights too — sometimes on her mother's side, sometimes on her husband's, and sometimes from a new direction altogether. All three were too busy quarreling over Juan to pay any attention to him.

Old Dog was the only reason Juan didn't run away. Juan used to say that he would like to cross the mountains and get a job over on the Pecos wrangling horses. But Old Dog was too old and sleepy to run away with him, so he couldn't go.

On the other hand, there was one thing that Juan's father, mother and grandmother were agreed on — they didn't like Old Dog. He was a nuisance. He was always in everybody's way, and there was the extra expense of food for him. The Izquierdos were poor, and Old Dog ate as much as two people.

All these troubles simmered and boiled for a long time. Then one winter day they exploded. Juan had been sick with a cold and fever. Mr. Izquierdo had brought out the doctor. His mother-in-law had taken all the correct precautions against the evil of *brujas* — witches. The older country people still clung to many such superstitions. Mr. Izquierdo himself took witches seriously enough to wrangle with his mother-in-law about the proper way to fling salt in order to ward off evil. When she happened to find one of the little creatures called Child-of-the-Earth — a kind of cricket that comes out of the ground at night, and a dread omen — Mr. Izquierdo threw salt on *her* as if she herself might be a *bruja*. This sent her into a rage.

The doctor said Juan would have to stay in bed — there was danger of pneumonia. And it was while he was lying there helpless that Juan's parents and grandmother decided to get rid of Old Dog. With all the worry about Juan and the expense of the doctor, Old Dog's presence had become unbearable.

It was a gray day, with a booming northwest wind and some rain and spitting snow. Mr. Izquierdo's truck got stuck in the mud going past our place. He had to confess why Old Dog was with him in the truck, away from Juan's side for the first time in years. Mr. Izquierdo was taking him to a friend who ran a gun club. The friend would do away with Old Dog.

Lone Dog

By Irene Rutherford McLeod

I'm a lean dog, a keen dog, a wild dog, and lone;
I'm a rough dog, a tough dog, hunting on my own;
I'm a bad dog, a mad dog, teasing silly sheep;
I love to sit and bay the moon, to keep fat souls from sleep.

I'll never be a lap dog, licking dirty feet,
A sleek dog, a meek dog, cringing for my meat,
Not for me the fireside, the well-filled plate,
But shut door, and sharp stone, and cuff and kick and hate.

Not for me the other dogs, running by my side,
Some have run a short while, but none of them would bide.
O mine is still the lone trail, the hard trail, the best,
Wide wind, the wild stars, and hunger of the quest!

Mr. Izquierdo was shamefaced and defiant at the same time. He said over and over, "We got to, we got to. We'll all go crazy. We got to."

After he had freed his truck and gone on, my mother had to restrain me from going to tell Juan what was happening. Here was real tragedy. What would Juan do when he found Old Dog gone?

I never did know who told Juan. Maybe he overheard something — or maybe he only sensed it. In any case he found out. And when Mr. Izquierdo came back in his empty truck, Juan had disappeared.

Mrs. Izquierdo ran all the way to our place. She arrived almost fainting from lack of breath. "Juanito! Juanito! Juanito is out in the rain!"

We all roared down the road to the Izquierdos' house in our old car. The grandmother was lying

"Lone Dog," from Songs to Save a Soul, *is reprinted by permission of The Viking Press, Inc.*

on the floor in Juan's room, sobbing. Juan's window was wide open.

We learned that Mr. Izquierdo had gone out toward the foothills, looking for Juan. Then we went back to our place, and Mother telephoned the doctor and the sheriff. I caught up my horse, Buddy, and rode out on the mesa. But I didn't see anything of Juan. On the way back, I saw Mr. Izquierdo racing down the road in his truck. It was taking the turns wildly, the rear wheels throwing up fountains of wet sand.

The doctor appeared a little later, with a deputy sheriff and an Indian to make up a search party. Everyone drove down to the Izquierdo place, and soon Mr. Izquierdo returned in his truck. Old Dog was with him, sound asleep.

Mr. Izquierdo explained that his friend at the gun club had not been home, and so Old Dog was still living. Mr. Izquierdo was very calm and gentle. He spoke so softly you could scarcely hear him, but his eyes crackled like electricity. The doctor went to his car and came back with a bottle. "Take a long drink," he said.

Mr. Izquierdo said, "Thank you," and his voice broke. Then he picked up Old Dog and carried him into Juan's room.

Old Dog woke up and got to his feet and tottered to the empty bed. Everyone watched him. It was amazing for him to wake up without Juan calling him. He put his chin on the edge of the bed and whined. Mrs. Izquierdo buried her face in her hands.

Suddenly Mr. Izquierdo said, "Old Dog, where's Juanito? Find Juanito!"

Old Dog blundered excitedly here and there. The deputy sheriff said, "Wouldn't any dog have much nose with all this rain."

"It hasn't rained since noon," the doctor said.

The Indian — a little, stump-legged old man — stepped forward. He grasped Old Dog by the scruff of the neck and dragged him to the window. Then he picked him up and dumped him out, and climbed out after him. Everyone else charged out the door and around the house. The Indian, his hand on Old Dog's shoulder, was already moving away through the mesquite trees. Old Dog's nose was to the ground. He began to run— a remarkable sight—and right away he fell down like a tumbleweed hitting a fence. The Indian set him on his feet again and ran beside him, holding the hair of his neck.

It was late afternoon by then, and almost dark. The mountains Juan had wanted to cross looked high and black, and a long way off. Old Dog and the Indian reached the first foothills. The rest of us followed, running as hard as we could.

The Indian and Old Dog disappeared into a wash. When we came up they were standing beside Juan, who lay asleep under an overhang of rock. He woke up and gazed at us in surprise. Then he saw Old Dog, and remembered. But he didn't say a word. The doctor wrapped him in a blanket.

"He's all wet," said Mr. Izquierdo. For some reason he whispered, although Juan was wide awake now in Mrs. Izquierdo's arms.

"Sweat," the doctor said. "It might be good for him."

The next day I left with my family for a visit with friends in the East. So I didn't hear the rest of the story until weeks later. When we returned, we found Juan and Old Dog constant companions as before. But there was a great change in the Izquierdo family. Mr. Izquierdo was always polite to his mother-in-law, and she was very polite to everyone, and they never argued about anything. "A miracle," everyone said. But Juan told us the truth. They believed Old Dog was a *bruja,* he said. And they knew they had to behave well to gain his good will.

For they had discovered something when Old Dog was searching for Juan. Something Juan had known and kept secret for a long time. Old Dog was blind.

There's a Catch

TO CATCH a crocodile you need only the following simple pieces of equipment: a deck chair, a dull book, a telescope, a pair of tweezers and a matchbox. The method is equally simple. You place the deck chair on a riverbank, sit in it and start to read. Becoming bored, you soon fall asleep, and the book slips off your lap. A crocodile spies the book and comes up out of the water to investigate. After reading a few pages, he too is asleep. Now you wake up again. You grab your telescope and, looking at the crocodile down the wrong end of it, you just pick him up with the tweezers and pop him in the matchbox.

The Real Sherlock Holmes

BY IRVING WALLACE

SHERLOCK HOLMES was the first of all the storybook detectives, and he is still the greatest. He is perhaps known to more people than any other character in fiction. You must have seen pictures of him — a powerful man of six feet two, dressed in a cape and deerstalker hat, with a pipe in his mouth and a magnifying glass in his hand.

Yet it was not his appearance that made Sherlock Holmes famous, but his marvelous powers of detection. In *The Adventure of the Norwood Builder,* a popular Sherlock Holmes story, a young man rushes into Holmes's sitting room at 221B Baker Street, London. "I am John McFarlane," he says, panting heavily.

Sherlock Holmes lazily replies, "You mentioned your name as if I should recognize it. I assure you that beyond the obvious facts that you are a bachelor, a lawyer, a Freemason and an asthmatic, I know nothing whatever about you."

Of course, Holmes was doing no more than using his eyes cleverly. He noticed that his visitor's clothes needed repairing — a sign that he was not married. A legal form sticking out of the man's pocket told Holmes that he was a lawyer. From his watch chain hung a charm worn only by members of the Society of Freemasons. He was also panting in a way that suggested he had asthma.

John McFarlane was in serious trouble. He was suspected of having murdered a builder in Norwood. In fact, the builder hadn't been murdered at all. For reasons of revenge, he had staged his own "murder," leaving evidence to show that McFarlane had killed him and destroyed the body in a fire. Holmes solved the case brilliantly, and the wicked builder was soon dis-

Adapted from The Saturday Review of Literature, *published by Saturday Review Associates, Inc., with editorial additions*

covered, hiding in a secret passage in his house.

When you read how Holmes can tell so much about someone he has only just met, you may wonder if such a thing is possible. "It's all very well in a book," you may say, "but no one could do that in real life." Well, there was someone who did it in real life. He was a well-known surgeon in Edinburgh, and his name was Dr. Joseph Bell.

For fifty years Dr. Bell taught at Edinburgh University. He used to tell his pupils that if they were to become good doctors they must first learn to use their eyes properly.

"Most people see," he said, "but they do not observe. Look at a man, and in his face you will find clues to where he comes from. His hands will show what work he does. The rest of the story is told by the clothes — even by a piece of lint sticking to his coat."

He would glance at some stranger, then remark, "A cobbler, I see." Later he would point out to the students that a cobbler's trousers were always worn smooth on the inside of the knee, for that was where he held the shoe he was repairing.

One of Dr. Bell's pupils was a young man called Arthur Conan Doyle. He graduated from the university in 1881, and for six years struggled to make a living as a doctor. At last he found himself so short of money that, in desperation, he turned to writing. He decided to try a detective story.

Wanting a new kind of detective for his book, Conan Doyle thought of his old teacher, Dr. Bell. If the surgeon had been a detective, he would surely have treated detection as a science, instead of the romantic game it was at that time. So Conan Doyle invented his scientific detective, Sherlock Holmes. But Holmes's brilliant methods are really those of Dr. Bell.

Dr. Bell's Methods

One afternoon Dr. Bell was at his desk in the hospital when somebody knocked at the door.

"Come in," called the surgeon. A man entered. Dr. Bell stared at him. "Why are you worried?"

"How do you know I am worried?"

"The four knocks. Those who have no cares in the world only bother to knock twice or, at the most, three times."

It turned out that the man *was* worried.

On another occasion, when Conan Doyle was acting as Dr. Bell's assistant, a patient entered the room.

"Did you enjoy your walk over the golf links today, as you came in from the south side of the town?" Dr. Bell asked.

"Why, yes, did you see me?" said the patient.

Dr. Bell said he had not seen him. "But," he explained, "on a showery day, the reddish clay of the golf course sticks to the shoes. There is no clay like that anywhere else."

The Case of the Retired Sergeant

Sherlock Holmes not only follows Dr. Bell's methods. There are times when he actually uses bits of his detective work. When people came into his consulting room, Dr. Bell would tell them what was wrong with them before they had time to open their mouths. He would even give them details of their past lives, and he hardly ever made a mistake.

One day, as a new patient entered, Dr. Bell studied him carefully and said, "Well, you've served in the Army, in a Scottish regiment, and you have only just retired."

"Aye, sir," said the man.

"You were a sergeant, and you were stationed in Barbados."

"Aye, sir."

Dr. Bell turned to his students. "You see, gentlemen, he is a polite man, but he did not remove his hat when he came into the room. They do not do so in the Army. But if he had been out of the Army for long, he would have learned civilian habits. Clearly he is used to giving orders, as a sergeant would. He is obviously Scottish, so he was probably in a Scottish regiment. As to Barbados, he is suffering from a disease that is common in the West Indies."

There is an incident almost the same as this one in the Sherlock Holmes story *The Greek Interpreter*.

Sherlock Holmes soon became very popular, as he still is today. He seems like a real detective, because he always tells you exactly how he solves each crime. In a way, of course, he was real, and perhaps that is why he appears so lifelike.

Dr. Bell, the original Sherlock Holmes, once caught a man out beautifully. He was teaching some students when a patient walked into the room.

"Gentlemen," said Dr. Bell, "this man has been a soldier in a Highland regiment. He probably played in the band."

The surgeon pointed out that when the patient walked he swaggered a little, like a Highland piper. But the man quickly said that he was a shoemaker, and that he had never even been in the Army.

The surgeon then asked him to remove his shirt. He did so, and the students saw a little blue *D* branded on his chest. Dr. Bell explained that soldiers who deserted from the Army in the Crimean War were branded with a *D* when they were caught.

The man finally confessed that he had once played in the band of a Highland regiment. Dr. Bell turned to his audience, and used the words Sherlock Holmes was to make famous:

"It was really elementary, gentlemen."

Anyone Can Be a Detective

Dr. Bell believed it was vital for doctors and detectives to use their eyes intelligently. He also said that anyone who found his life dull could change it into one of excitement and adventure, just by practicing his powers of observation.

His sister once described how he made train journeys more exciting. "When the family traveled in a train, he would tell us where the other passengers came from, where they were going, and even something about their jobs. Then he would ask them whether he was right or not. He was right so often that we thought him a magician."

However, Dr. Bell would show that his detective feats were not due to magic, but to good observation.

"The work that a man does leaves its mark on his hands," he used to say. "The scars of a coal miner are quite different from those of a man who works in a quarry. The hands of both the carpenter and the stonemason grow hard, but not in the same way."

Yet even Dr. Bell sometimes made mistakes. Luckily, he also had a sense of humor. When people asked him to give examples of his skill as a detective, he liked to tell this story:

One day he and his pupils were examining a patient in a hospital bed. "Aren't you a musician?" Dr. Bell asked him.

"Aye," admitted the sick man.

"You see, gentlemen, it is quite simple. This man has a disease of the cheek muscles, from too much blowing on wind instruments. We need only ask him, and he will admit it. What musical instrument do you play, my man?"

The man got up on his elbows. "The big drum, doctor!"

A Clever Cabdriver

Conan Doyle used to tell this story of how he met an admirer of Sherlock Holmes in Paris.

The "cabbie" who had driven him to his hotel studied him closely and then said, "Dr. Doyle, I see you have recently been in Constantinople and Buda. Also it is clear that you were not far from Milan."

Conan Doyle gasped with surprise, and asked the amateur detective how he had discovered all this.

"I looked at the labels on your suitcase," replied the artful driver!

The Adventure of the Speckled Band

In which Sherlock Holmes and his faithful friend Dr. Watson solve a hair-raising mystery. One of Conan Doyle's most famous tales and NOT *to be read at bedtime!*

BY SIR ARTHUR CONAN DOYLE

EARLY one April morning I woke to find Sherlock Holmes standing, fully dressed, by my bed. He was a late riser as a rule, and I blinked up at him in surprise.

"Very sorry to wake you up, Watson," said he, "but a client, a young lady in a considerable state of excitement, insists upon seeing me. She is waiting now in the sitting room."

I had no keener pleasure than in following Holmes in his professional investigations, and in admiring the rapid deductions, as swift as intuitions, and yet always founded on a logical basis, with which he unraveled problems.

I was ready in a few minutes to accompany my friend downstairs. A lady dressed in black, and heavily veiled, rose as we entered the sitting room.

"Good morning, madam," said Holmes cheerily. "My name is Sherlock Holmes. This is my intimate friend and associate, Dr. Watson, before whom you can speak as freely as before myself. Pray draw up to the fire, for I observe that you are shivering."

"It is not cold which makes me shiver," said the woman in a low voice.

"What, then?"

"It is fear, Mr. Holmes. It is terror." She raised her veil as she spoke, and we could see that her face was all drawn and gray, with restless, frightened eyes. Her features and figure were those of a woman of thirty, but her hair was shot with premature gray.

Sherlock Holmes looked her over with one of his quick, all-comprehensive glances. "You must not fear," said he soothingly, bending forward and patting her forearm. "We shall soon set matters right. You have come in by train this morning, I see."

"You know me, then?"

"No, but I observe the second half of a return ticket in the palm of your left glove. You must have started early, and yet you had a good drive in a dogcart, along heavy roads, before you reached the station."

The lady stared in bewilderment.

"There is no mystery, my dear madam," said he, smiling. "The left arm of your jacket is spattered with mud in no less than seven places. There is no vehicle save a dogcart which throws up mud in that way, and then only when you sit on the left-hand side of the driver."

"You are perfectly correct," said she. "I started from home before six. I can stand this strain no longer; I shall go mad if it continues. Oh, sir, can you throw a little light through the dense darkness which surrounds me? My fears are so vague, my suspicions depend so entirely upon small points that they may seem to you only the fancies of a nervous woman."

"I am all attention, madam. And now I beg

Condensed from The Complete Sherlock Holmes *with the permission of the Sir Arthur Conan Doyle Estates*

you to lay before us everything that may help in forming an opinion upon the matter."

The Terror of the Village

"My name is Helen Stoner," she said, "and I am living with my stepfather, the last survivor of one of the oldest Saxon families in England, the Roylotts of Stoke Moran, in Surrey."

Holmes nodded his head. "The name is familiar to me," said he.

"The family was at one time among the richest in England. Now, however, nothing is left save a few acres of ground, and the two-hundred-year-old house, crushed under a heavy mortgage. The last squire dragged out the horrible life of an aristocratic pauper; but his only son, my stepfather, obtained a medical degree and went out to Calcutta, where he established a large practice. In a fit of anger, however, he beat his native butler to death. He suffered a long term of imprisonment and afterwards returned to England a morose and disappointed man.

"When Dr. Roylott was in India he married my mother, Mrs. Stoner, the young widow of Major-General Stoner, of the Bengal Artillery. My sister Julia and I were twins, only two years old at the time. Shortly after our return to England my mother died. Dr. Roylott took us to live with him at Stoke Moran. My mother had bequeathed her entire income, not less than one thousand pounds a year, to Dr. Roylott, with a provision that a certain annual sum should be allowed to each of us in the event of our marriage. The money was enough for all our wants, and there seemed to be no obstacle to our happiness.

"But now a terrible change came over our stepfather. He shut himself up in his house and seldom came out save to indulge in ferocious quarrels with whoever might cross his path. At last he became the terror of the village, and the folks would fly at his approach, for he is a man of immense strength, absolutely uncontrollable in his anger.

"He now has no friends at all save the wandering gypsies, and he gives these vagabonds leave to encamp upon the few acres of bramble-covered land which represent the family estate. He has a passion also for Indian animals; he has at this moment a cheetah and a baboon, which wander freely over his grounds and are feared by the villagers almost as much as their master. You can imagine that my poor sister Julia and I had no great pleasure in our lives.

She died two years ago, and it is of her death that I wish to speak to you.

"Our aunt, Miss Honoria Westphail, lives near Harrow, and we were occasionally allowed to pay her short visits. Julia met there a major of marines, to whom she became engaged. My stepfather offered no objection to the marriage; but within a fortnight of the day fixed for the wedding, a terrible event occurred."

A Wild Scream

Sherlock Holmes had been leaning back in his chair with his eyes closed and his head sunk in a cushion, but he half opened his lids now and glanced across at his visitor. "Pray be precise as to details," said he.

"It is easy for me to be so, for every incident is seared into my memory. Only one wing of the old manor house is now inhabited. The bedrooms are on the ground floor; the first is Dr. Roylott's, the second my sister's, and the third my own. There is no communication between them, but they all open out into the same corridor. Do I make myself plain?"

"Perfectly so."

"The windows of the three rooms open on the lawn. That fatal night Dr. Roylott had gone to his room early, though we knew that he had not retired to rest, for my sister was troubled by the smell of the strong Indian cigars which it is his custom to smoke. She left her room, therefore, and came into mine, where she sat for some time, chatting about her approaching wedding. At eleven o'clock she rose to leave me, but she paused at the door. 'Tell me, Helen,' said she, 'have you ever heard anyone whistle in the dead of night?'

"'Never,' said I. 'Why?'

"'Because during the last few nights I have heard, about three in the morning, a low, clear whistle. I cannot tell where it comes from — perhaps from the next room, perhaps from the lawn. I wondered if you had heard it.'

"'No, I have not. It must be those wretched gypsies.'

"'Very likely. Well, it is of no great consequence, at any rate.' She smiled back at me, closed my door, and a few moments later I heard her key turn in the lock."

"Indeed," said Holmes. "Was it your custom always to lock yourselves in at night?"

"Always. I mentioned to you the cheetah and the baboon. We had no feeling of security unless our doors were locked."

"Quite so. Pray proceed."

"I could not sleep. A vague feeling of impending misfortune oppressed me. It was a wild night. The wind was howling outside, and the rain was beating against the windows. Suddenly, amid all the hubbub of the gale, there burst forth the wild scream of a terrified woman. I knew that it was my sister's voice. I sprang from my bed, wrapped a shawl round me, and rushed into the corridor. As I opened my door I seemed to hear a low whistle, such as my sister described, and a few moments later a clanging sound, as if a mass of metal had fallen. As I ran down the passage, my sister's door was unlocked, and slowly opened. I stared at it horror-stricken. By the light of the corridor lamp I saw my sister in the doorway, her face blanched with terror, her hands groping for help, her whole figure swaying to and fro. I ran and threw my arms round her, but her knees gave way and she fell. As I bent over her she suddenly shrieked, 'Oh, my God! Helen! It was the band! The speckled band!'

"There was something else which she would fain have said, and she stabbed with her finger into the air in the direction of the doctor's room, but a convulsion seized her and choked her words. I rushed out, calling loudly for my stepfather, and I met him hastening from his room in his dressing gown. When he reached my sister's side she was unconscious, and, though he sent for medical aid from the village, all efforts to revive her were in vain."

The Warning Whistle

"One moment," said Holmes. "Are you sure about this whistle and metallic sound?"

"That was what the coroner asked me. It is my strong impression that I heard it, and yet, amid the crash of the gale and the creaking of the old house, I may have been deceived."

"Was your sister dressed?"

"No, she was in her nightdress. In her right hand was found the charred stump of a match, and in her left a matchbox."

"Showing that she had struck a light and looked about her when the alarm took place. That is important. And what conclusions did the coroner come to?"

"He investigated the case with great care, for Dr. Roylott's conduct had long been notorious in the county, but he was unable to find any satisfactory cause of death. My evidence showed that the door had been fastened upon the inner side, and the windows were secured every night by old-fashioned shutters with broad iron bars. It is certain, therefore, that my sister was quite alone when she met her end. Besides, there were no marks of violence."

"How about poison?"

"The doctors examined her for it, but without success."

"What do you think that this unfortunate lady died of, then?"

"It is my belief that she died of pure fear and nervous shock, though what frightened her I cannot imagine."

"What did you gather from this allusion to a band — a speckled band?"

"Sometimes I have thought that it was merely delirium, sometimes that it referred to a band of gypsies. The spotted handkerchiefs so many of them wear over their heads might have suggested the strange adjective which she used."

Holmes shook his head like a man who is far from satisfied. "These are very deep waters," said he. "Pray go on."

"Two years have passed since then, and my life has been until lately lonelier than ever. A month ago, however, a dear friend whom I have known for many years did me the honor to ask my hand in marriage. His name is Percy Armitage. My stepfather has offered no opposition, and we are to be married in the spring.

"Two days ago some repairs were started in the west wing of the house, and my bedroom wall has been pierced, so that I have had to move into the chamber in which my sister died, and sleep in the very bed in which she slept. Imagine, then, my terror when last night, as I lay awake thinking over her terrible fate, I suddenly heard the low whistle which had been the herald of her own death. I sprang up and lit the lamp, but nothing was to be seen in the room. I was too shaken to go to bed again, so as soon as it was daylight I got a dogcart at the inn, and drove to the train. I have come to ask your advice."

"You have done wisely," said my friend.

A Sinister Business

There was a long silence, during which Holmes leaned his chin upon his hands and stared into the crackling fire. "This is a very deep business," he said at last. "If we were to come to Stoke Moran today, would it be possible for us to see these rooms without the knowledge of your stepfather?"

"As it happens, he spoke of coming into town today. It is probable that there would be nothing to disturb you."

"Excellent. Then we shall both come. What are you going to do yourself?"

"I have one or two things to do now that I am in town. But I shall return by the twelve-o'clock train, and shall look forward to seeing you again this afternoon."

The lady rose, dropped her thick black veil over her face, and glided from the room.

"And what do you think of it all, Watson?" asked Holmes, settling back into his chair.

"It seems to me to be a most dark and sinister business."

"Dark enough and sinister enough. But what do you make of these nocturnal whistles, and the very peculiar words of the dying woman?"

"I cannot think."

"When you combine the ideas of whistles at night, the presence of a band of gypsies, the doctor's probable interest in preventing his stepdaughter's marriage, the dying allusion to a band, and, finally, the fact that Miss Helen Stoner heard a metallic clang, which might have been one of the window bars falling back into place, I think the mystery may be cleared along those lines."

"But what, then, did the gypsies do?"

"I cannot imagine," Holmes said. "But — what in the name of the devil!"

An Angry Visitor

Our door had been suddenly dashed open, and a huge man had framed himself in the opening. He wore a black top hat, a long frock coat, and a pair of high gaiters. So tall was he that his hat actually brushed the crossbar of the doorway, and his breadth seemed to span it from side to side. A large face, seared with a thousand wrinkles, burned yellow by the sun, and marked with every evil passion, turned from one to the other of us. His deep-set eyes and his high, thin nose gave him somewhat the resemblance to a fierce old bird of prey.

"Which of you is Sherlock Holmes?" asked this apparition.

"My name, sir; but you have the advantage of me," said my companion quietly.

"I am Dr. Grimesby Roylott, of Stoke Moran."

"Indeed, Doctor," said Holmes blandly. "Pray take a seat."

"I will do nothing of the kind. My stepdaughter has been here. I have traced her. What has she been saying to you?"

"It is a little cold for the time of the year," said Holmes.

"You put me off, do you?" shouted our new visitor furiously. "I know you, you scoundrel! I have heard of you before. You are Holmes, the meddler."

My friend smiled.

"Holmes, the busybody!"

Holmes chuckled heartily. "Your conversation is most entertaining," said he. "When you go out close the door, for there is a decided draft."

"I will go when I have said my say. Don't you dare to meddle with my affairs. I am a dangerous man to fall foul of! See here."

With that, Dr. Roylott stepped swiftly forward, seized the poker, and bent it into a curve with his huge brown hands.

"See that you keep yourself out of my grip," he snarled, and hurling the twisted poker into the fireplace he strode out of the room.

"A very amiable person," said Holmes, laughing. "I am not quite so bulky, but if he had remained I might have shown him that my grip was not much more feeble than his own." He picked up the steel poker and, with a sudden effort, straightened it.

"This incident gives zest to our investigation," he said. "Now for some breakfast. Afterwards I shall walk down to Doctors' Commons, where I hope to get some data which may help us in this matter."

It was nearly one o'clock when Sherlock Holmes returned from his excursion.

"I have seen the will of the deceased wife," said he. "Dr. Roylott's total income is now not more than seven hundred and fifty pounds. Each daughter could claim an income of two hundred and fifty pounds, in case of marriage. It is evident, therefore, that if both girls had married, this brute would have had a mere pittance; if even one married, it would cripple him. And now, Watson, this is too serious for dawdling; we shall call a cab and drive to Waterloo Station. I should be very much obliged if you would slip your revolver into your pocket. That and a toothbrush are, I think, all that we need."

We Go to Stoke Moran

We caught a train for Leatherhead, where we hired a trap at the station inn and drove for four or five miles through the lovely Surrey lanes. It was a perfect day, with a bright sun and a few fleecy clouds in the heavens. The trees and wayside hedges were just throwing out their first green shoots, and the air was full of the pleasant smell of moist earth. My companion sat in the front of the trap, his hat pulled down over his eyes, buried in the deepest thought. Suddenly, however, he started, tapped me on the shoulder, and pointed over the meadows. "Look!" said he. "That must be Stoke Moran."

"Yes, sir, that be the house of Dr. Grimesby Roylott," remarked the driver.

"We have come to inspect some repairs to the building," said Holmes. "We will walk to the house across the fields."

We got off, paid our fare, and the trap rattled back on its way to Leatherhead. As we approached the house, Miss Stoner came hurrying out to meet us with a face which spoke her joy. "I have been waiting so eagerly for you," she cried, shaking hands with us warmly. "All has turned out splendidly. Dr. Roylott will not be back before evening."

"We have had the pleasure of making the doctor's acquaintance," said Holmes, and in a few words he sketched what had occurred. Miss Stoner turned white to her lips.

"Good heavens!" she cried. "He is so cunning that I never know when I am safe from him."

"He may find that there is someone more cunning than himself upon his track. Now, we must make the best use of our time, so kindly take us at once to the rooms."

The Mysterious Bell Rope

The building was of gray stone, with a high central portion and two curving wings, like the claws of a crab. One of these wings was a picture of ruin, but the right-hand block was comparatively modern. Some scaffolding had been erected against the end wall, and the stonework had been broken into, but there were no signs of any workmen at the moment of our visit.

Holmes walked slowly up and down the ill-trimmed lawn and examined the windows with deep attention. "This, I take it, belongs to the room in which you used to sleep, the center one to your sister's, and the one next to the main

building belongs to Dr. Roylott's chamber?"

"Exactly so. But I am now sleeping in the middle room."

"Pending the alterations, as I understand. By the way, there does not seem to be any very pressing need for repairs at that end wall."

"There were none. I believe that it was an excuse to move me from my room."

"Ah! That is suggestive. Now, would you have the kindness to go into the middle room and bar your shutters?"

Miss Stoner did so, and Holmes, after a careful examination through the open window, endeavored in every way to force the shutter open, but without success. Then with his magnifying lens he tested the hinges, but they were of solid iron, built firmly into the massive masonry. "Hum!" said he, scratching his chin in some perplexity. "No one could pass these shutters if they were bolted. Well, we shall see if the inside throws any light upon the matter."

A small side door led into the whitewashed corridor from which the three bedrooms opened. The room in which Miss Stoner was now sleeping, and in which her sister had met her fate, was a homely little room with a low ceiling. A brown chest of drawers stood in one corner, a narrow white-counterpaned bed in another, and a dressing table on the left side of the window. These articles, with two small wickerwork chairs, made up the furniture in the room save for a square of Wilton carpet in the center. The paneling of the walls was of brown, worm-eaten oak, old and discolored. Holmes remained silent, his eyes traveling round and round and up and down, taking in every detail.

"Where does that bell communicate?" he asked at last, pointing to a thick bell rope which hung beside the bed, the tassel lying upon the pillow.

"It goes to the housekeeper's room."

"It looks newer than the other things?"

"Yes, it was put there only a couple of years ago."

"Your sister asked for it, I suppose?"

"No, I never heard of her using it."

Holmes walked over to the bed and spent some time staring at it and running his eye up and down the wall. Finally he gave the bell rope a brisk tug. "Why, it's a dummy," said he. "This is very interesting. You can see now that it is fastened to a hook just above the little opening for the ventilator."

"How very absurd! I never noticed that."

"Very strange," muttered Holmes, pulling at the rope. "There are very singular points about this room. For example, what a fool a builder must be to open a ventilator into another room, when, with the same trouble, he might have communicated with the outside air!"

"That is also quite new," said the lady.

"Done about the same time as the bell rope?" remarked Holmes.

"Yes, there were several changes carried out about that time."

"They seem to have been of a most interesting character — dummy bell ropes, and ventilators which do not ventilate. With your permission, Miss Stoner, we shall now carry our researches into the inner apartment."

Some New Clues

Dr. Grimesby Roylott's chamber was larger, but as plainly furnished. A camp bed, a small wooden shelf full of books, mostly of a technical character, an armchair beside the bed, a plain wooden chair against the wall, a round table and a large iron safe were the principal things which met the eye. Holmes examined each of them with the keenest interest.

"What's in here?" he asked, tapping the safe.

"My stepfather's business papers."

"There isn't a cat in it, for example?"

"No. What a strange idea!"

"Well, look at this!" He took up a small saucer of milk which stood on the top of it.

"No; we don't keep a cat. But there is a cheetah, and a baboon."

"Ah, yes, of course! Well, a cheetah is just a big cat, and yet a saucer of milk does not go very far in satisfying its wants, I daresay. There is one point which I should wish to determine."

He squatted in front of the wooden chair and examined the seat through his magnifying lens. Then he rose and put the lens in his pocket. "Hello! Here is something interesting!"

A small dog lash hung on one corner of the bed. The lash, however, was curled upon itself and tied so as to make a loop of whipcord.

"What do you make of that, Watson?"

"It's a common enough lash. But I don't know why it should be tied."

"That is not quite so common, is it? Ah, me! It's a wicked world, and when a clever man turns his brains to crime it is the worst of all."

I have never seen my friend's face so grim or his brow so dark as it was when we turned from the scene of this investigation. We had walked several times up and down the lawn before he roused himself from his reverie. "It is essential, Miss Stoner," said he, "that you should follow my advice in every respect."

"I am in your hands."

"In the first place, you must confine yourself to your room, on pretense of a headache, when your stepfather comes back. Then, when you hear him retire for the night, you must open the shutters of your window, put your lamp there as a signal to us, and then withdraw quietly to the room which you used to occupy. The rest you will leave to us."

"But what will you do?"

"We shall spend the night in your room, and investigate this noise which has disturbed you."

"I believe, Mr. Holmes, that you have already made up your mind. For pity's sake, tell me what was the cause of my sister's death."

"I should prefer to have clearer proofs before I speak."

"You can at least tell me whether my own thought is correct, and if she died from some sudden fright."

"No, I do not think so. I think that there was probably some more tangible cause. And now, Miss Stoner, we must leave you, for if Dr. Roylott saw us our journey would be in vain. Good-by, and be brave."

"Just in Time"

Sherlock Holmes and I had no difficulty in engaging a room at the village inn. Our window commanded a view of Stoke Moran manor house. At dusk we saw Dr. Grimesby Roylott drive past, his huge form looming up beside the little figure of the lad who drove him. The boy had some slight difficulty in undoing the heavy iron gates, and we heard the hoarse roar of the doctor's voice and saw the fury with which he shook his clenched fists at him. The trap drove on.

"Do you know, Watson," said Holmes as we sat in the gathering darkness, "I have really some scruples as to taking you tonight. There is a distinct element of danger."

"Can I be of assistance?"

"You might be invaluable."

"Then I shall certainly come. You have evidently seen more in these rooms than was visible to me."

"No, but I may have deduced a little more. I imagine that you saw all that I did."

"I saw nothing remarkable save the bell rope, and what purpose that could answer I confess is more than I can imagine."

"You saw the ventilator, too?"

"Yes, but I do not think that it is very unusual to have a small opening between two rooms. It was so small that a rat could hardly pass through."

"I knew that we should find a ventilator before ever we came to Stoke Moran."

"My dear Holmes!"

"Oh, yes, I did. You remember, Miss Stoner said that her sister could smell Dr. Roylott's cigar. Now, of course that suggested a communication between the two rooms. It could only be a small one, or it would have been remarked upon at the coroner's inquiry. Therefore, I deduced a ventilator."

"But what harm can there be in that?"

"Well, there is at least a curious coincidence of dates. A ventilator is made, a cord is hung, and a lady who sleeps in the bed dies."

"I cannot as yet see any connection."

"Did you observe anything very peculiar about that bed?"

"No."

"It was clamped to the floor. The lady could not move her bed. It must always be in the same relative position to the ventilator and to the bell rope."

"Holmes," I cried, "I seem to see dimly what you are hinting at. We are only just in time to prevent some subtle and horrible crime."

"We shall have horrors enough before the night is over; so for goodness' sake let us have a quiet pipe and turn our minds for a few hours to something more cheerful."

A Tense Vigil

It was about eleven o'clock when a single bright light shone out suddenly from the dark manor house.

"That is our signal," said Holmes, springing to his feet. "It comes from the middle window."

There was little difficulty in entering the grounds, for unrepaired breaches gaped in the old park wall. Making our way among the trees, we reached the lawn, crossed it, and were about to enter through the window when out from a clump of laurel bushes there darted what seemed to be a hideous and distorted child. It threw itself upon the grass with writhing limbs and then ran swiftly across the lawn into the darkness.

"My God!" I whispered. "Did you see it?"

Holmes was for the moment as startled as I. His hand closed like a vise upon my wrist. Then he broke into a low laugh and put his lips to my ear. "A nice household," he murmured. "That is the baboon."

Where was the cheetah, I wondered; perhaps we might find it upon our shoulders at any moment. I confess that I felt easier in my mind when, after following Holmes's example and slipping off my shoes, I found myself inside the bedroom. My companion noiselessly closed the shutters, moved the lamp onto the table, and cast his eyes round the room. All was as we had seen it in the daytime. Then, creeping up to me, he whispered into my ear so gently that it was all that I could do to distinguish the words: "The least sound would be fatal to our plans."

I nodded to show that I had heard.

"We must sit without light. He would see it through the ventilator."

I nodded again.

"Do not go to sleep; your very life may depend upon it. Have your pistol ready. I will sit on the side of the bed, and you in that chair."

I took out my revolver and laid it on the corner of the table. Holmes had brought a long thin cane, and this he placed upon the bed beside him. By it he laid a box of matches and the stump of a candle. Then he turned down the lamp, and we were left in darkness.

How shall I ever forget that dreadful vigil? I could not hear a sound, not even the drawing of a breath, and yet I knew that my companion sat tensely within a few feet of me. We waited in absolute darkness. From outside came the occasional cry of a night bird, and once at our very window a long-drawn catlike whine, which told us that the cheetah was indeed at liberty. Far away we could hear the deep tones of the parish clock. Twelve struck, and one and two and three, and still we sat waiting silently.

"You See It, Watson?"

Suddenly there was a momentary gleam of light up in the direction of the ventilator. It vanished immediately, but was succeeded by a strong smell of burning oil and heated metal. Someone in the next room had lit a dark lantern. I heard a gentle sound of movement, and then all was silent once more, though the smell grew stronger. For half an hour I sat with straining ears. Then suddenly another sound became audible — a very gentle, soothing sound, like that of a small jet of steam escaping continually from a kettle. The instant that we heard it, Holmes sprang from the bed, struck a match, and lashed furiously with his cane at the bell pull.

"You see it, Watson?" he yelled. "You see it?"

But I saw nothing. At the moment when Holmes struck the light I heard a low, clear whistle, but the sudden glare flashing into my weary eyes made it impossible for me to tell what it was at which my friend lashed so savagely. I could, however, see that his face was deadly pale and filled with horror and loathing.

He had ceased to strike and was gazing up at the ventilator when suddenly there broke from the silence of the night the most horrible cry to which I have ever listened. It swelled up louder and louder, a hoarse yell of pain and fear and anger all mingled in the one dreadful shriek. They say that away down in the village, and even in the distant parsonage, that cry raised the sleepers from their beds.

"What can it mean?" I gasped.

"It means that it is all over," Holmes answered. "And perhaps, after all, it is for the best. Take your pistol, and we will enter Dr. Roylott's room."

With a grave face he lit the lamp and led the way down the corridor. Twice he struck at the chamber door without any reply. Then he turned the handle and entered, I at his heels, the cocked pistol in my hand.

On the table stood a dark lantern with the shutter half open, throwing a brilliant beam of light upon the iron safe, the door of which was ajar. Beside this table, on the wooden chair, sat Dr. Grimesby Roylott, clad in a long dressing gown, his bare ankles protruding beneath, and his feet thrust into slippers. Across his lap lay the dog lash which we had noticed during the day. His chin was cocked upward and his eyes were fixed in a dreadful, rigid stare at the corner of the ceiling. Round his brow he had a peculiar yellow band, with brownish speckles, which seemed to be bound tightly on his head. He made neither sound nor motion.

"The band! The speckled band!" whispered Holmes.

I took a step forward. In an instant the doctor's strange headgear began to move, and there reared from his hair the squat diamond-shaped head and puffed neck of a loathsome serpent.

"It is a swamp adder!" cried Holmes. "The deadliest snake in India. He has died within ten seconds of being bitten. Let us thrust this creature back into its den, and we can then remove Miss Stoner to some place of shelter and let the police know what has happened."

He drew the dog whip swiftly from the dead man's lap, and throwing the noose round the reptile's neck he drew it from its horrid perch and, carrying it at arm's length, threw it into the iron safe, which he closed.

How Holmes Knew

Such are the facts of the death of Dr. Grimesby Roylott, of Stoke Moran. The little which I had yet to learn of the case was told me by Sherlock Holmes next day.

"I had," said he, "come to an erroneous conclusion which shows, my dear Watson, how dangerous it always is to reason from insufficient data. The presence of the gypsies, and the use of the word 'band,' put me upon an entirely wrong scent. I reconsidered my position when my attention was drawn to this ventilator and the dummy bell rope. The discovery that the bed was clamped to the floor gave rise to the suspicion that the rope was there as bridge for something passing through the hole and coming to the bed. The idea of a snake occurred to me, since the doctor had other creatures from India. The idea of using a poison which could not possibly be discovered by any chemical test was just such a one as would occur to a clever and ruthless man who had Eastern training.

"Then I thought of the whistle. Of course he must recall the snake before the morning light revealed it to the victim. He had trained it, probably by the use of the milk, to return when summoned. He would put it through this ventilator with the certainty that it would crawl down the rope and land on the bed. It might or might not bite the occupant; perhaps she might escape every night for a week, but sooner or later she must fall a victim.

"An inspection of his chair showed me that he had been in the habit of standing on it, which would be necessary in order that he should reach the ventilator. The safe, the saucer of milk and the loop of whipcord were enough to dispel any doubts. The metallic clang heard by Miss Stoner was obviously caused by her stepfather hastily closing the door of his safe upon its terrible occupant. Having once made up my mind, you know the steps which I took. I heard the creature hiss and attacked it, driving it through the ventilator.

"The blows of my cane roused its snakish temper, so that it flew upon the first person it saw. In this way I am no doubt indirectly responsible for Dr. Grimesby Roylott's death, and I cannot say that it is likely to weigh very heavily upon my conscience."

QUIZZLES-TWO

(*Answers and explanations on page 198*)

CAN YOU SEE STRAIGHT?

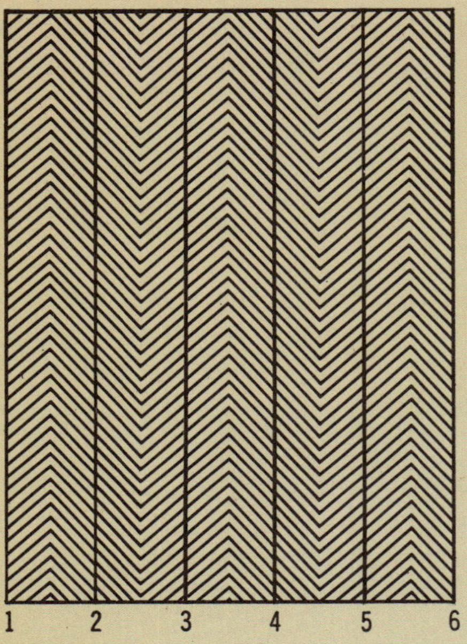

All you have to do here is to say which of these lines are parallel.

THE MAGIC SQUARE

	5	

This is an ordinary square divided into nine small squares, but it used to be considered very lucky. This is because the numbers 1 through 9 can be arranged each in a different square, so that every column across, down, and even diagonally, adds up to 15. The figure 5 must be in the middle. Can you find the right places for the other eight numbers?

WORDS WITHIN WORDS

The first word of each pair can be fitted into the second one, to make another familiar word. For instance, in No. 1, NOW goes into SING and gives you SNOWING. See if you can do the other five.

1. NOW SING . . . . .SNOWING. . . . .
2. STAR CUD . . . .
3. THE FEAR . . . .
4. ISLE MAD . . . .
5. ATE NEST . . . .
6. ACE MEND . . . .

"Words Within Words" by Jack Barrett is adapted from The Saturday Evening Post

CAN YOU PLAY LEAP-SHEEP?

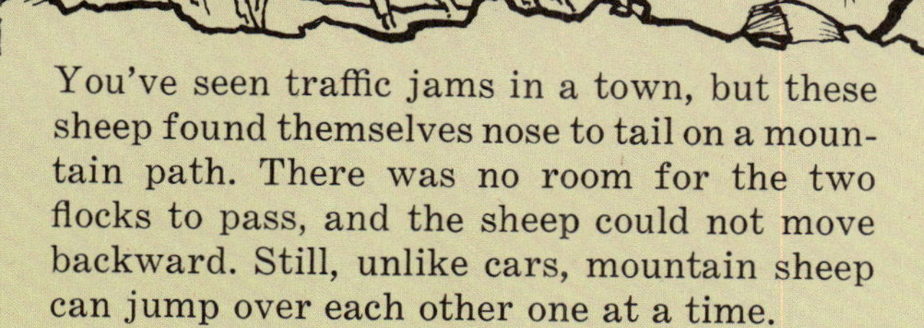

You've seen traffic jams in a town, but these sheep found themselves nose to tail on a mountain path. There was no room for the two flocks to pass, and the sheep could not move backward. Still, unlike cars, mountain sheep can jump over each other one at a time.

When the flocks met, there was a gap between the black leader and the white leader exactly the length of one sheep. So the white leader moved into the gap, and the black leader jumped over him. How did the sheep continue moving until both flocks could go on their way? They solved the problem. Use matchsticks and see if you can too.

AUNT EMILY LIKES–

When Nancy went to stay with her Aunt Emily, she soon found that her aunt disliked a very large number of things. She was very fond of COFFEE, but would not even taste TEA. She wouldn't have a CAT in the house, but the place was overrun with DOGS. Particularly strange was that she loved CIGARS, but had never been seen smoking a CIGARETTE. Though she was always very kind to her NIECES and NEPHEWS, she refused to speak to her BROTHER or SISTER. She wouldn't write LETTERS or watch TELEVISION, yet she enjoyed going to the MOVIES.

Nancy discovered that the things her aunt hated were all alike in one way. Can you discover the secret too?

HOW FIRM ARE YOUR FISTS?

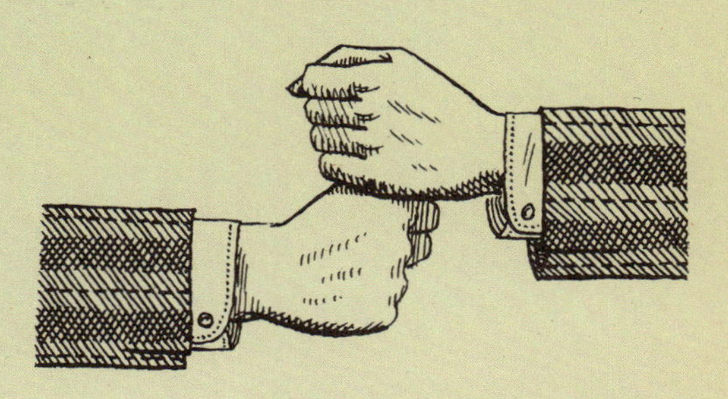

Here is a way to impress your friends with your strength. Tell the biggest of them to clench his fists and place them one on top of the other as firmly as he can. You will find it easy to knock them apart with only two fingers. Yet when your friends try to do the same to you, they will not be able to move your fists. The reason is on page 198.

Joby was just fourteen, but the general needed him

The Drummer Boy of Shiloh

BY RAY BRADBURY

IN THE April night blossoms fell from the orchard trees. They lighted with rustling taps on the drumhead. At midnight a peach stone, left on a branch through winter, fell swift and unseen. It struck once, and jerked the boy upright. In silence he listened, for a moment, to the beating of his own heart. After that he turned the drum on its side, where its great moon face peered at him whenever he opened his eyes.

His face was solemn. It was a solemn night for a boy just turned fourteen — in the peach orchard near Owl Creek not far from the church at Shiloh.

In the shadows, forty thousand men lay crazily askew in their uniforms. Their rifles lay beside them in the orchard grass. A mile farther on, another army was strewn helter-skelter. Now and again the boy heard a vast wind stir the air — the army whispering in the dark. Some men were talking to others. Some were murmuring to themselves, dreaming of battles yet unfought.

The boy could only guess what the men whispered. And he guessed that it was, "Me, I'm the one who'll live through it. I'll go home. The band will play. And I'll be there to hear it."

Yes, thought the boy, *that's all very well for them. They can give as good as they get. Me, I got only a drum and two sticks to beat it.*

The boy turned on his side. If he stayed very still, the soldiers might go away at dawn, taking the war with them. Perhaps they would not notice him lying small here.

"Well, by thunder now," said a voice. Someone stood over the boy. "Well," said the voice quietly, "here's a soldier crying *before* the fight. Good. Get it over. Won't be time once it all starts."

A hand must have come down out of the night. For there was a little *rat-tat* as the fingernails brushed the drum. "Why, it's the drummer boy, isn't it?" said the voice. The boy nodded, not knowing if the nod was seen.

The man bent still closer. He smelled as all fathers should smell — of salt sweat, tobacco, horse, and boot leather. He had many brass buttons. He could only be, and was, the general. "What's your name, boy?" he asked.

"Joby, sir," whispered the boy, starting to sit up.

"All right, Joby, don't stir. How long you been with us, Joby?"

"Three weeks, sir."

"Run off from home, boy?"

Silence.

"Darn-fool question. Do you shave yet? There's your cheek, like a peach blossom off the tree overhead. And the others here, not much older. Mighty raw, the lot of you. You ready for tomorrow or the next day, Joby?"

"I think so, sir."

"You want to cry some more," said the general, "go on ahead. I did the same last night."

"You, sir?"

"God's truth. Thinking of everything ahead. Both sides figuring the other will just give up, and the war done in weeks. Well, that's not how it's going to be. Maybe that's why I cried."

"Yes, sir," said Joby.

The general must have taken out a cigar now. For the dark was suddenly filled with the Indian smell of tobacco. "It's going to be a crazy time," said the general. "Counting both sides, there's a hundred thousand men out there tonight. Not one can spit a sparrow off a tree or knows a horse clod from a Minié ball. We should turn tail and train four months. They should do the same. But here we are, taken with spring fever, going to be a hero, going to live forever. It's wrong, boy. Sometime this week more innocent men will get shot than ever got shot before."

The boy opened his lips to say something, but did not say it. The general heard the boy's breath and spoke himself. "Why am I telling you this? Well, when you get a bunch of wild horses on a loose rein, somehow you got to bring order, rein them in. These lads don't know what I know — that men actually die in war. So each is his own army. I got to make one army of them. And for that, boy, I need you."

Adapted from The Saturday Evening Post, *© 1960 by The Curtis Publishing Co.*

"Me!" The boy's lips barely twitched.

"You, boy," said the general quietly. "You are the heart of the army. Listen to me now."

And Joby listened as the general spoke. If he, Joby, beat slow tomorrow, the heart would beat slow in the men. They would lag by the wayside. They would drowse in the fields on their muskets. They would sleep forever after that — in those same fields, their hearts slowed by a drummer boy and stopped by enemy lead.

But if he beat a sure, steady, ever faster rhythm, then their knees would come up in a long line down over that hill — one knee after the other, like a wave on the ocean shore. That was it. That's what he needed. He gave the orders, but Joby set the pace.

So bring the right knee up and the right foot out and the left knee up and the left foot out, one following the other in brisk time. Move the blood up the body and make the head proud and the spine stiff. Put steel armor all over the men. For blood moving fast in them does indeed make them feel as if they'd put on steel. He must keep at it, long and steady! Then, even though they were shot or torn, they would feel less pain.

The general stopped. After a moment he said, "So there you are. You're the general of the army when the general's left behind. Will you do that for me, boy?"

"Yes, sir."

"Good. And, God willing, many years from now when you're far older than I, they will ask what you did in this awful time. And you will tell them, one part humble and one part proud, I was the drummer boy at the battle of Owl Creek, or the Tennessee River. Or maybe they'll just name it after the church there — I was the drummer boy at Shiloh."

The general stood up. "God bless you, boy. Good night."

"Good night, sir." And tobacco, brass, boot polish, salt sweat and leather, the man moved away through the grass.

Joby lay for a moment, staring, but unable to see where the man had gone. He swallowed. He wiped his eyes. He settled himself. Then, very slowly and firmly, he turned the drum so it faced upward toward the sky.

He lay with his arms around it. And he felt the tremor, the muted thunder, as all the rest of the April night in the year 1862, near the Tennessee River, not far from Owl Creek, very close to the church named Shiloh, the peach blossoms fell on the drum.

The Queen Behind Columbus

Isabella of Spain led her country in battle —and dared to believe in the strange dream of an unknown Genoese sailor

BY DONALD CULROSS PEATTIE

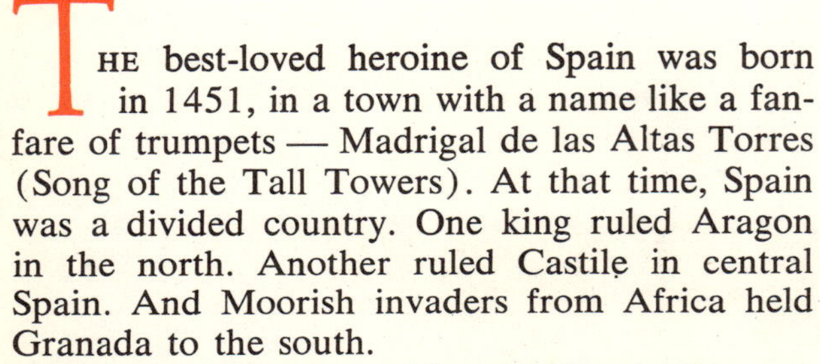

THE best-loved heroine of Spain was born in 1451, in a town with a name like a fanfare of trumpets — Madrigal de las Altas Torres (Song of the Tall Towers). At that time, Spain was a divided country. One king ruled Aragon in the north. Another ruled Castile in central Spain. And Moorish invaders from Africa held Granada to the south.

Isabella's father was king of Castile. Her native village was fortified against his enemies by the high towers for which it was named. The sun beat down upon it, and strong winds swept through it. For it was set on a wide, treeless plateau. In this bleak place the little princess grew up. Everyone could see that she had a warm heart and a keen mind, and that she was fated for greatness.

Isabella was still a child when her father died. Her mother became ill with grief and never got well again. So the crown of Castile passed to the princess's wretched half brother, Henry. And the young Isabella was brought to his gloomy court in Madrid. She was by then a serious girl with blue eyes, wavy red-gold hair and an apple-blossom complexion.

At seventeen, she had three offers of marriage. One was from the rich and wily old king of Portugal, one from a weakling brother of the king of France. The third was from Ferdinand of Aragon, the kind of prince she had dreamed about since childhood. This gallant young man was the choice of her secret heart, and of all the people of Castile.

Henry wanted his half sister to marry the hateful king of Portugal. He was so furious when she chose Ferdinand that Isabella had to flee back to her native town. Once safely there, she sent to Ferdinand an acceptance of his offer, and he sent her a ruby necklace that had been his mother's.

When Henry's spies told him of this, he was angrier than ever. He lined the frontier with guards, who were to seize Ferdinand when he stepped into Castile. Luckily, none of the guards paid any heed to a young mule driver who drove his cart across the border. Ferdinand's dirty face and dingy clothes disguised him perfectly. Yet when he met Isabella for the first time, in a palace room in Valladolid, he looked the prince and soldier that he was. A few days later the two young people were married.

When Henry died in 1474, the throne of Castile stood empty for Isabella. But she had to be crowned at once because a pretender was laying claim to it. And she had to be crowned alone — for Ferdinand was away in Aragon. On December 13 Isabella, clad in ermine, rode a white horse into the main square of Segovia. There was a gorgeous procession. Pages carried the crown of the absent Ferdinand on a pillow. And the red-haired princess was crowned Queen of Castile.

The Beginnings of Greatness

All this was good news to the greedy king of Portugal. He thought that Ferdinand and Isabella were too young to know how to defend their country. Besides, he knew that Henry had wasted Spain's treasure, and that the Spanish army was small. So he laid claim to the throne, and marched twenty thousand well-drilled soldiers into the heart of Castile.

Now Isabella began to show her greatness. She mounted her horse and, in full armor, rode about the country like a Joan of Arc. She begged for troops and for money. Men flocked to her, and Ferdinand drilled them for the army.

In the battles that followed, Isabella saw that fresh horses were always waiting for her beloved husband. She urged the troops forward and rounded up food for them. At night she studied maps by lamplight, and found a fatal weakness in the Portuguese lines. But during the battle that finally brought victory she was on her knees in prayer. It was Ferdinand who won the fight and the glory.

Then Isabella boldly faced the tasks of peace. In Henry's time the grandees, or noblemen, did whatever they pleased. They were often cruel to the commoners. Isabella traveled the roads of her kingdom, punishing the wicked and protecting the poor. Because she was always just, the people trusted her. Spain began to grow strong.

Spain Becomes a Battlefield

Isabella was a truly regal queen. But she made all Ferdinand's fine cambric shirts with her own needle. And she was a good mother to her five children. Above all, she was a devout Christian.

This was a time when Christianity was in danger. The infidel Moors in the south were still three million strong. From their mountain strongholds they raided the border, sacked towns and stole women. At Christmastime 1481, the Moorish king of Granada captured a border fortress, and Spain became a battlefield. To the east, the Moslem world rallied behind the Moors. From England, France and Ireland, allies of Ferdinand and Isabella sped to meet the attack. Their Majesties took command of the Christian crusade.

While the king led the armies at the front, the queen supplied them with food and transport. She sent to Germany for expert gunpowder makers. She had her engineers build roads over impassable mountain trails, and bridges across the deepest chasms. When many of the soldiers were struck down with sickness, she set up hospitals at their camps. She brought in doctors, medicines and bandages, and she paid for them all with her own money.

Inspired by their Spanish leaders, the Christian armies turned the tide of battle. They swept into the kingdom of Granada, to the gates of the Moorish city of Baza. Then — with victory in sight — they ran short of food and ammunition. That was when Isabella sold her rubies and pearls, her gold and silver plate, and even the crown of Saint Fernando of Castile. Thus she was able to send fourteen thousand mules loaded with supplies from the far corners of her realm. She was able to hire soldiers all the way from Switzerland. When she herself arrived at the front, Baza surrendered. Her presence so fired the spirits of the troops that they could not lose.

A Daring Plan

Once again there was peace. And now a new dream came to Isabella. Three years before, a tall sailor named Christopher Columbus had come to her from Genoa to unfold a daring plan. The queen could not forget his honest eyes and his passion for the Christian faith. His idea that the world was round haunted her. Let others shake their heads. She believed in it. This bold seaman wanted to sail into the unknown West to reach the Eastern nations of Japan and India. He might discover new lands for Crown and Cross.

The queen had been excited by this magnificent plan. But Ferdinand and a court council had been against it. Since Isabella always acted together with her husband, there was little she could do. She had given Columbus some money, and told him to come back when the war was over.

In the fateful year 1492 Granada fell at last. For the first time in seven hundred and seventy-seven years Christians walked freely through its streets. And there, in the Alhambra palace, the starry-eyed sailor once again faced Ferdinand and Isabella. Once again the greatest enterprise in history was denied its chance.

Columbus was turned from the gates of Granada. Sorrowfully, he rode away on his mule. But the power of his presence remained at court and worked upon the queen. So did Luis de Santangel, Spain's greatest banker. He saw that the sailor's noble dream might also lead to untold riches. When he explained this to Ferdinand, the king listened with new interest. A messenger was sent flying after the plodding mule to bring back its rider.

So it was agreed that Columbus would be given three ships to venture into the unmapped West. He would be called the "Admiral of the Ocean Sea." Luis de Santangel gave half the money needed for the venture. Columbus borrowed from his friends; and Isabella levied upon the seaport of Palos de la Fronterra for two of the ships and sailors to man them. Thus it was that the sails of the *Niña*, the *Pinta* and the *Santa María* disappeared over the western sea line.

How often must Isabella's thoughts have followed those vanished ships! She went about her kingdom, founding schools and hospitals. She taught her people the ways of peace. Yet she shared in spirit the immortal voyage. Where has the wind blown those frail vessels? she must have wondered. Have they sunk in a gale? Or smashed on a hidden reef? Then suddenly, out of the blue, came news of Columbus.

Early in 1493 Isabella received a letter from Lisbon. It said that the Admiral had crossed the western sea, and claimed vast lands for their Majesties. The *Santa María* had gone aground in Santo Domingo and the *Pinta* had been delayed by storms, but on March 15 the *Niña* under Columbus's own command dropped anchor in Palos.

Columbus came to the court in Barcelona, where Ferdinand and Isabella sat in state upon their thrones. With him were some feathered and painted Indians, bearing gaudy parrots and gifts of gold. The king and queen rose for Columbus, as they would have done for no other commoner on earth. For this sailor had opened up half the world as a new home for the Spanish people, a new kingdom for souls of the Christian faith. Their Majesties heard his tales and admired his gifts. Then they and all their court knelt in a service of thanksgiving for the Great Discovery.

Columbus made three more voyages to the Americas. Each time it was Isabella who found the ships, the men and the money he needed. She provided farm animals, seeds for crops, colonists and priests for the settlements in the New World. In November 1504, after his last voyage, the Admiral of the Ocean Sea was on his way to her when he learned that she had died.

All of Spain mourned the spirited queen with the beautiful red-gold hair. For in just thirty years she had united her divided country. She had brought peace to her people. And her faith in an unknown sailor had made possible one of the greatest adventures in history.

UPI

The Niña II, *shown here, left Palos, Spain, in September 1962 and reached San Salvador on Christmas Day. Modeled after the smallest of Columbus's three ships, this little caravel is built of oak and is roughly three times as long as a rowboat. Aboard her were Lieutenant Carlos Etayo of the Spanish Navy, Robert Marx, an American underwater explorer and geographer, and seven sailors. They carried no engine, radio or other modern equipment, relying on fifteenth-century navigational instruments and a copy of a map said to have been used by Columbus to guide them in following his historic route across the Atlantic. Their only food was what seamen had in 1492: beans, lentils, rice, cheese, honey and sea biscuits. Even this soon had to be rationed as they ran into hurricanes and line squalls which ruined their stores. And, before the voyage ended, they were catching and eating sharks to keep from starving. Their trip took almost twice the time taken by the* Niña, *the* Pinta *and the* Santa María. *But these brave men and their gallant little ship were greeted by a brass band in San Salvador, and there was dancing on the beach in their honor.*

The thrilling story of a hunter and his quarry, by a master teller of animal tales

Krag, the Kootenay Ram

BY ERNEST THOMPSON SETON

KRAG was a joy to behold. As he bounded up the jagged cliffs of the Gunder Peak in the Kootenay Rockies of the far Northwest, he was more a spirit thing than a three-hundred-pound ram with ten-year rings on his horns. And such horns, curling in one great sweep, a circle and a quarter! Tucked away under their shadow were his golden eyes with dark misty depths.

For five years Krag had taught his band of mountain sheep to stay away from the lowlands. The only land of safety was the open windswept peaks, where neither lions nor riflemen could approach unseen. But at length an old hunter, Scotty McDougall, arrived at a shanty on Tobacco Creek. The first time he saw Krag through his field glasses, he exclaimed, "What horns!" Then he added, "Them's mine!"

Then a visitor came to Scotty's shanty — a cattleman named Lee, with three Russian wolfhounds. Soon men and dogs were on the trail of the ram. One day they got a glimpse of him far away, above them.

The men hurried along by the hollows toward the spot. They found his great hoofmark, but there were no other signs on the hard rocks. The dogs, nosing in all the near hollows and thickets, broke suddenly into a loud clamor. And up jumped the ram.

Adapted from The Lives of the Hunted, *published in 1901 by Charles Scribner's Sons. This selection also appears in* Ernest Thompson Seton's America, *© 1954 and published by The Devin-Adair Co.*

Over the bushes, over the broken rocks he bounded — soaring, floating, certain, splendid. He bore the curling wonders on his head as lightly as a lady might her earrings. Then, from various other coverts, his band sprang up and joined him.

Away they went, the ram forging quickly to the lead and the others stringing along after — over the upland, flying, sailing, leaping and swerving. Krag, cut off from the peak by the dogs, dashed southward. Now it was a straight race. One, two, three miles, and the chase was sweeping along a rocky ridge that ends in the sudden gash of Skinkler's Gulch. A minute more and the crowd of sheep were rounded up and cornered on the final rock. They huddled together in terror — five hundred feet of dizzy canyon all around, three fierce dogs and two fiercer men behind.

Krag had no fear of the dogs. He could fight them. But the rifles were sure death. There was one chance left. The granite walls of the Yak-in-i-kak River could prove no harder than the human foe. The dogs were within two hundred yards now. There was no time to hesitate. He, the leader, wheeled to the edge and *leaped*.

Down, down went Krag, but he had not leaped blindly to the bottom. Thirty feet downward, across the dizzy canyon, was a little jut of rock, no bigger than his nose. It was the only one in sight. But Krag landed fairly, and poised just a heartbeat. In a flash his blazing eyes took in another point, on the other side, hidden under the overhanging rocks he had leaped from. He floated across. From there he ricocheted to another point — then back, to a mere roughness of the rock, on which his hoofs gripped for an instant. With a final drop of twenty feet, he reached a ledge of safety far below.

The other sheep followed fast. Just as the last had reached the second slender foothold, three white-and-yellow creatures whirled past in the air to perish in the boiling Yak-in-i-kak below. The brave hounds never hesitated to follow a foe.

Lee and Scotty stood blankly at the edge. Scotty uttered harsh words. Lee had a choking feeling in his throat. "Bran! Rollo! Ida!" he called. But the only response was the western wind that whistled down Skinkler's Gulch.

During the years that followed, more than one hunter feasted his eyes on the great ram's horns. Their fame even reached the cities. Men offered fabulous prices for the head that bore them.

Tempted by such an offer, Scotty prepared for a long hunt, even though winter was beginning. All he carried were his rifle, his blanket, his pipe, matches, tobacco, a cooking pot, some jerked venison and a few pounds of chocolate. He followed the track of the ram in the snow. Though it wound everywhere, partly hidden by the tracks of Krag's own band, Scotty always knew it by its size.

One day old Krag heard a *crack!* A stinging something touched one horn and tore the hair from his shoulder. Krag was dazed for a moment. Then he gave the signal, which in our speech is, "Everyone for himself now."

The Long Hunt

So the band scattered. But Scotty's one thought was old Krag. When the ram made straightaway eastward down the hill, Scotty followed. The ram crossed the Flathead River on the ice. Keeping to the roughest ground, he traveled all day northeastward. Scotty stayed steadily on the trail.

On the fifth day a blinding snowstorm hid him from Scotty's view. The snow covered the great ram's tracks. The trail was lost.

Next day Scotty scanned the vast expanses between him and Kintla Lake. He saw a moving speck below. He quickly ran toward it. But when he got to the spot he had aimed at, there — five hundred yards away, on the next ridge — stood the famous ram. Each was in plain view of the other. Scotty fired. But the distance was too great.

The ram made eastward. Sometimes the trail was easy to follow. Sometimes it was blotted out by new-fallen snow. But day after day they went. The ram seemed to have learned that five hundred yards was the farthest range of the rifle. Still, it seemed as though he wanted to have the hunter within sight, for then he knew where he was. One time Scotty stole a march. He would have had a close shot had not the fateful west wind borne the taint. Krag was warned in time.

By the end of the first month, the long pursuit began to tell on the ram. The man had his dried venison and chocolate, enough for many days. When they were gone, he could shoot a hare or a grouse and hastily cook it. But the ram required hours to seek the scanty grass that lay under the snow. His belly was pinching up, and he was growing weak with hunger.

Then for two weeks they were daily in sight of each other. In the morning Scotty would rise, wolflike, from his frosty lair. He would call out, "Come, Krag. Time we wuz a-movin'."

And the ram on the distant ridge would stamp defiantly. Then, setting his nose to the wind, he would move on — now fast, now slow, keeping the safe five hundred yards ahead. When Scotty sat down to rest, the ram would graze. Once when Scotty rose and scanned the northern distance for the ram, he heard the long snort far behind. Turning, he saw old Krag impatiently waiting. The wind had changed, and Krag had changed his route to suit.

Another day Scotty had a hard two hours crossing a stream over which old Krag had leaped. When he reached the other side, he heard a snort. He looked around to find that the ram had come back to see what was keeping him.

For twelve long weeks now the ram had led Scotty through the snow, over ten long mountain ranges — five hundred rugged miles. Both were growing hollow-eyed, gaunter every day. The man's hair had bleached since he set out on this mad pursuit. And the head and shoulders of the ram were grizzling.

A Cunning Plot

One morning they sat at rest — Scotty on one ridge, the ram six hundred yards away on the next. Then some evil spirit entered into Scotty, and he thought of a cunning plot. He cut some birch rods and gathered some stones. Then he moved to the edge of the ridge and made a dummy of himself, using what clothing he could spare. Keeping exactly behind it, he crawled backward over the ledge and disappeared. After an hour of crawling and stalking, he came up on a ridge behind the ram.

There Krag stood, majestic and graceful, with horns that rolled around his brow like thunderclouds about a peak. He was gazing intently on the dummy, wondering why his partner was still for so long. Scotty, less than three hundred yards away, lay down. He threw snow on his back till he was all whitened. Then he set out to crawl two hundred yards, watching the great ram's head. Once old Krag looked about sharply. Nearer, nearer crawled the hunter. Then he reached some sheltering rocks, and rested.

For the first time Scotty saw the famous horns quite close. He saw the great, broad shoulders, the curving neck, still massive, though the mark of famine was on all. He saw this splendid fellow creature blow the hot breath of life from his nostrils. And he even got a glimpse of the light in those glowing amber eyes. He slowly raised the gun. And the hand that had never trembled before now shook as though in fear.

But the hand grew steady. The hunter's face was calm and hard. The rifle sang. Scotty hid his head. He heard a rattling on the distant stones, then a long-drawn *snoof!* Two minutes later all was still, and he timidly raised his head.

There on the snow lay a great gray-brown form. And at one end were the splendid horns of a splendid creature. Scotty walked slowly over. He gazed, not at the dear-won horns, but at the calm yellow eyes — unclosed, and yet undimmed by death. He sat down twenty yards away, with his back to the horns. He did not know what he himself felt.

There was a long silence. Then Scotty said, "I'd give his life back to him if I could."

Four years went by. Scotty, now known as Old Man Scotty, had never hunted since. One day an old partner stopped at his shanty.

"Let's see him, Scotty," he said.

"Suit yourself." The old man jerked his head toward the draped thing on the wall.

The stranger pulled the cloth off the head, and the firelight lent a red and angry glare to the glassy eyes. "Kivver him up when you're through," said Scotty.

"Why don't ye sell him?"

"I'll nivver sell him — I'll nivver part with him. I stayed by him till I done him up, an' he'll stay by me till he gets even. He broke me down on that trip. He's made an old man o' me. But he ain't through with me yet. Thar's more o' him around than that head. I tell ye, when that old chinook comes a-blowin' up the Terbakker Crik, I've heared noises that the wind don't make. I've heared him just the same as I done that day when he blowed his life out through his nose, an' me a-layin' on my face afore him."

Old Scotty is forgotten. But the ram's head hangs on a palace wall today, a treasure among kingly treasures. And men — when they gaze on those marvelous horns — still talk of the glorious Gunder ram who grew them far away on the heights of the Kootenay.

The great author and naturalist Ernest Thompson Seton spent most of his life outdoors in the western United States and Canada. There he studied the ways of the Indians and of the wild creatures he loved. He wrote more than forty books, including Wild Animals I Have Known *and* The Lives of the Hunted, *from which the story of Krag is taken. Mr. Seton, who died in 1946, aged eighty-six, was also chief scout for the Boy Scouts of America and wrote the first boy-scout manual.*

Try Your Skill at Tracking

You need not go into the wilderness as Scotty MacDougall did to try *your* skill at tracking. All around you—in fields and woods and farmyards—there are animal footprints that you can learn to "read."

Although no two animals' prints are exactly alike, the tracks you are most likely to find near home fall roughly into five types: 1. *Hoofs (deer, cows, pigs, sheep, etc.)* 2. *Completely hairy feet with no visible pads (rabbits, hares, etc.)* 3. *Completely naked feet with pads often indistinct (mice, rats, muskrats, etc.)* 4. *Hairy feet and naked toes with the naked pad or pads visible in the track (dogs, cats, foxes, etc.)* 5. *Horny feet (birds).*

WHITE-TAILED DEER: The hoofs have sharp points and are more gracefully shaped than those of domestic hoofed animals. When a deer is going full speed, its dewclaws also leave marks.

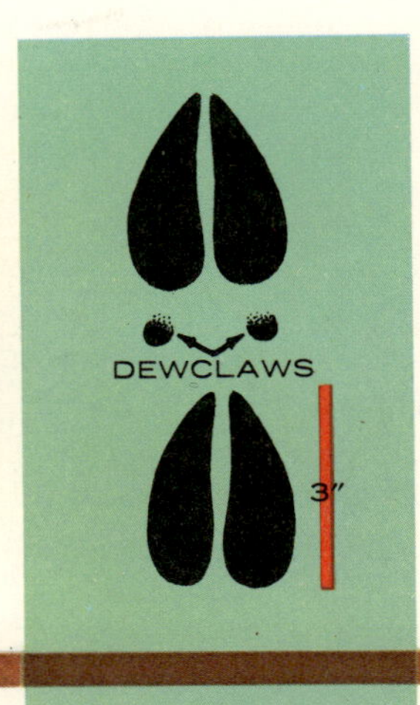

COW: The front hoofs of the cow are wider than the hind hoofs. Large flat cakes of dung are commonly found with cow tracks.

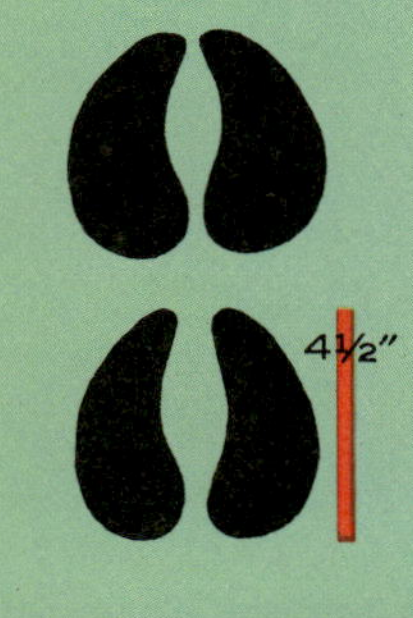

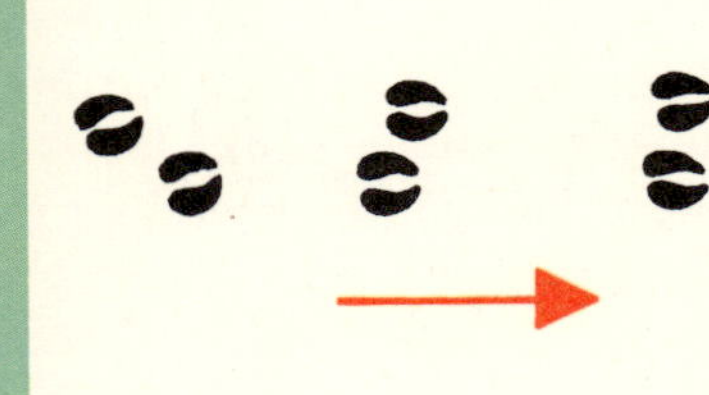

RABBIT: This is the print of a cottontail rabbit. The prints of jackrabbits and other hares are larger, with more distance between bounds. The cottontail's puff of white tail only touches the ground when he is sitting on it; but the jackrabbit's tail leaves a straight drag mark in snow, between and behind the prints of his hind feet.

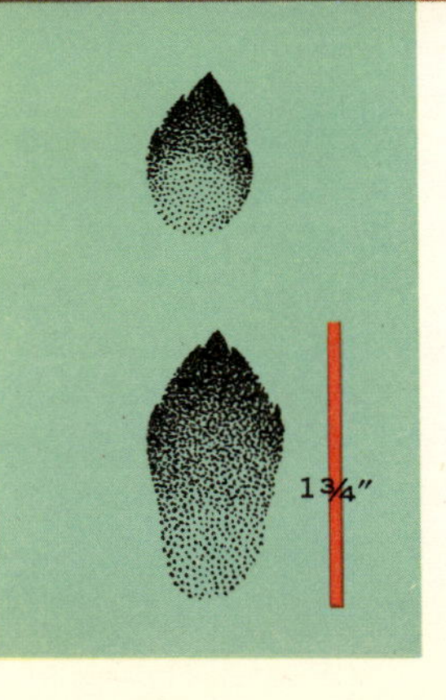

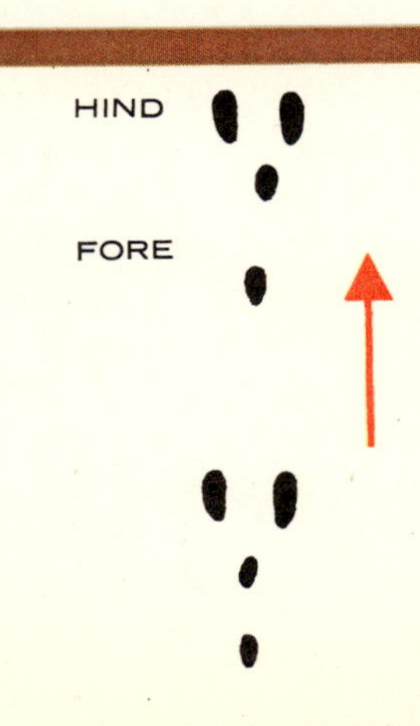

All animals make deeper impressions in soft earth, sand, mud or snow than on hard, bare ground. Tracks are also easier to see when the shadows are long—that is, in early morning or late evening. When you are following a trail, or succession of tracks, look as far ahead as possible instead of at the ground right in front of your feet. You will soon get tired if you walk all hunched over. Take along a pencil and a pad of paper so you can make sketches of what you find and study them later.

Some tracks tell a story about the animal who has made them. When a four-footed animal bounds across a field, for instance, the hind-feet tracks get ahead of the front-feet tracks. The faster the animal goes, the farther ahead the tracks of his hind feet get. A four-footed animal with a lame leg or sore foot will step more lightly on the injured part, leaving a lighter track with that foot. It may even walk on only three legs. An injured bird may hop on just one leg. And when you find the tracks of one kind of animal following those of another, you will know that you are not the only "hunter" on the trail.

Here are the tracks of a number of common animals. How many of them have you seen?

MEADOW MOUSE: The tiny forefeet have four toes each; the hind feet, five toes each. Meadow mice make networks of little trails, about an inch wide, around their burrows.

CHIPMUNK: The chipmunk's delicate track shows four toes on each forefoot, five toes on each hind foot. Chipmunks place their forefeet diagonally behind their hind feet when bounding.

SQUIRREL: The tracks of the gray squirrel, at right, show heel prints on the hind feet. The red squirrel's tracks are similar, but slightly smaller, and they show no heel prints on the hind feet.

WOODCHUCK (or GROUNDHOG): The woodchuck's tracks show small pads. Only four clawed toes of the forefeet leave marks because the thumbs are too stubby to make an impression. All five clawed toes of the hind feet show plainly.

RACCOON: The forefeet tracks are shorter than those of the hind feet and close together when the coon runs. Each foot shows five distinct toes with claws. Coon tracks are generally found along the banks of streams or near the trees in which these little animals live.

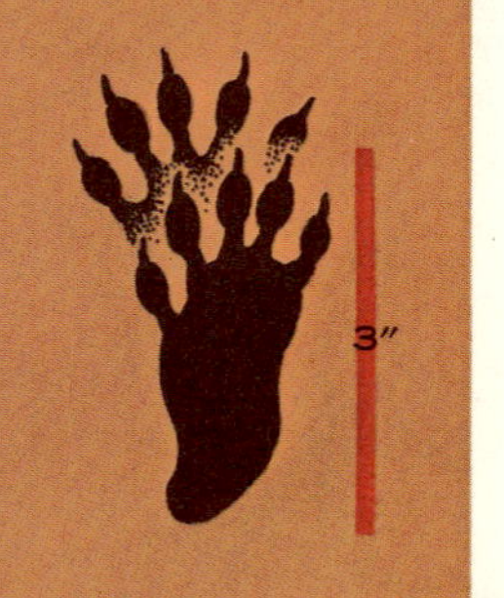

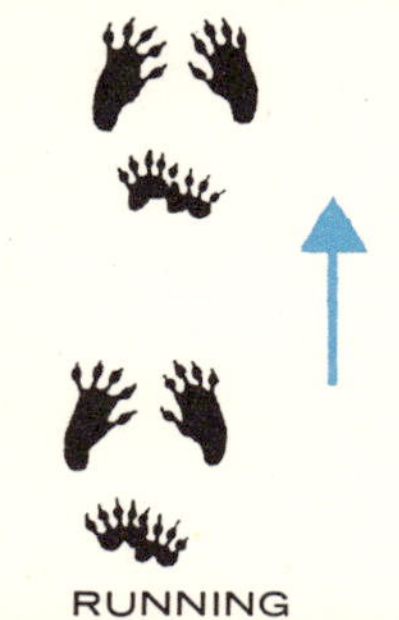

SKUNK: Skunks have five toes on each foot. Since they do a lot of digging, the claws on their forefeet are well developed and leave a clear impression. The claws on their hind feet usually do not show at all. A galloping skunk leaves a diagonal trail.

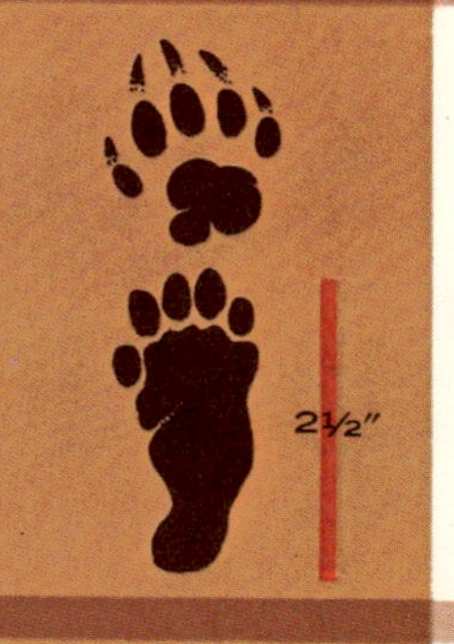

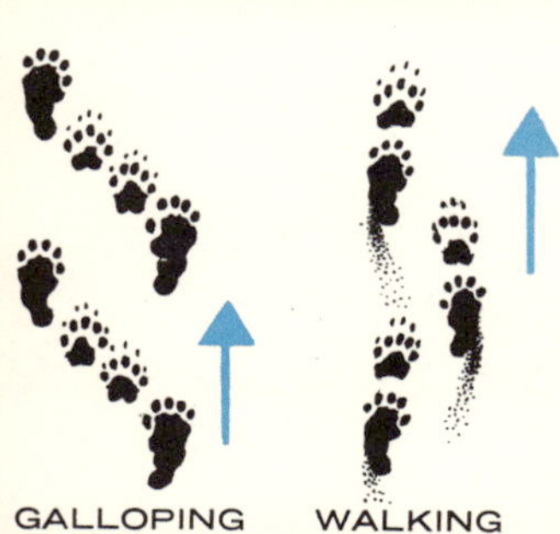

OPOSSUM: Five toes show on each foot. All but the thumbs of the hind feet leave claw marks. Possum tracks are often found near woodland streams or after a late spring snow.

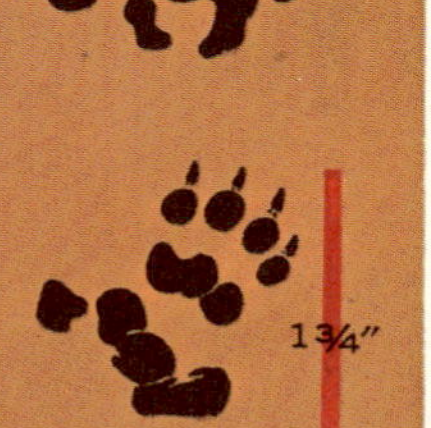

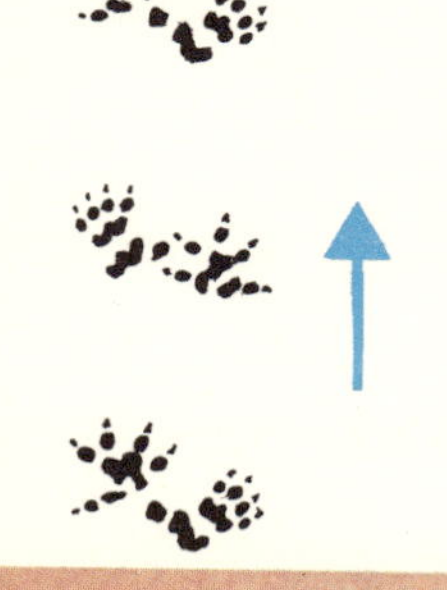

TURTLE: The snapping turtle's long tail leaves a wavy drag mark with footprints on either side. The tail of the little painted turtle, shown here, makes a straight drag mark between its footprints.

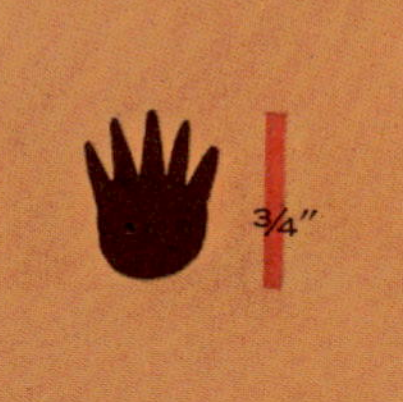

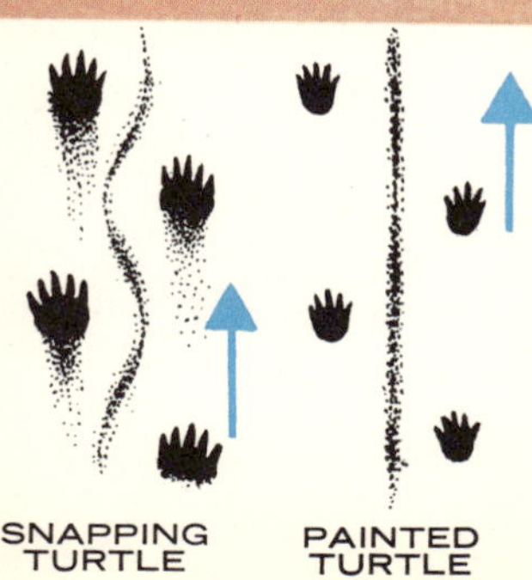

FOX: The fox leaves a narrow trail because his feet are set nearly in a straight line. In snow, his brush leaves a soft, shallow, slurry mark, sometimes every yard and sometimes not for fifty steps.

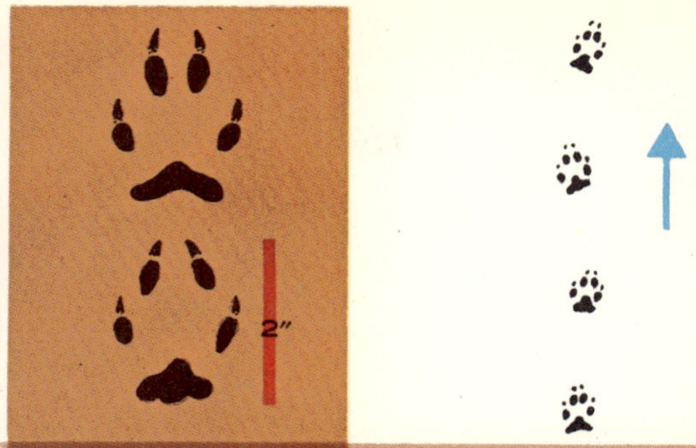

2"

DOG: Dogs cannot pull in their claws, and so they leave clear claw marks. The smudge shown in the track is made because, unlike cats and foxes, dogs drag their toes.

VARIABLE

CAT: A house cat normally keeps its claws sheathed, so no claw marks show in its tracks. A bobcat (or lynx) has a similar, but larger, track. The prints of all cats show four toes on each paw. Cats are considered "perfect trackers" because they place their hind feet neatly in the tracks of their forefeet.

1"

PHEASANT: In mud or light snow, only the toes make a track. But deep snows show the print of the whole foot.

4"

LIGHT SNOW

WALKING IN HEAVY SNOW

HERON: These tracks are large, with three long, forward-pointing toes and a short, broken toe mark behind.

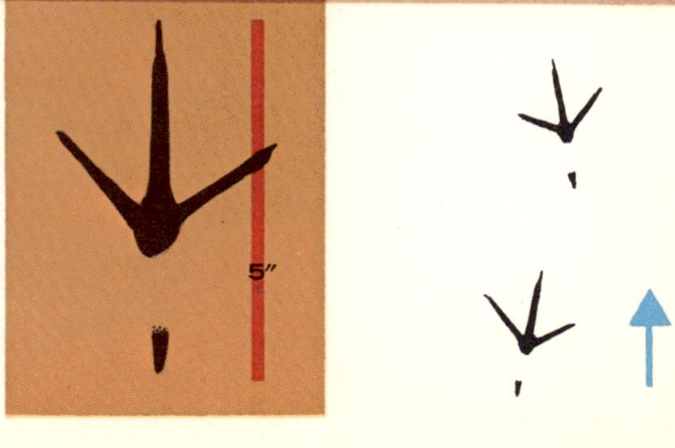

5"

This desperate race across two continents proved that the automobile had come to stay

The "Impossible" Race from Peking to Paris

BY J. D. RATCLIFF

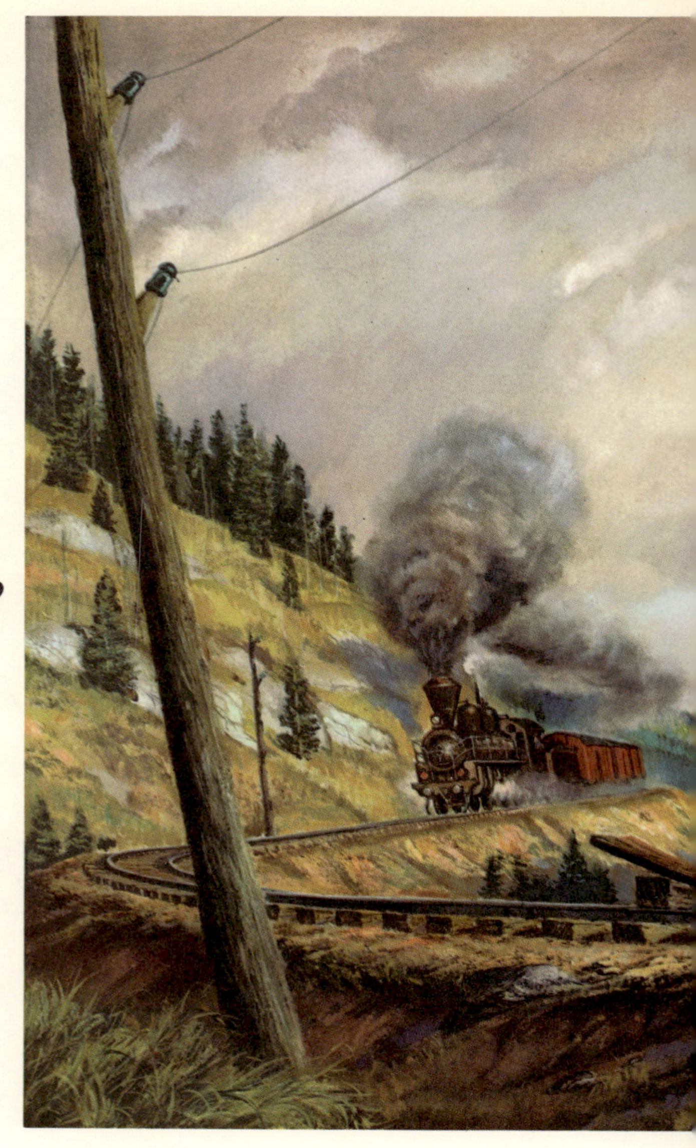

IN 1957, Luigi Barzini, Jr., an Italian journalist, asked permission to cross Soviet Russia by car in an attempt to drive from Peking to Paris. The trip would take him across northern China's mountains, over the Gobi Desert, through the Siberian wilderness, over the Ural Mountains, and then on to Moscow, Berlin and Paris.

The Russians rejected the proposal: such a drive was "impossible." But they were wrong. Half a century before, Barzini's father had made the same trip in a wheezy 1907 car.

It was history's most amazing car journey.

Early in the twentieth century, most people believed that the rattly little cars of those days could never replace the reliable horse. A small group of motorists felt otherwise. To settle the question the French newspaper *Le Matin* proposed a most difficult test for the automobile: a race from Peking to Paris.

For three quarters of the journey there were no roads, only caravan trails, forest paths and mountain passes. If any car could manage that trip (estimated at eight to ten thousand miles), the automobile must indeed have a future.

A strange little group of cars accepted the challenge and entered the race. There were two French De Dion-Boutons, whose engines were only equal in power to one of today's smaller outboard motors. A Dutch Spyker, only a bit more powerful, was to be driven by Jean Godard. A bouncy little six-horsepower Contal three-wheeler had been entered by August Pons. The fifth car was

Adapted from The Kiwanis Magazine, © *1957 by Kiwanis International*

a very powerful forty-horsepower Itala. It carried Prince Scipione Borghese, his chauffeur, Ettore Guizzardi, and the Italian journalist Luigi Barzini.

Prince Borghese, a noted explorer and sportsman, spent a long time preparing for the race. Before the start he made a three-hundred-mile ride on horseback to study the mountains north of Peking. He measured the narrow, rocky passes with a bamboo cane to see if there was room for a car. He arranged for fuel, tires and spare parts to be stored along the way. Some supplies were carried to the storage points by camel caravan from Peking. Others were sent from Moscow by the Trans-Siberian Railway.

Borghese's car was equipped with extra fuel tanks and heavy-duty tires. The frame of the car had been strengthened, and there was a huge collection of tools, including crowbars, shovels and axes. Much of this equipment was later thrown from the car along the way to lighten the load.

They're Off!

On the morning of June 10, 1907, the cars moved out of Peking. A French military band marched in front of them. Ladies fluttered their handkerchiefs and some of the Chinese threw firecrackers to wish them well. It was the last moment of triumph the drivers were to know for weeks to come.

There was trouble almost immediately. At the outskirts of Peking, a hard rain soaked the racers

in their open cars. Ropes loosened and luggage began to tumble. Pons's little three-wheel car jumped like a frightened rabbit. Its wheels didn't fit the ruts in the road. When it threatened to fall apart Pons turned back, deciding to send his car by rail over the first part of the journey, from Peking to Nankow.

The mountains that separate northern China from the Mongolian plains presented fantastic difficulties. Narrow trails cut out of rock hung on the sides of seemingly bottomless gorges. Huge boulders blocked the trail all along the way. There was only one way to get through — clear the path and drag the cars. Ropes were hitched on, and coolies, horses and mules went to work.

Doubts began to arise. Could cars ever become a quick method of transport? Camel caravans easily passed the struggling cars. Chinese merchants, riding in their sedan chairs, smiled as they glided by.

Going uphill was bad; going downhill was often worse. With ropes hooked on the rear, coolies tried to hold cars back. Once Borghese's car got away. With the chauffeur, Guizzardi, at the wheel, it plunged down the rocky path like a maddened bull. By some miracle, it got to the bottom without diving into the gorge beside the trail.

At the end of the fifth day, Borghese was in the lead, but he had traveled only a hundred and fifty miles. At this speed it would take nearly a year to reach Paris. And the fearsome Gobi Desert lay ahead. Pons took one look at the Gobi and knew that his little three-wheeler would never get across. He turned back. The four remaining drivers decided to try.

Over the Gobi Desert

Borghese was the first to start across the sandy waste, following the telegraph line. In that tropical heat the car engine boiled steadily, using up precious water. Although the danger was great, even the few quarts of drinking water that remained in reserve finally went to cool the engine.

Gasoline, brought by caravan, was waiting at the tiny settlement of Pong-Hong, in the middle of the Gobi Desert. From here Barzini was able to telegraph his story to his paper in Italy. He noticed that his telegram was marked "No. 1."

"The first today?" Barzini asked. No, he was told. It was the first telegram *ever* sent in the six years there had been a railroad station in Pong-Hong.

Crossing the Gobi showed that the automobile might, after all, be better than the caravan or the sedan chair in some ways. Borghese's car did it in four days, as against seventeen days for the fastest caravan. As he left the city of Urga (now called Ulan Bator), on the far side of the desert, the De Dion-Boutons had just arrived. The Dutch Spyker was still somewhere in the middle of the Gobi.

Two days of hard driving over mountain trails, and Borghese reached the Russian frontier town of Kyakhta. Now it seemed that they would have a clear way ahead, since Russian maps showed

roads stretching across Siberia. But events soon proved that the roads existed only in the map maker's mind.

Through the Siberian Wilderness

There had been a military road but it was abandoned when the Trans-Siberian Railway was built. For three thousand miles the Itala struggled through downpours of rain that turned Siberia into a sea of mud. It caked Borghese's radiator so that the engine steamed constantly. It splattered the clothes and smeared the faces of the people in the car.

Many rivers crisscross Siberia, and the wooden bridges that had been part of the old road were ready to collapse. Borghese took them at a fast run, hoping to get his car across before the bridge fell apart.

Where the bridges were completely gone, rivers were forded. The sensitive electrical equipment was removed and the engine coated with grease. Then horses or oxen had to be found to drag the car across.

At times, bridges of the Trans-Siberian Railway would be used. Wheels on one side of the car would be inside a rail, those on the other outside a rail, only inches away from the unguarded edge. With ears strained for the sound of approaching trains, they bumped carefully over the abyss.

Once they got stuck in the tracks before an oncoming train. With levers, the car was pried out just in time.

At one point a wheel collapsed. No replacement was available within a thousand miles. Borghese seriously considered giving up the race. But a local carpenter, working with only a hatchet, chopped out a sturdy new wheel. Sometimes the gasoline was not waiting for them at the supply points. In one tiny village the car was hopelessly stalled. Then Borghese discovered that for some strange reason a local shop had a large supply of benzine. It was dumped into the car's tanks. Smoking like a coke oven, the Itala chugged on.

On July 20 the car reached a marble signpost in the Ural Mountains. On one side was ASIA, on the other, EUROPE. Another week, and the Itala rattled triumphantly into Moscow. The three other cars in the race were seventeen days behind, still fighting their way across Siberia.

On to Paris

From Moscow on, the journey was easier. There was only one incident to mar the final lap to Paris. In a Belgian village a policeman stopped the car for going faster than the eight-miles-per-hour speed limit.

When one of the dirty, ragged trio in the car announced, "I am Prince Borghese — we have just driven from Peking, China," the policeman could not believe him. Finally, when papers were produced to prove it, he waved the car on.

At four p.m. on August 10, 1907, sixty-one days after leaving Peking, the Itala limped into Paris. It had won victory in a race that stretched nearly halfway around the earth.

While Borghese was being honored in Paris, the other racers still struggled over the road. Because of ill health, Jean Godard, driver of the Dutch car, had to give up in Berlin when triumph was in sight. The two De Dion-Boutons completed the journey on August 30.

The automobile had proved itself. As one Italian motoring magazine said a few years ago, "It remains the most sensational automobile achievement in history."

PARIS!
99
Paris is in sight! Throw a one to enter the city.
98
97
Stopped by Belgian policeman for going more than eight miles per hour. Miss two turns.
96
95
Engine trouble. Back two squares for repairs in Berlin.
94
93
92
91
Map mistakenly shows a right turn. Take long way around to Berlin.
90
89
Hurry through St. Petersburg. Advance to 93.
88
87
86
Delayed by celebration in Moscow. Miss one turn.
85
84
83
Get food supplies in Russian village. Advance to 85.
82
81
80
79
78
77
You have a narrow escape on a hairpin turn in the Ural Mountains. Back up six squares and try again.
76
75
74
73
You are now leaving Asia and entering Europe. Take an extra turn.
72
71
70
69
Cross over bridge before it collapses. Advance to 72.
68
67
66
65
Road washed out by floods. Go back to 61.
64
63
Chased by bandits on horseback. Hurry on five squares to escape them.
62
61
60
59
58
57
Car goes in gully. Miss one turn while oxen pull it out.
56
55
54
53
52
51
50
49
Beautiful inn and lake in distance. Take detour to investigate.
48
47
Inn and lake are only a mirage. Throw a four to get back on your route.

1
2
3
Luggage drops off car and is lost. Go back to Peking. You need not throw a two or a six to start again.
PEKING
4
5
Pick up speed going downhill. Move on three squares.
6
7
8
9
10
Boulders block road. Miss one turn while coolies drag them away.
11
12
13
14
15
16
A sedan chair passes you. Take an extra turn to catch up with it.
17
18
19
20
21
Wheel collapses. Miss one turn while village carpenter makes new one.
22
23
24
25
Car running well. Advance to 29.
26
27
28
29
30
Make detour around mountain.
DETOUR
31
32
33
Engine boils over in desert. Wait two turns while water is fetched from oasis.
34
35
36
Camel caravan crossing road. Go back to 32.
37
38
39
Stuck on railroad tracks before oncoming train. Throw a six to get free.
40
41
42
43
Take short cut to 55 to send telegram from Pong-Hong.
44
5

Your Own Peking-to-Paris
Automobile Race

INSTRUCTIONS: Two or more can play this game. You'll need one counter each, which you can name for an old car—also one of a pair of dice. To start you must throw a two or a six. The first one to get from Peking to Paris is the winner.

KING OF JAZZ

BY GILBERT MILLSTEIN

LOUIS "SATCHMO" ARMSTRONG is known and loved all over the world. When he plays his famous trumpet his audiences go wild with pleasure and call for more and more, as if they could listen to him forever.

When he performed in London, the Royal Philharmonic Orchestra was to play the last piece on the program. It could not do so for forty-five minutes because the audience refused to let Satchmo go. In Ghana he played for twenty-five thousand Africans, and the chief of police had to ask him to play slower music because the audience was getting too excited!

When he played in West Berlin, jazz fans behind the Iron Curtain risked their lives by slipping across the border to hear him. In Norway, the police had to squirt hoses on a thousand of his fans who were raging because they could not get into one of his concerts.

Because he is so popular, and wins so much good will wherever he goes, Louis Armstrong has been called "America's secret weapon." He has also earned the unofficial title of Ambassador. One of America's highest statesmen says he is "a much more important American than I will ever be."

But Louis doesn't believe it. "Ambassador?" he says. "It's not serious. My public, they ain't thinkin' about politics when they call me Am-

Adapted from Mayfair, *© 1957 by Crombie Publishing Co. Ltd., with editorial additions*

bassador. They thinkin' about that horn and them notes and that music."

His way of being an ambassador is friendly and easy — if a little unusual. When he first played at a London music hall, over twenty-five years ago, King George V was in the Royal Box. As he was about to begin one tune, Satchmo bowed toward the King and said, "This one's for you, Rex." Just a few years ago he was no less gracious to Princess Margaret. "We've got one of our special fans in the house," he told the audience, "and we're really goin' to lay this one on for the Princess."

Satchmo's Road to Fame

Satchmo spent his early years in a poor, honky-tonk district of New Orleans, where he was born in 1900. It was a rough neighborhood, and as he grew up he saw brawls and knifings and shootings. Louis went to school just long enough to learn to read and write. And in the streets he found jazz.

There were many bands in the Negro districts of New Orleans in those days, making their own music from the African rhythms of their ancestors. These bands played everywhere — in saloons and dance halls, for weddings and funerals, at picnics, parades and fish fries. Little Louis was called "Satchel-mouth" or "Satchmo" because of his great big grin. He was one of the ragged army of children that followed the bands. At night he stood outside the cafés, listening to music played by Negroes who were later to become famous jazz musicians.

Louis knew what it was like to be really poor. To make a little money he carried coal, worked on a junk cart and sold newspapers. Sometimes he had to hunt for food in restaurant garbage cans. He was not quite twelve when he formed his own small band and went around playing for pennies.

He firmly believes that his early life did him good. As a child he saw plenty of both good and bad. And he learned one lesson that he often repeats today: "You don't have to do a thing that's bad unless you *want* to."

Yet it was a piece of mischief — though a fairly innocent one — that set Louis Armstrong on the road to fame. One New Year's Eve he went out to celebrate. Just for fun he took along as a noisemaker an old pistol of his stepfather's. He had just fired his last blank cartridge when the police collared him and hauled him off to the juvenile court. He was sent to the Colored Waifs' Home for Boys for eighteen months. And it was there that he learned to play the cornet.

When he was set free, Satchmo got a part-time job in a band. He earned $1.25 a night plus tips. He also ran errands for the wife of the great jazz

London, 1956: Satchmo plays "St. Louis Blues" with the London Philharmonic Orchestra. Leopoldville, the Congo, 1960: Jubilant fans carry him on their shoulders after triumphant concert. West Berlin, 1959: He's mobbed by young autograph hunters while on concert tour of Western Europe.

WIDE WORLD UPI WIDE WORLD

musician Joe "King" Oliver. In return, Oliver gave him music lessons. Then, in 1918, when Oliver went north to Chicago, Louis was offered his place in Kid Ory's band — on condition that he get himself a pair of long pants. Soon he was known as the best cornet player in New Orleans.

Oliver kept asking him to come to Chicago, which by that time was the capital of jazz. So, one day in August 1922, Louis packed his bag and caught a train. In Chicago he soon became a finer musician than his former teacher. Some records he made in the 1920s with his "Hot Five" and "Hot Seven" bands became jazz classics. By then he had switched from the cornet to the trumpet, because his manager thought the larger horn looked more impressive.

The Lord Helps the Poor

The sales of Louis's records were so successful that he decided to make a tour of Europe. On his second tour of the Continent in 1933, he was received in capital after capital — "like a visiting monarch." In Copenhagen, ten thousand people greeted him at the station. He was received by the Prince of Wales (now the Duke of Windsor), the Crown Prince of Sweden, the King of the Belgians and the King of Italy. And he is still going strong. In recent years he has played for the King of Thailand, the King of the Ashantis (a Ghanaian tribe) and a princess of India.

Louis came to earn hundreds of thousands of dollars a year, but he bothers himself as little as possible with money. His manager has to keep him from giving too much of it away!

Like most musicians who play wind instruments, Satchmo suffers from something rather like corns on his lips. He uses vast quantities of a German lip ointment, which has now been named after him. He also drinks a mixture of honey and glycerin, and uses a special gargle for the sake of his naturally hoarse voice. That famous rasp has been compared to the sound of "a tired piece of sandpaper calling to its mate."

"There's no time of day I ain't doin' somethin' for them chops and that horn," he says. "The Lord helps the poor, but not the poor lazy. All a lot of these modern cats want is to sit down and make that high note, and they're too lazy to keep themselves in shape to do it. How many modern trumpet players could play my solos? You'd have to carry them out on stretchers."

Jazz played by other people can be noisy and unpleasant, but one famous critic has called Louis's jazz "the work of an artist." Few other jazz musicians have received so much praise from so many critics. As Satchmo himself would say, "Them cats really dig ol' Pops!"

Some Things You Should Have Remembered from Picture on Page 23

1. Mother's white apron 2. Daughter's red dress 3. Rag doll 4. Father's orange juice 5. Dog with collar 6. Tiger-striped cat 7. Ball with red stripes 8. Father's white chair 9. White cloth on table 10. Basket of bread 11. Bowl of fruit 12. Father's bacon and eggs 13. Daughter's apple 14. Sugar bowl 15. Father's cup and saucer 16. Father's spoon 17. Sideboard 18. Toaster 19. Salt and pepper shakers 20. Coffeepot 21. Clock 22. Mirror 23. Chandelier 24. Blue curtains in dining room 25. Daisies on dining-room wallpaper 26. Picture of cat 27. Picture of dog 28. Bare trees in yard 29. Snow on ground 30. Cardinal at bird feeder 31. Wall telephone 32. Yellow kitchen curtains 33. Green-and-black kitchen floor 34. Flowerpot 35. Heart mold 36. Sink 37. Cupboards 38. Two saucepans 39. Dog bowl 40. Ceiling light

Musical Instruments FROM ODDS AND ENDS

BY CORINNE M. MURPHY

The name of Louis Armstrong conjures up the rhythm and beat so characteristic of jazz. How would you like to have your own rhythm instruments to play with your friends or along with your favorite records? Here are some you can make yourself; they begin with the easiest and demand more skill as you proceed. All are fun to make and to play, and the materials are cheap and easy to find.

RHYTHM BLOCKS

With a crosscut saw cut two pieces of wood, each measuring about 1 x 3 x 5 inches. Or they can be square or round if you prefer. Sand each block smooth, first with coarse sandpaper and then with fine. With a brush or pad of cheesecloth, coat both sides of each block with shellac, thinned a little with denatured alcohol. When this is thoroughly dry, sand the blocks lightly with fine sandpaper.

Now you are ready for the handles. They can be made from two strips of leather, about 1 x 4 inches; or from narrow blocks of wood, about ½ x 1 x 3 inches, which should be sanded smooth and given a coat of shellac. Or you can get your handles ready-made in the form of wooden drawer pulls, available in various sizes at hardware stores. If you use drawer pulls, drill a hole in the center of one side of each block and screw the pull in place. Handles of the other types can be secured with fine nails.

If you want a natural finish, completely coat each block again with shellac, and sand lightly when dry. For an attractive appearance, decorate the tops of your blocks with poster paints or enamels before applying the second coat of shellac. (Be sure to clean, in alcohol, the brush you used for shellac.)

When clapped together, these blocks can make a fine rhythmic accompaniment.

MUSICAL GLASSES

Here is a simple way to begin making a tune. Find eight glasses of the same size and shape (the dime-store variety will do for the first adventure), and line them up in a row. Fill a pitcher with water and, starting at the left, fill the glasses with the different amounts shown. The left-hand glass will be your lowest note, so it should be filled almost to the top. Give the glasses less and less water as you go up the scale.

You "play" the glasses by gently tapping the tops with a pencil or spoon. But first you will need to tune the notes. Starting at the left with **do,** go up the scale, adding or taking away a little water as necessary, until you have completed the scale: **do, re, mi, fa, sol, la, ti, do.**

If your glasses are not exactly the same, the levels of the water will vary and you will have to experiment with them in order for the scale to work. You may find that you need a smaller glass for your highest note. The sound is caused by the vibration of air in the glass, and the larger the glass, or the fuller it is with water, the lower the sound will be. Much also depends on the thickness of the glass. So do not worry if your scale does not look just like the one in the picture.

Number each glass as shown. Then take a familiar tune such as "Three Blind Mice" and work it out by number. Write the numbers down so that you can play the tune more quickly. It would be fun to set up two or three scales and play with your friends.

Here is how you would work out "Jingle Bells" on your glasses:

333 333 3512 3/ 4444 43333 3223 25
333 333 3512 3/ 4444 43333 5542 1

PAPIER-MÂCHÉ MARACA

Many musical compositions lend themselves to the soft rattle of the maraca. Here is a maraca you can make with everyday materials.

You will need: a burned-out light bulb, some newspaper, masking tape, wallpaper paste, tempera or poster paints, paintbrushes, and shellac or plastic spray.

Tear some newspaper into strips about one inch wide and three to six inches long. Then mix the wallpaper paste according to the instructions on the package. Coat one side of a newspaper strip with paste (or simply dip the whole strip into the paste) and place it over the light bulb, continuing in crisscross fashion until the bulb is completely covered.

Make a short roll of newspaper and attach it with tape to the bottom of the light bulb. This will be the handle of your maraca.

When the first layer of papier-mâché is dry, stick another layer over the entire shape, including the bottom of the handle. Make three or four more layers in the same way, ending with a layer of paper-towel strips which will give you a good surface on which to paint.

Allow the last layer to dry, then take the maraca by its handle and hit the bulb section on a hard surface to break the glass inside — this will create the rattle. Decorate the maraca with your tempera or poster paints and, when these are dry, finish off with a coat of shellac or plastic spray. If you make several maracas, you and your friends could learn a South American folk song and put them to really good use.

MARIMBA

Are you ready for something a little more difficult? The marimba has rhythm and tune too.

For a one-octave marimba you will need: a 7-foot length of pine, redwood, basswood or poplar (1 x 1½ or 2 inches); a length of rope; some tacks or brads.

With a ruler and pencil, mark off the eight divisions on your wood. These will be your notes, as follows:

do 12″ re 11½″ mi 11″ fa 10¾″
sol 10¼″ la 9¾″ ti 9¼″ do 9″

Cut, with a crosscut saw, the 12-inch bar first. If you want to tune it precisely, tune it to C on a piano or a tuning fork. Sand or saw to make any needed adjustment.

Cut the next bar, and so on until your whole scale is cut and tuned. Make a loop in the rope and center the bars on it as shown. They need not be tacked in place, but simply laid on the rope to cushion them.

Now try tapping out some simple tunes. You can use small mallets, or dowels with wooden beads glued to the ends. Put a felt tip at the end of one stick for a softer sound.

You can take your marimba apart easily this way. But if you want a more permanent instrument you can make a frame of narrow lumber, ½ x ½ inch, like the one below.

To assemble the marimba, first center the frame on top of your bars and draw a line, on the bars, around the outside of the frame. Remove the frame and lay the rope in its place, following the lines you have drawn. Tack the rope to each bar. Lift rope and bars onto the frame, and tack the ends of the rope to the narrow end of the frame. Now tack the rope to both sides of the frame between bars 2 and 3, and 6 and 7.

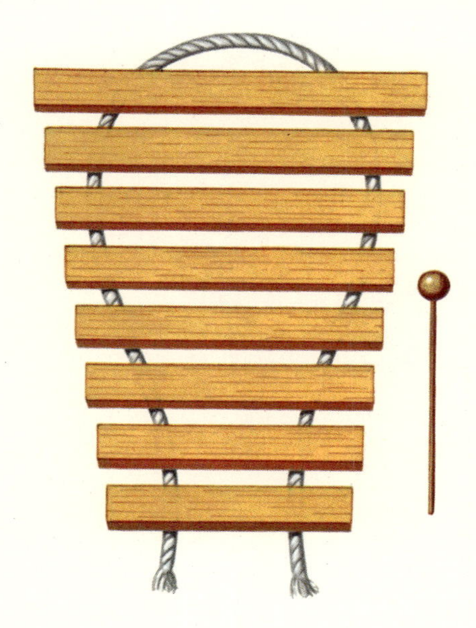

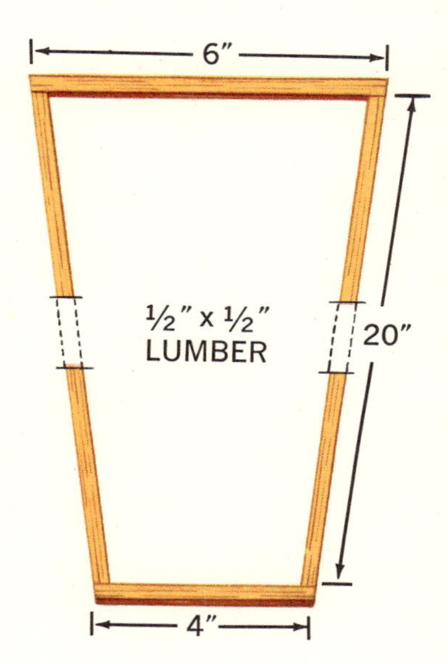

COFFEE-CAN DRUM

Nothing can capture the spirit and tempo of jazz quite like a drum. You will want two or three for your rhythm band. Here is a simple one you can make with the following everyday materials: an empty coffee can, some parchment-like paper from an art store, or an old inner tube, enamel paints and paintbrushes, sturdy cord or lacing.

With a can opener remove the bottom of the coffee can, so that it is open at both ends. Give the outside of the can a coat (or two, if the first doesn't cover the print) of enamel paint, and let it dry. Decorate with oil or enamel paints.

Cut two circles of parchment or inner tube, about two inches larger than the diameter of the can. Pierce holes around the rim of each circle, about ¾ inch apart and at least ½ inch in from the edge. If you are using parchment, wet the parchment until it is limp.

Tape the circles over each end of the coffee can, or have a friend hold them in place, while you lace the cord through the holes crisscross from top to bottom. Lace the cord loosely all the way around, then gently but firmly tighten it until the drumheads are taut.

Tie the ends of the cord tightly with a square knot.

Make a handle by attaching a cord to the cross cords, as shown below.

This drum is held in the hand and played with the fingers or with a small beater.

CLAY DRUM

This drum takes longer to make, but you will be able to enjoy it for years. You will need: two or three pounds of moist clay, oilcloth to cover your work table, a piece of rawhide for the drumhead, some rawhide thonging, the use of a kiln.

Wedge, pound and cut the moist clay until the air bubbles are out. Start by making a flat disk of clay about 1/2 inch thick. Then roll the rest of the clay on the oilcloth (wrong side up) into long pieces that you can build into the coils shown here.

Wind the coils upward around the outside of the flat base, making the sides of the drum. Gather in the middle section as shown, then widen out at the top for the drumhead. Remember that the farther the sound vibrates, the lower the note will be; so if you want a deep, resonant sound, make the drum taller.

Join the coils of clay by overlapping them a bit and squeezing each one gently into the preceding coil. Continue coiling until the shape is complete. If your clay was quite moist, you may need to let it set for a while at this stage to avoid pushing it out of shape. Do not let it harden, however, before smoothing together the coils with your fingers. You can use a popsicle stick to get into the inside areas.

When your drum is quite hard, do any finishing touches such as sanding the rough areas and scratching in a surface design. Also make a shallow groove around the drum about one inch from the top.

Let the drum dry thoroughly. This may take from a few days to several weeks, depending on the humidity. Obtain the use of a kiln, and fire the drum once — the bisque (or biscuit) firing, as it is called — without any glaze. When the clay has come out of the kiln, let it cool. You are then ready to put on the drumhead.

Cut a circle of rawhide at least two inches larger all the way around than the top of the drum. Either buy rawhide thonging, or cut a thong from a circle of rawhide as shown. Soak the drumhead in water until it is soft and limp. Then have a friend hold it gently in place while you pull the edges down around the top of the drum and secure it tightly with the rawhide thong. Keep the drumhead straight and firm and make sure that the thong follows the shallow groove in the clay. When the drumhead is dry you are ready to play.

THE BETTMAN ARCHIVE

"THERE GOES THE PONY EXPRESS!"

BY DONALD CULROSS PEATTIE

STEAMBOAT whistles screamed with gladness. Locomotives hooted joyful answers. The band played, flags waved. And the men and women of St. Joseph, Missouri, cheered wildly as a chestnut-colored horse danced out of Pike's Peak Livery Stables.

Young Billy Richardson leaped to the saddle, revolvers in his holsters. Wheeling his mount, he galloped to the post office. The eastern mail for California had just been slung off the train here in "St. Joe," where the railroad tracks ended. It was ready in the locked pockets of the mail pouch.

Billy strapped the pouch to his saddle pommel — and with a wave of his hand was off on the first westward dash of the Pony Express.

At the same hour, on that same day, April 3, 1860, a similar pouch of eastbound mail was tossed aboard a steamer in San Francisco Bay, bound upriver to Sacramento. Not long afterward, in Sacramento, Billy Hamilton, riding a white mustang, started east. This was the first run of the long and dangerous relay which, like a spark of the American spirit, leaped the nineteen hundred miles between the "post offices" of East and West.

Through Snow and Sagebrush

Neither telegraph line nor railroad track yet crossed the prairies, deserts and mountains between St. Joe and Sacramento. Once a month a creaking old stagecoach lumbered from Missouri to California — when snows and Indians and highwaymen let it go through. A roundabout southerly coach route took twenty-one days. Mail also could go, in three or four weeks, by steamer to Panama, across the Isthmus and then by ship to San Francisco.

By 1860 there were half a million gold seekers, homesteaders and other settlers west of the Rocky Mountains. In vain had these pioneers sought the aid of Congress for a faster overland-mail service. But now the Pony Express was to carry the nation's news across the continent, faster than it had ever been carried before. The

Adapted from St. Louis Post-Dispatch, © *1944 by The Pulitzer Publishing Co.*

announcement of the new service stirred the imagination: "Mail for California, Oregon, Washington Territory, British Columbia, the Pacific Mexican ports, the Russian Possessions, the Sandwich Islands, China, Japan and India."

Billy Hamilton, they say, rode the first twenty miles of the eastward dash in fifty-nine minutes. Changing horses every five, ten or fifteen miles, he galloped on thirty-seven miles farther to Sportsman's Hall, twelve miles east of Placerville. There he dismounted and fastened the mail pouch to the saddle of the next rider. This was Warren Upson, who carried it over the Sierra Nevada. In those icy divides the Pony Express company had to keep a drove of pack mules moving on the trail, in order to clear away the thirty-foot snowdrifts. On the next lap, "Pony Bob" Haslam carried the pouch across the sagebrush desert of Nevada to Fort Churchill.

So, from horse to horse, from rider to rider, from station to station, night and day, the mail went through. And somewhere beyond Salt Lake City the eastbound rider met the westbound. They passed at a gallop with a wave of the hand — two flying shuttles on the loom of the continent, weaving the fabric of the Union.

The westbound mail, because of weather, made that first trip in slightly the shorter time: nine days and twenty-three hours. It was after midnight when it arrived in San Francisco, but late hours were nothing to that wide-open town. Theaters, bars, hotels, restaurants and homes emptied. Whistles screamed. Bells pealed. Bonfires blazed in the streets. Crowds cheered. And one fashionable lady took off her expensive bonnet and tied it on the pony's head. The Pony Express had cut in half all previous overland-mail time. It had proved to be three times as fast as the steamship.

The Pick of the West

The new service was organized by Russell, Majors and Waddell, a well-known express firm of Leavenworth, Kansas. Details had been carefully worked out. The firm had set up a hundred and ninety relay stations manned by four hundred stationmasters. It had bought four hundred and eighty horses — the best that money could buy. The eighty riders were the pick of the West. They rode for salaries of fifty to a hundred and fifty dollars a month — depending on the length and dangers of the run — and for love of adventure.

The company had to defend its lonely way stations and precious saddle horses against constant attacks by Indians and rustlers. Yet the men of the Express had orders not to shoot unless surrounded. They were to depend on the superior speed of their mounts and their own unbeatable horsemanship. Several riders were wounded. One was ambushed and killed by Indians. His pony escaped and came in riderless to the next relay station, with the mail sack safe.

Most of the riders were in their early twenties, and were almost as small as jockeys. Only men of good character were chosen. Each was required to take an oath: "I will use no profane language, will drink no intoxicating liquors, will not quarrel or fight with any other employe." Most of them kept their word faithfully. The firm presented each man with a little Bible when he took his job, and expected him to uphold high standards, even in the rough-mannered, tough-living towns of the Old West. The riders trained for their jobs as athletes or pilots do today. They were the idols of the people.

The Mail Got Through

The famous writer Mark Twain once saw the Pony Express while he was traveling by stagecoach to California. He later wrote of it, "Now the driver exclaims: 'Here he comes!' Every neck is stretched, every eye strained. Away across the endless dead level of the prairie a black speck appears against the sky. Soon it becomes a horse and rider, rising and falling, sweeping nearer and nearer, and the flutter of hoofs comes faintly to the ear. Another instant a whoop and a hurrah from our upper deck, a wave of the rider's hand, but no reply, and man and horse burst past our excited faces and go winging away like a belated fragment of a storm!"

Many were the stories of the riders' gallant endurance. Once, when his relief rider failed, Bob Haslam continued for a hundred and eighty-five miles through desert full of Ute Indians. At a station he snatched some sleep. Then, awakened by the incoming mail, he started back with it. He was sure he would get a fresh mount at the next station. But when he got there, he found the place a smoldering ember, the stationmaster dead, and all the stock stolen. On he rode, completing the trip only three hours late.

This most dashing and dangerous job was the dream of all boys of the period. One who applied was a slim lad of fourteen who gave his name as William F. Cody. The manager hesitated. The

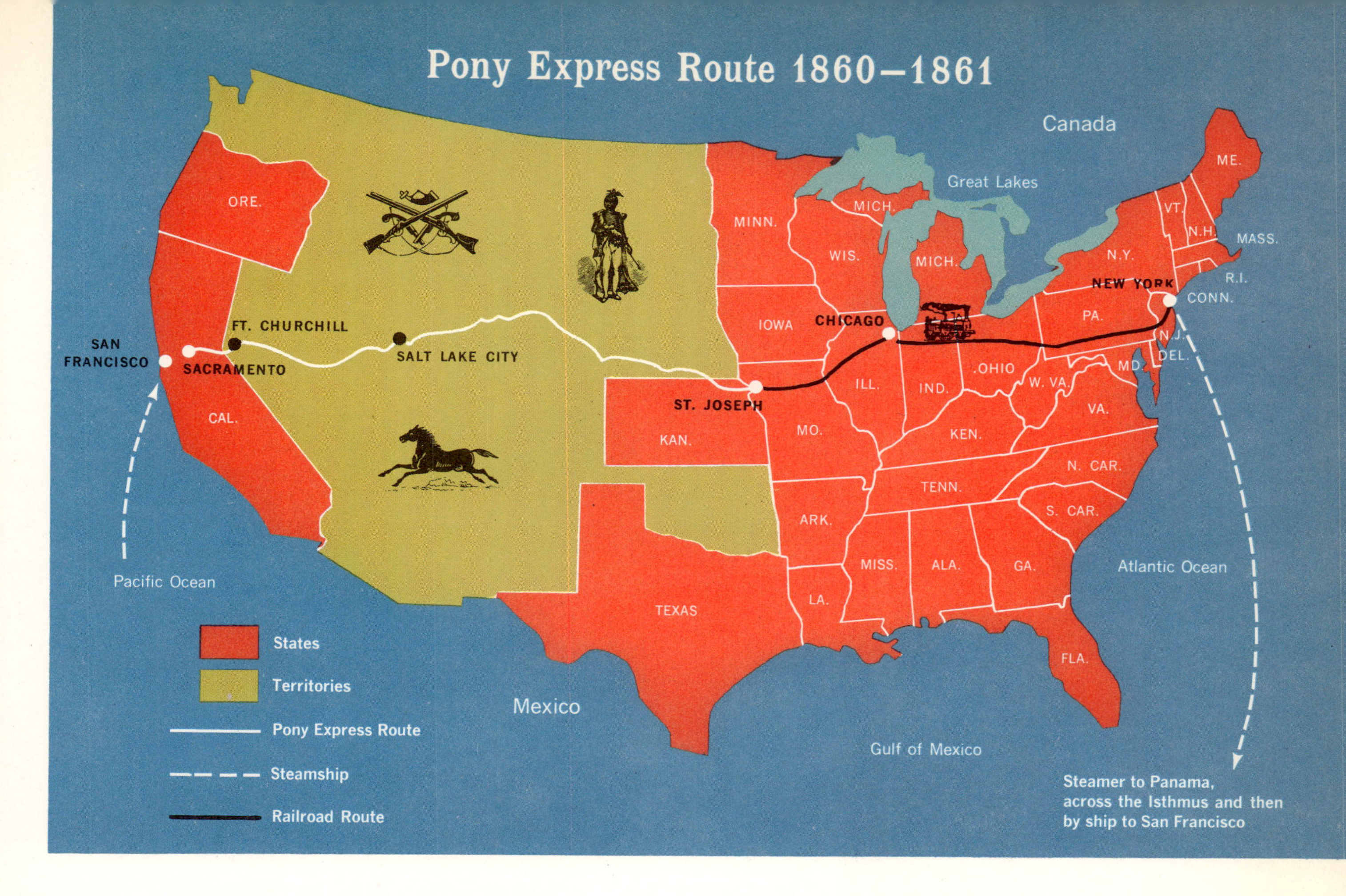

run in his division was one of the most dangerous. He could not know that this boy would go down in fame as "Buffalo Bill." But young Cody got the job. And he soon broke all endurance records in a run of three hundred and eighty-four miles without a stopover. Surrounded once by fifteen armed Sioux, he escaped by outriding them on his swift pony for twenty-four miles.

Cody's experiences were like those of almost all the other young horsemen. Yet in eighteen months the Pony Express riders covered six hundred and fifty thousand miles. They carried thirty thousand pieces of mail and lost only one pouch. The mail, then as now, got through.

The service soon ran twice a week. It carried an average of fifteen pounds of mail. Eastern newspapers kept correspondents in St. Joseph to telegraph western news from there as soon as the riders brought it in. The British government used the service for important Asian mail.

News in the United States was never more vital than at that moment, for it was just before the Civil War. The Pony Express bore westward the news of Lincoln's election, the firing on Fort Sumter and the President's call to arms.

The great days of the Pony Express came to an end in October 1861, when telegraph lines finally joined the East and the West. On its abandoned route were laid the tracks of the Union Pacific Railroad, the first transcontinental rail system, which was completed in 1869.

But the Pony Express had played an important part in American history. Its bold young riders were true pioneers. Theirs was a high-hearted conquest over time and space and hardship. Remembering them, put your fingers on your pulse. And you'll hear those hoofbeats galloping again!

The Punishment Fits the Crime

A SCHOOLTEACHER was taken to court for driving past a stop sign. "So you are a teacher," said the judge. "I can now say what I have wanted to say all my life. You sit right down at that table, madam, and write 'I went through a stop sign' five hundred times." —*Adapted from* Kablegram

GREAT WEAPONS *of* PIONEER AMERICA

BY WILL BRYANT

SURVIVAL in the New World would not have been possible for the American pioneer without guns and gunpowder. For more than two hundred and fifty years, guns were household items in frontier families – as necessary as the cooking kettle and spinning jenny, mostly for hunting, sometimes for defense. A family's chances for survival in the wilderness could often be measured by its guns and how they were used. Frontier boys learned early to make the single shot in a muzzle-loading rifle count. Girls, too, learned to reload, to make bullets from melted bar lead with ladle and mold, shown below, and, often, to shoot as straight as their brothers.

The great Kentucky rifle, which first appeared about 1730, took half a minute to load with loose powder and ball. It was fired when the flint, held between jaws of the hammer, struck the earlike steel tang, or frizzen, opening the pan and dropping a shower of sparks into the priming powder, which in turn ignited the main charge through a touchhole. These guns were made entirely by hand by gunsmiths, and no two were exactly alike. A rifle is no better than the man who shoots it – in the hands of an expert, the Kentucky rifle was a superb instrument; it fed, clothed and protected generations of Americans for more than a hundred years.

By 1820, the percussion caplock was replacing the flintlock. Here, a copper cap filled with explosive pellet is fired by hammer impact, igniting powder charge through hollow tube.

FAVORITES of the PONY EXPRESS

Mail riders looked mostly to fast horses for safety, and every ounce of weight was important. Fine, light percussion revolvers were the six-shot .36-caliber Colt Navy model of 1851 and the five-shot .31-caliber Colt pocket model of 1849, above. The latter weighed less than two pounds loaded. At right, Smith & Wesson .32, one of the first successful cartridge guns.

The year of the Pony Express, 1860, was a key year in the development of firearms. In that year appeared the first successful repeating rifles, the Henry and the Spencer, which later evolved into the Winchester. President Lincoln himself test-fired and approved the Spencer for service use. All modern firearms may be traced back to the development of the metallic cartridge and its use in repeating mechanisms.

Seven years after he rode for the Pony Express, young Bill Cody earned the name "Buffalo Bill" with a single-shot Springfield which he called "Lucretia Borgia." Hunting for the Kansas Pacific Railroad, he shot 4280 buffalo in eighteen months.

Father mined a lot of silver,
but he paid through the nose

The Revenge of the Tommyknockers

BY RUTH WOODMAN

HALLOWEEN had a special meaning in our family. It was the date on which Father always broke his nose.

The first time it happened we were giving a Halloween party in our home in Rye, New York. We used to make cider from our own apples. And just before the guests arrived, Father and I went down to the cellar to tap the cider. This lot must have been really working there in the dark. When Father bent over and began tapping briskly on the side of the barrel, the bung shot out with terrific force. It caught him smack on the bridge of the nose. Cider poured out of the bunghole. Blood gushed from Father's nose. I didn't know where to hold the jug.

We went upstairs, where Mother was putting out doughnuts and cookies to go with the cider.

"Bessie, I've broken my nose!" groaned Father.

"Nonsense, George," said Mother. "You always make a big show about things." But when Father wiggled and creaked his nose to prove it, she turned pale. She sent him to Dr. Bassett, who put two neat splints on his nose, and that was that.

By the time another Halloween rolled around, we'd almost forgotten about Father's accident. He

had a fine beak of a nose, and the break didn't even show.

Again we were having a Halloween party. We did all the usual things. We bobbed for apples, ate marshmallows off strings, dived for pennies in a pan of flour.

Father wanted to bob for apples too. He knelt beside the tub with his hands clasped behind his back. He pounced on a beautiful red apple. But a little boy on the other side of the tub had the same idea at exactly the same second. There was a loud *cr-r-r-ack!* Out of the tub came Father's bald head. Blood streamed all over the apple, which he held firmly clenched in his teeth.

This time Father telephoned Dr. Bassett. "Why do you always have to break your nose on Halloween?" the doctor asked crossly. That was the first it had occurred to any of us that this was the anniversary of the other fracture.

"It's the work of the tommyknockers," Father said to us.

"What are tommyknockers?" we asked.

"Tommyknockers," he explained, "are the imps who haunt mines. Whenever anything goes wrong underground — not big disasters, but little, bothersome things — it's because of the tommyknockers. They're like gremlins."

Father was a mining engineer. Back in 1896 he had gone out to Colorado during a big silver rush, and he had mined a lot of silver.

"Now," he said solemnly, "the tommyknockers are getting even with me for invading their haunts and stealing their treasure."

We asked why the revenge took this particular form, and Father grinned. "My nose for ore, of course," he said.

A Near Miss

The next Halloween Father announced that he would not take part in any of our party games. He'd help decorate the sun parlor, but that was all. It was enough.

He was standing on a stepladder, tacking up orange and black crepe-paper streamers, when the ladder tipped. It was just as if an unseen hand had pushed it, and Father plunged downward. As he fell, he struck his nose against an open French door. We could all hear the crack.

This third experience took the fun out of Halloween parties in our house. Of course, some people said that things always go in threes, so there was no chance of its happening again. But these same people had said that lightning never strikes twice in the same place.

So, the fourth year, we let somebody else give the party. Father and Mother stayed quietly at home alone. After dinner Father settled himself in a chair to read. Mother crocheted. And Prince, our black cocker spaniel, snoozed on the black bearskin rug in front of the fireplace. It was all very peaceful, not a bit like Halloween.

A log burned through and fell with a shower of sparks. Father got up and took another log out of the woodbox. As he crossed to the fireplace, he didn't see Prince, camouflaged against the black rug. He tripped over the dog and pitched headlong against the brass fender.

Mother and Prince both yelped.

"Drat that dog!" Father bellowed. "Nearly broke my neck!"

"Never mind your neck," said Mother. "How about your nose?"

Miraculously, it was unhurt. It had missed one of the brass knobs on the fender by a nostril.

The Masked Intruder

Around nine o'clock there was a scampering of feet on the front porch. Father got up to lock the front door. But just then it flew open. In swarmed a bunch of masked children carrying brown paper bags filled with dried beans and flour. They scattered the beans and flour all around the front hall.

One figure in a sheet and pillowcase slipped into the music room and hurled a handful of the stuff into Mother's new baby-grand piano. Father was furious. He pounced on the little girl, who wriggled out of his clutches and made a beeline for the front door. On the porch Father grabbed the pillowcase. He was about to rip it off when the child dived down the porch steps. At the same time a foot kicked Father square in the face. It was a kick that would have done a mule proud.

Father came back into the house with his nose lying over on one cheek. For several days he had to stay home from work. He was ashamed to tell anyone that a little girl had kicked him in the face. So he made up a story about how he had overpowered a masked intruder in a hand-to-hand struggle. The girls in Father's office thought he was terribly brave.

"How many times do the tommyknockers knock?" I asked Father.

Adapted from The Lion, *© 1961 by Lions International*

Father said that an old prospector he'd known in Colorado claimed the tommyknockers always struck a victim five times running. Of course, Father didn't believe it for a minute. He said the prospector was a "superstitious idiot." Still, this five-times-running superstition preyed on all our minds.

Mother Took No Chances

Halloween fell on a Wednesday that fifth year. That was the day that Patrick, the handyman, always waxed our floors. But when he rolled the rugs back Mother stopped him.

"Not this week, Patrick," she said. "Halloween, you know . . ."

Patrick understood. He nodded and rolled the rugs down again. The bearskin rug was taken out of the house, and Prince was taken to the vet's. My brother offered to lend Father his catcher's mask.

"Can you picture me going to work wearing a catcher's mask?" demanded Father.

"You're not *going* to work, George," announced Mother quietly. "You're spending the day right here at home."

When Father called his office to say he had a cold and wouldn't be in, his partner laughed. "Well, that changes the betting," he said.

Father turned from the telephone, red with anger. "Bessie," he said, "they're laying bets! Bets on my *nose!*" He banged his fist on the desk so hard that the brass inkwell jumped and nearly hit him. Mother quickly removed the inkwell.

We had invitations to parties that evening, but we said we couldn't go to them. We wanted to be home, in case anything happened. I couldn't decide whether I hoped it *would* or it *wouldn't.*

After dinner the family went into the living room, all but Father. Father stayed at the table, moodily drinking coffee and smoking a cigar. Suddenly, from the dining room, came the sound of a sharp *cr-r-r-ack!* We leaped to our feet and rushed in. There was Father picking the meat out of a walnut he'd just cracked.

"Well?" he asked.

We slunk away without a word.

By ten o'clock we'd all gone to bed. Around eleven Father switched off the light and settled down for the night. When Mother heard the clock chime half past eleven, she relaxed. Halloween was nearly over.

"You see?" said Father, who was thinking the same thing. "That idea of five in a row was all superstitious bunk." He kissed her good night. Mother breathed a little prayer of thanks.

A few minutes before midnight the telephone rang. Father jumped out of bed and started into the hall to answer it. But the door leading into the hall had blown partly open. Father was still half asleep and he ran slam into it. Anyone else would have stubbed his toe. But not Father. For the fifth — and last — time, he paid through the nose.

A "Nosey" Party Game

Do you want to have a good laugh? Have your friends form a circle. Then ask them to try to pass the cover of a small matchbox from nose to nose.

Young Master Caterpillar

BY DONALD CULROSS PEATTIE

The strange life of the "terrible children" of the insect world

ONCE, long ago, a weird procession passed through a small town in southern France. As they went, the marchers nibbled pine needles, killing all the pine trees. The townspeople had them tried in a law court for trespass, vandalism and theft. The judge ordered them to leave town at once. But the lawyer for the dreadful marchers said this would not be possible.

"They need more time," he said.

"Very well then," said the judge. "But in a few months they must go."

The sly judge knew he was quite safe in saying this. Winter was on the way and, when it came, the marchers would hide away in cocoons. In spring they would come forth again as harmless moths. For these marchers were caterpillars — the pine processionaries, which move in single file, head to tail, destroying pine forests. And this story is an old French folktale.

The "Children" of Butterflies

All caterpillars are the "children" of butterflies or moths. They are called larvae. And what brats these children are! They eat enormously and grow fast. They get into anything and everything. Some feed on crops, some on clothes. Most leave a trail of ruin behind them, though one, the silkworm, has been a useful and valuable friend to man from ancient times. In one way or another, all caterpillars are more important than the moths or butterflies they later become.

A butterfly, like all other true insects, has six legs. A caterpillar, however, may have either two

LIFE CYCLE OF A MONARCH BUTTERFLY

1 Baby caterpillars
2 Full-grown caterpillar (larva)
3 Larva shedding skin
4 Pupa
5 Pupa changing into butterfly
6 Adult butterfly

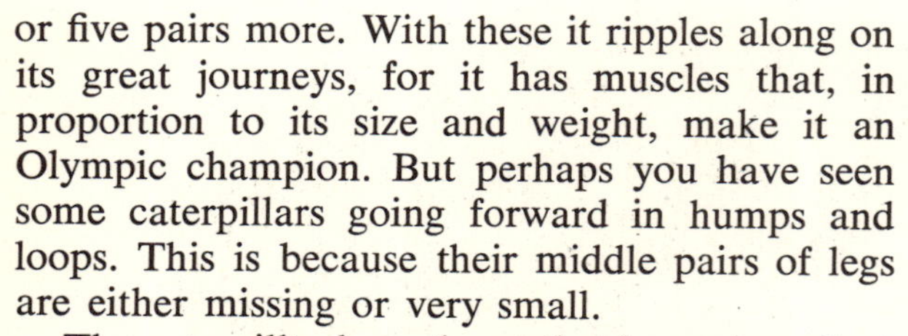

or five pairs more. With these it ripples along on its great journeys, for it has muscles that, in proportion to its size and weight, make it an Olympic champion. But perhaps you have seen some caterpillars going forward in humps and loops. This is because their middle pairs of legs are either missing or very small.

The caterpillar has a heart that keeps its yellow or green body fluid, or "blood," flowing slowly. But it has no lungs; instead, its body has pores that connect with a network of tubes and so provide air for the "blood." There is a crop for grinding up food, and a gut for digesting — trust these greedy creatures for that! And there are tireless jaws that move sideways, instead of up and down like ours.

Primitive organs, which will become the eyes of the adult insect, can distinguish light from dark. And the caterpillar has a keen sense of touch all over its body. Apparently without ears, it lives in a silent world, and cannot even hear the sound of its own constant munching.

Once a caterpillar starts doing something, it may be unable to stop. This was shown by the great French student of insect life, J. Henri Fabre. He set a group of pine-processionary caterpillars on the rim of a flowerpot. Beside the pot he laid a branch of pine, the caterpillars' favorite food. It would have been easy for them to reach the pine. Instead, they crawled around and around the rim of the pot for seven days.

Silly as this sounds to us, it made good sense to the caterpillars. For, like spiders, these creatures are spinners. Each one laid down a thread of silk to guide the one behind it. The threads formed a track which the crawlers could not leave. They were caught in a game of follow-the-leader.

Eat, but Don't Be Eaten!

To get born, the caterpillar pushes its way out through the shell of its egg. Usually the egg has been laid on a tasty plant. Right away, the greedy little larva can start its first meal.

But, to many a bright-eyed bird, Young Master Caterpillar looks like a good meal in himself. So, for safety's sake, some wary caterpillars do their own feeding at night or under the ground. Others are protected from their enemies by thick coats of hair which can give you a rash.

But even hairless caterpillars have tricks for staying alive. Many of them are the very same color as bare, dead twigs on the trees; and they can hold themselves at just the same angle of growth as real twigs. The larva of the puss moth puts on a false face by pulling down an extra fold of skin. The result is a furious red "face," two big scary "eyes" and a false, fierce "mouth." It even shoots from its hindquarters what looks like the forked tongue of a serpent. Are its enemies *really* scared by all these goings-on? No one knows for sure. But it is an amazing show.

Though caterpillars have wonderful ways of protecting themselves, Nature has her own methods of getting rid of them. When I was a boy, an army of caterpillars invaded my neighborhood. People began making plans to poison and burn them. Just then a flock of warblers came through on their seasonal migration and saw the in-

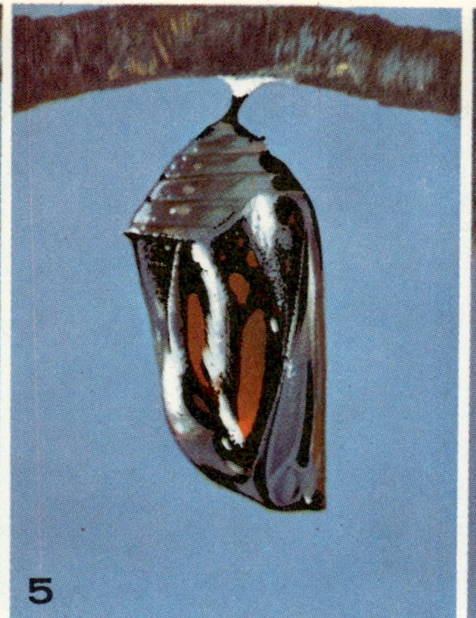

vaders. Soon there was hardly a caterpillar left.

Another time when I was a boy I captured the full-grown larva of a polyphemus moth. I put it with some oak leaves in a box in my room. Before long my caterpillar began restlessly weaving its head back and forth in a way that meant it was about to spin a cocoon. The material for this comes from glands in the creature's head. It is a sticky fluid that hardens into a kind of silk when it meets the air. The cocoon is generally made in three layers: there is a coarse, loose outer casing made of a dead leaf, then a lining of fine silken floss, and finally a papery wrapping around the caterpillar itself. In the dark silence of my cocoon a miracle took place. The greedy larva became a gentle moth.

Secrets of the Cocoon

Many cocoons are expert little pieces of camouflage. The leaf-roller caterpillar snuggles down between two leaves and fastens them together with silk, so that the whole thing looks like one leaf blown in the autumn wind. The larva of the black hairstreak butterfly forms a hideaway that looks just like a bird-dropping on a twig. And the tiny cocoon of the hated clothes moth clings to fabric in such a way that your mother can hardly tell it from a speck of lint.

The silkworm has, for four thousand years, been raised by man just for its cocoon. When full-grown, this creamy-gray caterpillar is an amazing little worker. For three days it will spin without stopping. And from its cocoon skilled workers can reel off unbroken filaments up to 1200 yards long and only 1/1200 of an inch thick. These filaments are then unreeled and twisted into thread. It takes about twenty-five thousand cocoons to make one pound of raw silk!

Inside its cocoon every caterpillar changes secretly from a larva to a pupa, or chrysalis. If the larva is the "child," the pupa is the "teen-ager" waiting to become a grownup. Finally the great day comes when it makes a hole in the cocoon and crawls out, weak and damp. Its wings, crumpled like a leaf in bud, slowly open. It may wave them many times, drying and sunning them. And at last they are ready for the glory of flight!

The winged insect now has eyes and can see color. Butterflies delight in orange and red and yellow flowers. Moths, which fly mostly at night, prefer white blossoms that show in the dusk. Some flowers open at night, as if just for the moths, and give off their perfume after the sun has set. For these insects now have an exquisitely developed sense of smell.

Gone now is the greed of the caterpillar. These airy grownups live only on nectar. They reach deep into flowers for it with their long, uncurling tongues. There are even some who never eat or drink at all, but live only to mate and lay eggs.

Moths and butterflies live but a short while. Soon their lovely wings, faded and torn, carry them in a last flutter to the forest floor. Or the insects drift down to the waters of a lake, or are borne away by some stream. But somewhere, in some right place, their eggs have been laid. The light-winged mother does not stay to see more. The great circle of life—in which she has played her important part—is complete.

Learn to be a LEPIDOPTERIST*

BY EDWIN WAY TEALE

With nothing more than a pair of sharp eyes, you can have fun watching moths and butterflies. But, for collecting, you require some aids: a butterfly net, which costs very little; a killing bottle; a pair of tweezers; some jars, cans and pillboxes; a notebook; a magnifying glass and a butterfly guidebook (both of which you can buy at a ten-cent store for a start). You will also need collecting boxes, mounting pins, and wood to make a setting board.

The killing bottle, which should be kept at home, is used to put your insects painlessly to sleep. Wet a wad of absorbent cotton with Carbona and place it in the bottom of a wide-mouthed container, such as a pint mason jar. (Be sure to use the Carbona with great care, following the instructions on the label, as the fumes can be dangerous.) Over the wad of cotton place a piece of wire screen, cut to fit, as shown in Figure 1. This prevents the insects from getting wet or from crawling under the cotton. They should be left in the jar *a full twelve hours.*

For carrying your specimens home and for holding live insects, you will find it useful to have a collection of empty bottles, cans and jars.

In handling butterflies and moths, use tweezers instead of your fingers. If this is impossible, pick them up by their legs or antennae rather than by their wings.

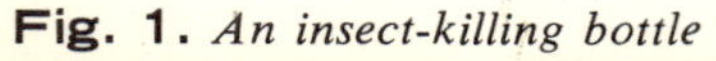

Fig. 1. *An insect-killing bottle*

A notebook may sound like work. But you will find that your fun is increased manyfold if you take notes on the insects you collect. Put down the date, the place, the time of day, the weather conditions, the plants on which the creatures were feeding, and anything unusual you observe. Such notes will help you in future hunting and will make your collection really worth while.

Off to the Hunt

The best days for butterfly hunting are clear, still ones when the sun is its brightest. Cool, cloudy or windy days are usually bad times for collecting. On a morning after an evening thunderstorm you may find some of the best specimens. The storm is thought to kill off old and ragged butterflies and produce the right atmospheric conditions to enable the new insects to break from their chrysalises.

Most butterflies can be approached best when they are feeding. Good places for all-around hunting are weed lots bordering woods, clover fields on sheltered hillsides, and open stretches where thistles, milkweed and orange butterfly weed are abundant. The common blue buddleia, or butterfly bush, attracts these gaily colored insects in large numbers.

In the movies, butterfly collectors always dash madly across a meadow flailing the air with their nets. In real life, the skillful insect hunter stalks his prey, and uses his brains instead of his feet. When you approach a butterfly, have the sun to one side or in front of you. If it is at your back, it will cast your shadow ahead and may frighten

---

* *When you handle a moth or butterfly, your fingers will soon become covered with colored dust. These particles are actually tiny, flattened scales which cover the creature's wings, overlapping like shingles. They give the name to the order to which moths and butterflies belong: the Lepidoptera (Lep'-i-dop'-tera), which means scaly-winged. A lepidopterist is someone who collects and studies these insects.*

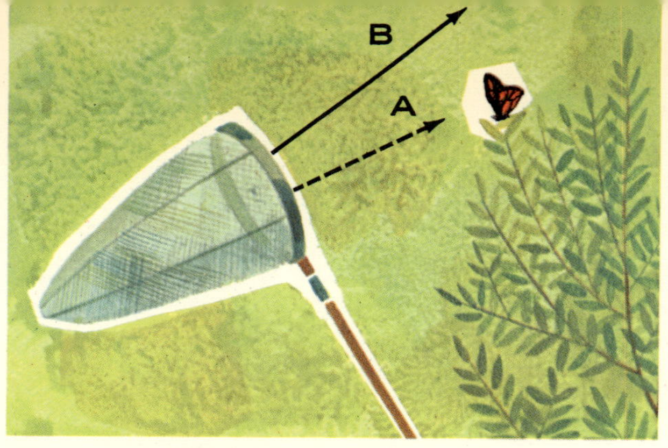

Fig. 2. *In catching a monarch, the net should follow line B instead of A*

the insect before you are within reaching distance. In most cases, when catching a butterfly, you give a quick sidewise swoop and then, with a twist of your wrist, turn the net so the bag folds over the hoop, imprisoning the creature within.

If possible, try to keep from knocking the flowers from the plants in making the swoop. The tallest plants in a field are favorite resting places of the butterflies. And where you catch one, you may catch another, if you leave the plant undamaged.

Part of the fun of butterfly hunting is learning the habits of the insects so you know where to find them, what sort of flowers each prefers and what they will do when startled. When the monarch is surprised, it leaps straight up into the air. Consequently it is best to aim the net just above the flower, as shown in Figure 2. The royal fritillary, on the other hand, drops into the grass when it is frightened. Insects that rest on the ground are caught by clapping the net down over them, rather than by making a side swoop.

At first, you will be out for any game you can catch. But, as your collection grows, you will find yourself hunting particular butterflies to fill in gaps. Here is where knowledge of the different species will aid you most of all. The tiny tailed blue, for example, shows a marked preference for white flowers. Some butterflies, like the grayling, or wood nymph, haunt shady roads and paths through woodlands. Others, like the orange sulphur, or puddle butterfly, disappear as soon as the sun is obscured. They are often found in clusters, basking in the midday heat and sipping moisture from the mud of roadside pools.

Some moths are active during the early hours of the night, others during the later hours. You will find that dark nights with a sultry, almost stormy atmosphere are best. Beautiful nights, when the moon is its brightest, are the least productive for the moth hunter.

"Working the lights" can be fun. By placing a white sheet in front of a lantern or porch lamp, you can get the night fliers to alight upon it. They walk about, charmed by the light, and you can collect them with ease.

Your local library should have reference books that will tell you more about the different butterflies and moths you will meet. As you go along, make it a habit to look up everything you can find about any new specimen you capture. It will make your collection more interesting and suggest things to watch for when you stalk the insects in the open fields.

Organizing Your Collection

From such supply houses as Ward's Natural Science Establishment in Rochester, New York, and the General Biological Supply House in Chicago, Illinois, you can buy mounting pins and ready-made boxes in which to store your specimens. Or a cigar box, with a layer of corrugated cardboard in the bottom, will serve very well. Common pins are not suitable for mounting insects. They bend and rust, and discolor the specimens. Special mounting pins should be used. They come in several sizes, for use with different insects.

When you take your specimens from the killing bottle, you can either mount them on the setting board straightaway, or you can place them in paper triangles (see Figure 3) for

Fig. 3. *How to fold paper triangles for holding insects*

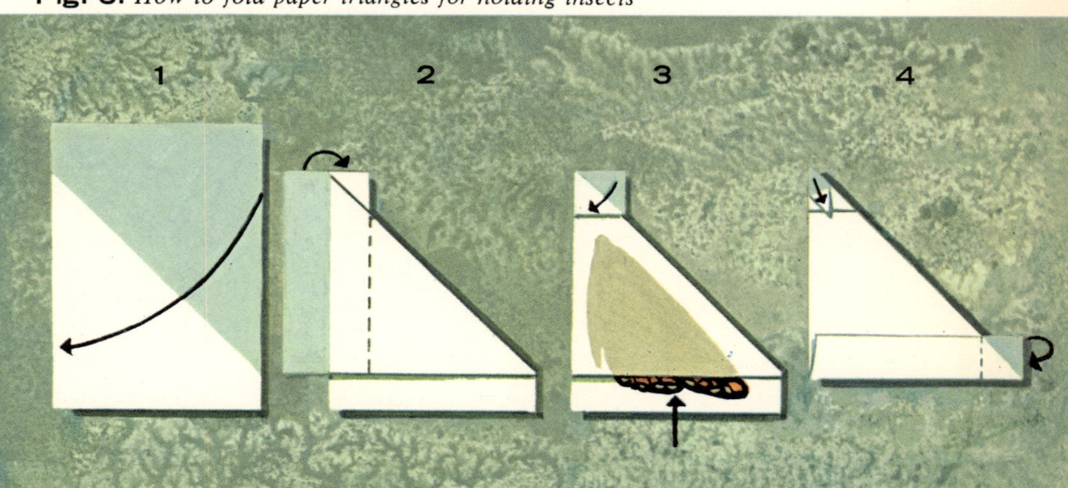

Adapted from The Junior Book of Insects *by Edwin Way Teale, with diagrams by the author. Copyright 1939, 1953 and published by E. P. Dutton & Co., Inc.*

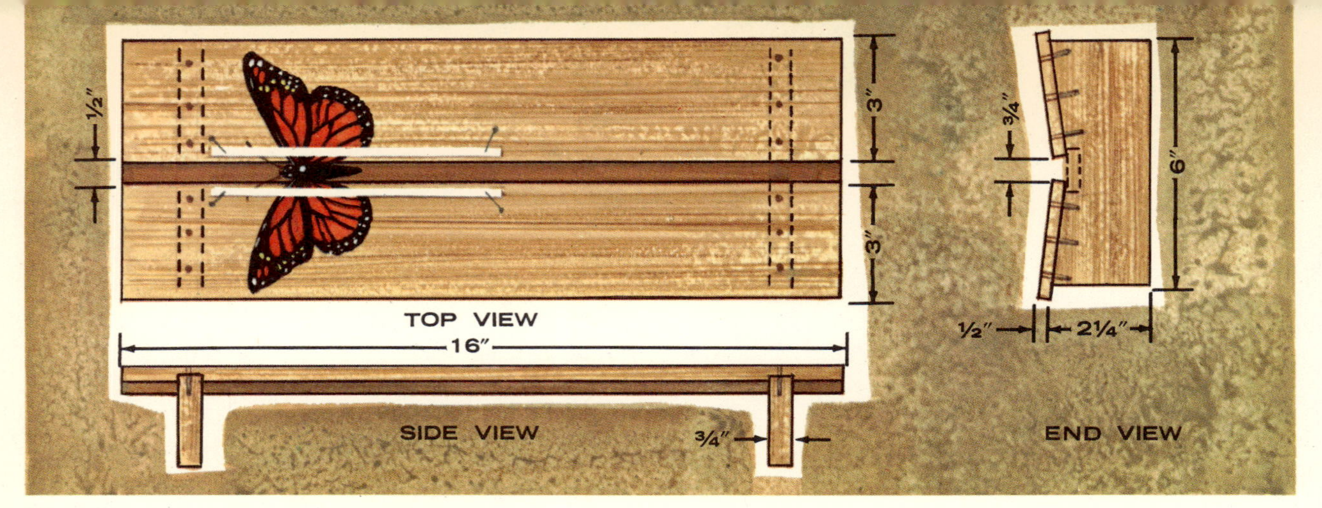

Fig. 4. *Construction of a setting board*

safekeeping until you have time to mount them. The insects can be left in the triangles for weeks without damage, though after some time they become stiff and have to be softened before they can be mounted. This is most easily done by placing them, in their triangles, between clean, slightly damp towels. When the specimens are sufficiently softened, you can move the wings without danger of breaking them. They are then ready for the setting board, where they are held in the desired position until they have dried again.

Figure 4 shows how the setting board is constructed. Use soft wood such as white pine. (Boards from packing cases are suitable.) If you make the center slit wider at one end than at the other, you can place the larger-bodied insects at that end. Place the body of the butterfly or moth in the slit and then adjust the wings until they are in their best position, pinning narrow strips of paper or muslin in place to keep them from moving until they are dry. A needle will help you with the delicate work of adjusting the wings without rubbing away the scales.

The insects have to remain on the setting board for several days until they are thoroughly dry. (They will dry more quickly if you have already stored them in paper.) Keep them in a protected place where mice and other pests can't get at them. When they are permanently dried in the desired position, the insects can be pinned in place in the boxes for storage and display.

Pin your specimens in the boxes in rows and columns, placing a male and a female together, and putting insects of the same species in the same box. You should pin them through the middle of the thorax, as shown on the facing page.

Usually the labels in display boxes are pinned on the left or above the specimen. To give a neat appearance to your collection, have all specimens and cards the same height above the bottom. On your labels give the common and scientific names of your specimen, the place where it was caught, the date, and, when possible, what it was doing when captured. If it was eating, what was it eating? Such information is really valuable and makes your collection far more than merely a cemetery for dead insects. Of course, you can't identify all the creatures you catch immediately. Doing that is part of the winter fun, when living insects are few and far between. Always, when you are not sure of your identification, place a small question mark on the label.

When you are exploring, give each specimen a number in your notebook and put the same number on the paper triangle into which you slip the insect. Then, later, when you have time, you can get insects and facts together and record the information as you mount the specimens.

Some Jewels of the Insect World

The first butterfly you are likely to see in the spring is the mourning cloak. It is one of the few insects that hibernate through the winter. It sleeps in hollow trees or crannies and comes out to flit about open glades in February and March when the sun is bright.

Two butterflies you soon will learn to recognize are the monarch, or milkweed butterfly, and its "look alike," the viceroy. Birds shun the monarch because it exudes a nauseating fluid. And since it has almost identical black and orange markings, the viceroy, which has *no* disagreeable taste and which belongs to an entirely different family, fools the birds and also escapes their attack.

Probably the biggest butterfly you'll capture will be the tiger swallowtail. If you live in the South you may encounter the giant swallowtail, which stretches as much as five and a half inches from wing tip to wing tip. The tiniest North American butterflies are the midget metalmarks and blues. Their wingspread is barely half an inch.

(continued on page 128)

BUTTERFLY ART JEWELRY CO. BROOKLYN 12, N. Y.

COMMON WOOD NYMPH
(Minois alope)

TAILED BLUE
(Everes comyntas)

REGAL FRITILLARY
(Speyeria idalia)

LUNA MOTH
(Actias luna)

MONARCH
(Danaus plexippus)

TIGER SWALLOWTAIL
(Papilio glaucus turnus)

VICEROY
(Limenitis archippus)

CECROPIA MOTH
(Hyalophora cecropia)

GIANT SWALLOWTAIL
(Papilio cresphontes)

PROMETHEA MOTH
(Callosamia promethea)
Female

PROMETHEA MOTH
(Callosamia promethea)
Male

POLYPHEMUS MOTH
(Antheraea polyphemus)

MOURNING CLOAK
(Nymphalis antiopa)

IO MOTH
(Automeris io)

EURYTHEME SULPHUR
(Colias eurytheme)

The biggest and most striking of the 8,800 species of moths are the giant silkworm moths: the cecropia, io, promethea, polyphemus and luna. Their velvety wings sometimes have a span of nearly half a foot. The io is decorated with great round eye spots and has brilliant red-and-yellow wings. The pale-green luna has two flowing tails. But the polyphemus, with its delicate shadings of brown and pearl, blue and yellow, is the prize of any collection.

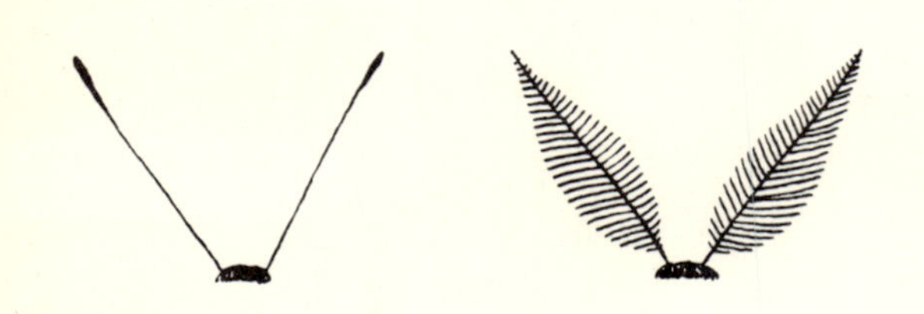

Moth or Butterfly? *Sometimes you may find it hard to distinguish butterflies from moths. In general, the following rules hold true: moths have feathery antennae (right); butterflies, smooth and knobbed antennae (left). When at rest, moths hold their wings out horizontally; butterflies hold their wings vertically above their bodies. Moths have thicker and more wedge-shaped bodies than butterflies.*

Solution to Circus Crossword

(see page 13)

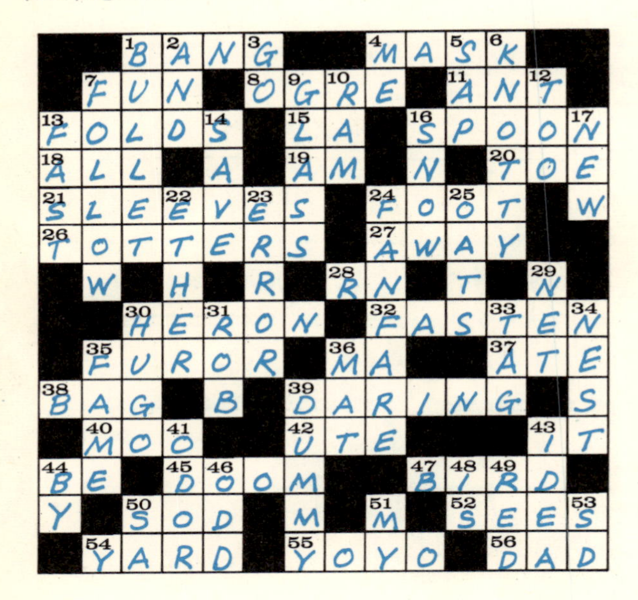

Answers to Can You Name These Birds?

(see page 31)

1. CARDINAL: *Only all-red bird with a crest.* Smaller than a robin. The male is all red except for a black patch at base of bill. The female, yellowish brown with a touch of red, is at once recognizable by its *crest and heavy red bill.*

2. CHIPPING SPARROW: A very small gray-breasted sparrow with a bright *rufous* (*or reddish*) *cap. Black line* through eye with *white line* over it. Immature birds in winter are buffier, with a striped crown and *gray rump.*

3. TREE SPARROW: Bright *red-brown cap.* A single *round black spot,* or "stickpin," in the middle of its breast. Also has two white bars on each wing.

4. REDHEADED WOODPECKER: Only eastern woodpecker with *entire head red.* In flight shows large square *white patches* on the rear edge of the wing. Immature bird is *dusky-headed.*

5. COMMON GOLDFINCH: A small bird. Male in summer is the *only small yellow bird with black wings.* Female in summer is dull olive-yellow with blackish wings and white wing bars. In winter, both look like the summer female.

6. BLUE JAY: A large bird, larger than a robin. Bright blue above, whitish below, and *crested.*

7. BLACK-CAPPED CHICKADEE: The only small birds with the combination of *black cap, black bib* and *white cheeks.* Smaller than sparrows.

8. MOURNING DOVE: A small *brown* pigeon. Its tail is *pointed,* rather than fan-shaped, and shows large white spots when the bird flies. Has a black spot behind the eye. Its wings make a whistling sound when it is in flight.

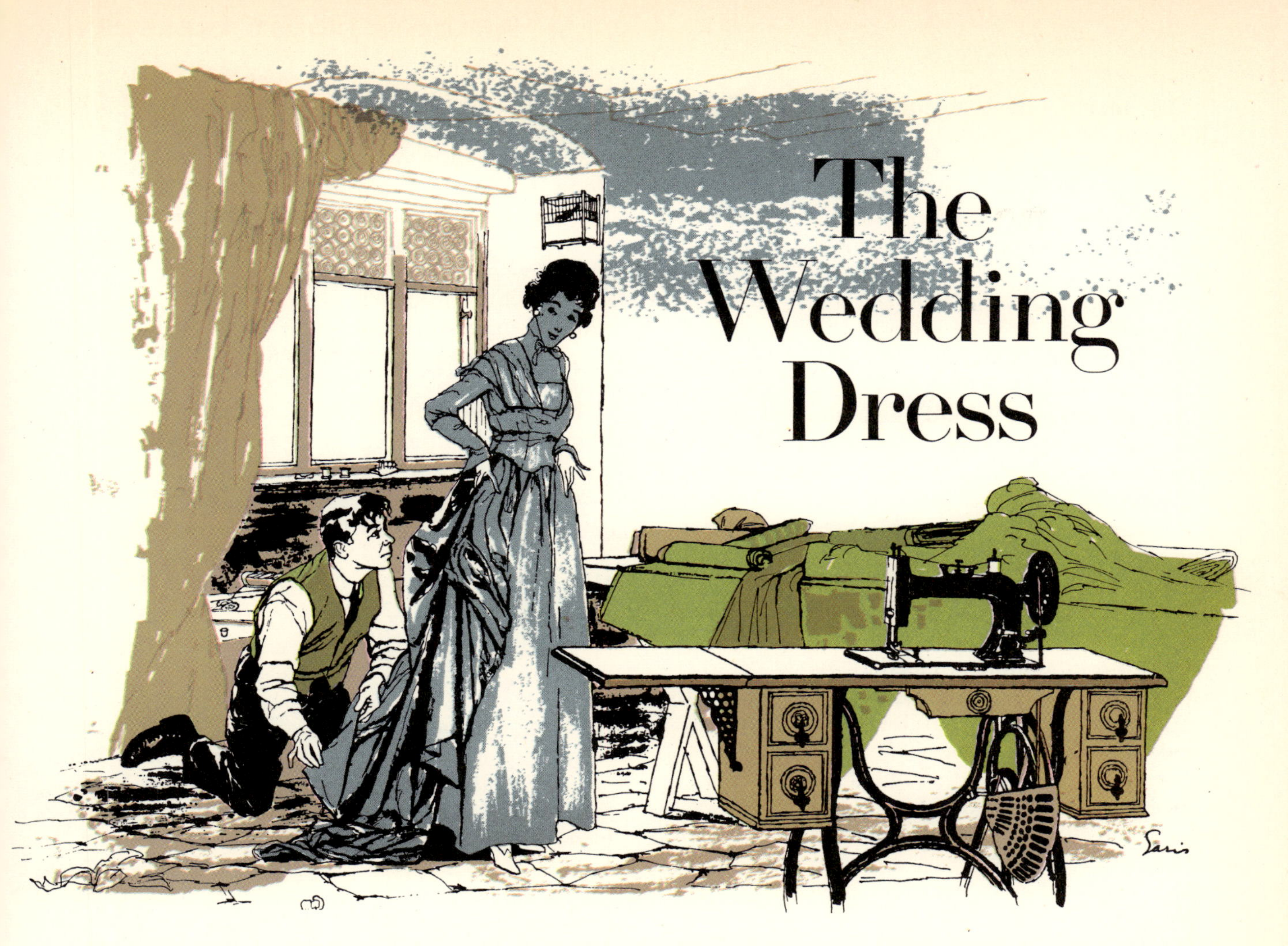

The Wedding Dress

The true story of a proud young beauty and the hidden message that changed her life

BY I. A. R. WYLIE

This story starts some years ago in a small hill town in southern Italy.

One of the gayest youngsters in the whole town was Lucia Gazzoni — a dark-haired, dark-eyed beauty of great charm. Lucia had many admirers, and she liked to keep them guessing. For a few days she would choose one young man as her favorite, and then she would change to another. Though she made them sad, they never got angry with her. And none of her suitors ever ceased to adore her.

If for some reason a man paid no attention to her, Lucia felt challenged. So she couldn't help trying to add Giuseppe Silva to her list of admirers. Giuseppe seemed not to notice her charms.

Giuseppe wasn't romantic-looking. He was rather short, and he had heavy shoulders. His face was plain except for his bright, kindly eyes. But many girls in the town wanted to marry him. For he was the only tailor in that region, and he was quite rich. He was a clever dress designer, who could do anything with a pair of scissors, a needle and a piece of material. The town boasted that you could go as far as the city of Naples and do no better.

An Evening at the Fair

Every spring the fair came to set up its booths in the town square. The day before it opened Lucia went to Giuseppe's little shop. She bought some thread. Then she lingered, as if she were shy.

"Why do you stay in this little place, signor?" she asked. "Everyone says that you are so clever. You could go to Naples and make a lot of money. . . ."

"The money I have, signorina, is enough," said Giuseppe.

"You have no ambition," Lucia said scornfully.

"It is foolish to be ambitious for things one does not really want — or for things one cannot have."

"What *do* you want?" she asked.

He went on stitching silently.

Suddenly she asked gaily, "Would you like to take me to the fair?"

Any other man would have jumped at the offer, but Giuseppe took his time. "I should be very pleased, signorina," he replied. And she had to be content with that cool answer.

At least Giuseppe had one thing all the other men lacked. He had money, and he spent it freely. Lucia dragged him into the booths, where he bought her sweet cakes and cheap trinkets to her heart's content. But he let her ride on the merry-go-round alone, and he waited for her patiently on the edge of the crowd.

So Lucia met Roberto Bellini. He rode the wooden horse next to hers. When she pretended to be afraid, he laughed and held her steady with a strong hand. She had heard about him. He had relatives in the town, whom he had come to visit at fair-time. Roberto was a steady, successful young wine salesman who had traveled all over Europe.

Giuseppe's Gift

Did it seem to Lucia's restless heart that Roberto was a way of escape from her drab little world? At any rate, she was delighted when he called at her home the next day. Lucia and her parents understood why he had come. A young man did not make a formal call like that unless he had a serious purpose.

Within a few weeks, Roberto was back with a proposal of marriage. He was going to America to sell wine, and he wanted to take Lucia with him.

There was no doubt of the answer. Lucia's parents might be sad at her going so far from them, but America was the golden land of an Italian peasant's dream. They were glad for her good fortune.

The news spread quickly. When Giuseppe heard it, he called on Lucia's parents and asked to be allowed to make her wedding dress. He said that it would be his wedding gift. They were thankful to accept. For they were poor and the dress would have been too expensive for them to buy.

So almost every day Lucia went, with a chaperone, to Giuseppe's little shop. He knelt at her feet, and he fitted and snipped and pinned the lovely silk. It was so rich and heavy that everyone knew Giuseppe must have made a special trip to Naples to find it. When the dress was finished, Lucia smiled happily at herself in the mirror. She hadn't known that she could be so beautiful.

The sun shone brightly the day of her wedding. That night her parents gave a party, and there was dancing in the square. But Giuseppe's house was closed and he had vanished. People said he had been called out of town to visit a sick relative. Lucia was too happy and excited to think of him. The next day she and her husband left for America.

The Tide Turns

At first, marriage was as wonderful as Lucia's dreams of it. Roberto was a good husband and a good businessman. They had a pleasant house in a suburb of New York City. In time they were blessed with two little girls as pretty and bright-eyed as their mother.

For a few years Lucia wrote home often, but then less and less. The little Italian town faded into the mists of her girlhood memories. She thought of Giuseppe Silva just once — when she laid the wedding dress away finally. It was already old-fashioned, but the material was still rich and lovely. Someday, perhaps, she would find a use for it.

Then slowly the tide of their fortunes began to turn. Business was no longer good. Though Roberto worked hard, he lost his job. Then he became seriously ill. Little by little, their savings were eaten up. And finally, one tragic day, Roberto died.

Lucia had no one to turn to. Her friends had troubles of their own. Her parents were dead. Her daughters, aged ten and seven, were too young to help her.

Frightened and sick at heart, she sold their home. She rented rooms in a cheaper neighborhood. She earned a little money by teaching Italian in a New York school, and by giving English lessons to new arrivals from Italy. Sometimes she would lie awake at night and wonder what would become of them all if she were to be taken ill.

There were other problems, too. Little Lucy, the younger girl, was almost ready for her First Communion, the first important event in her life. "What shall I wear, Mother?" she asked. Lucia knew what was at the back of the child's anxious questioning: would she have to be ashamed, as she was so often, of her shabby clothes? But what could Lucia do?

Then she remembered her wedding dress!

There it was — as rich, as lovely as ever. It was amazing to think that she had owned something so beautiful and had almost forgotten it. She began at once to rip it apart and cut it down to fit Lucy. As she undid the deep hem, she found — to her surprise — a neatly folded paper. On it, in faded but strong writing, was a message that had been waiting for her nearly fifteen years: *I shall always love you.*

Lucia sat for a long time, remembering. She saw the dark man with the square shoulders, really, for the first time. She thought of the unspoken love she had never known he felt for her. She cried her heart out with loneliness and grief.

That night she wrote a letter. It was addressed to a man who might now be dead. In any case, he must surely have long since forgotten her. But she felt she must tell him that she had found his message. And she wanted to thank him for a love she had done so little to deserve. Beyond telling him that her husband was dead, she said nothing about her misfortunes.

Weeks passed, and there was no answer. She did not expect one. Little Lucy wore the beautiful dress at her First Communion. She was the proudest, happiest girl of all her class. Watching her go up the church aisle to the altar, Lucia thanked Giuseppe for his goodness.

A Fairy-tale Ending

One day soon after, Lucia came home to find a man waiting in the poorly lit hallway of her apartment house. At first she did not recognize him. His shoulders had grown heavier and a little stooped. The once thick black hair was gray. Then she heard his voice: "It is still true, Lucia."

Though she had not written of her distress, he had known of it in his heart because he loved her. Giuseppe had come all the way to America on the brave chance that she might need him.

This story has a true fairy-tale ending. Giuseppe had done well for himself. He was able to start a tailoring business in the new country that had become hers. He made a good home for Lucia and her little girls. And they lived happily ever after.

What a Whopper!

Mrs. C. Koroscil, of the New York Liars Club, stepped off the curbing into a pool of water, but her feet didn't get wet. Looking down, she saw the water receding swiftly — the tongues of her shoes were lapping it up.

— *Albert Lea (Minn.)* Evening Tribune

Sure Bets

Say to a group of friends: "I bet any of you that if you put a penny under your cap on the table I can take it away without touching the cap."

One of them must then put a penny on the table, and his cap on top of it.

Conceal a penny in your hand and knock mysteriously on the table three times. Then reach under the table, knock three more times, and pull out your hand showing the penny in it. Your friend will pick up the cap to see if his penny is still there. Now is your chance to grab his penny — without touching the cap!

— *Based on a contribution by John Tazewell Jones*

Borrow a dollar bill (any piece of paper the same size will do) and ask a friend to hold it by one end so that the bill is hanging down. Place your thumb and forefinger on either side of the bill — as close as you like, without actually touching it — and try to catch it when your friend lets go. We bet you miss it!

— *Based on a contribution by Daryle Feldmeir in* Minneapolis Tribune

QUIZZLES-THREE

(Answers and explanations on page 199)

COMPLETE THE SQUARE

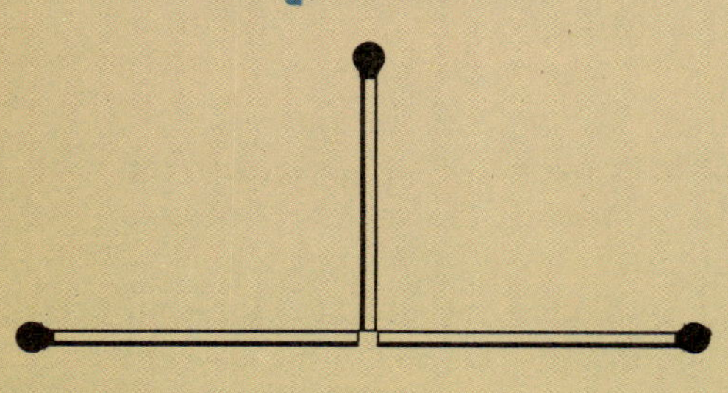

Arrange three matches like this. Now, without moving any of these three, add another match to make a square. But be careful — there's a catch in it.

YOU BE THE DETECTIVE

A detective would refuse to believe these two stories. Can you say why?

1

A man telephones the police with the news that his best friend is dead. He says he found a message written by his friend saying it was suicide. The police ask him where he found it. He replies, "Between pages 101 and 102 of his Bible."

2

A lady, dreaming she was drowning, became so frightened that she died of a heart attack in her sleep.

CAN YOU FIND THE WORD?

You are looking for a word, and you are given just three clues. There is a rhyme for it. There is a meaning for it when spelled backward. Lastly, there is a noun with which it can be joined to make yet another word.

For example, the answer to No. 1 is STAR. It rhymes with SCAR. Backward, it becomes RATS. And it joins with LIGHT to make STARLIGHT. Now try the other five.

IT RHYMES WITH	SPELLED BACKWARD IT MEANS	IT MAKES ANOTHER WORD WITH	THE WORD IS
1. Scar	rodents	light	. . STAR . .
2. Trial	placed flat	sun	. . . .
3. Fans	a fastening	sauce	. . . .
4. Broom	heath	bed	. . . .
5. Pail	untruthful person	road	. . . .
6. Flap	some	mouse	. . . .

"You Be the Detective" is from the radio program Double or Nothing.
"Can You Find the Word?" by Ben L. O'Dell is adapted from The American Magazine.

A CRAZY PICTURE

There are twelve mistakes in this picture. Can you find them?

WHICH HAND?

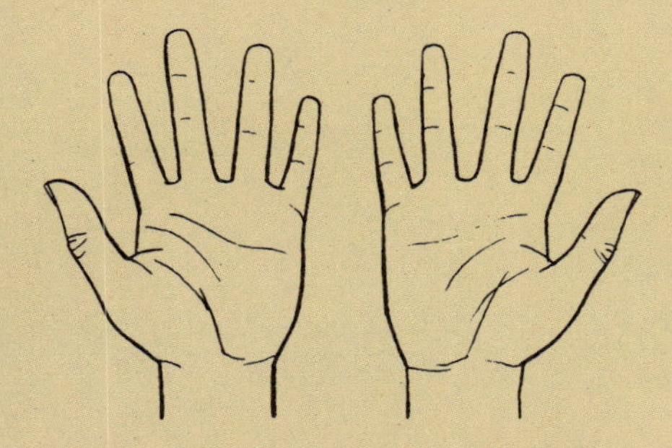

Here is an easy way to baffle a friend with your powers of mind reading. Ask him to think hard about either his right or his left hand, and to hold the hand above his head while your back is turned. After a minute tell him to lower his hand. Then turn around quickly and tell him which hand it was.

LOST, STOLEN OR STRAYED— ONE LETTER

ITERUIEEWOCKFOROLDIER

No, this is not some strange Indian war cry. It is just what happened to an ordinary English sentence when our printer could not find a certain letter of the alphabet. When you discover what the letter is, you will find that there are six words here, but we bet you will find it hard to say them quickly.

Lively Days at Sagamore Hill

To his six children President Theodore Roosevelt was the world's most exciting father

BY HERMANN HAGEDORN

FOURTH of July was always the children's day at Sagamore Hill — the great gabled house on Long Island Sound. All of Theodore Roosevelt's family and their neighbors gathered that day on the wide porch. On the lawn the firecracker brigade kept the sticks of punk lighted. Houseguests arrived by surrey. And in the evening the townspeople drove out to watch the pinwheels, Roman candles and skyrockets blaze in the night sky.

Sometimes there was a picnic or swimming — or an "initiation" for someone new at Sagamore Hill. But always there were gaiety and excitement. For the guiding spirit behind all the fun was Theodore Roosevelt, Colonel of the Rough Riders in the Spanish-American War, and President of the United States.

To his two little girls — Alice and Ethel — and his four boys — Ted, Kermit, Archie and Quentin — there was no one like "Father." The children knew him as a sturdy man with a drooping sandy mustache and eyeglasses. Yet for them he was also King Arthur and Daniel Boone rolled into one. They believed he could row a boat better, shoot a gun straighter, and set off firecrackers louder than anyone else in the world.

"Fight Hard and Fight Well"

Finally, on those Fourth of July evenings, the last rocket would burst in a shower of stars. Then Father would gather the children around him on the lawn. He would tell them stories of his frontier days in the Bad Lands of the Dakota Territory when he was a young man. He told of battling prairie fires with his cowboys, of chasing cattle thieves, of adventures with Indians and grizzly bears. He knew how to tell a story so that the children would feel the sting of smoke in their eyes, and see flames rushing nearer and nearer.

In all his stories Father hammered home the importance of courage and the challenge of life. "If you've got to fight, fight hard and fight well," he would tell the children.

He would also say to them, "There are two things I want you to make up your minds to. First, that you are going to have a good time as long as you live — I have no use for a sour-faced man — and next, that you are going to do something worthwhile. You are going to work hard and accomplish what you set out to do."

Father also had strong views on safety, especially the safe handling of firecrackers. He taught each child how to look after himself. But he never preached "safety first." Once he wrote to his sister: "We have found a large hollow tree, the hollow starting from an opening twenty feet up.

Adapted from The Roosevelt Family of Sagamore Hill, *copyright 1954 by Hermann Hagedorn and published by The Macmillan Co., with editorial additions*

The other day, with much labor, I got up the tree and let each child down in turn with a rope."

New guests at Sagamore Hill were usually initiated by a dizzy slide down Cooper's Bluff. This sandy bluff sloped sharply two hundred feet to the beach.

"There is a little path down," Father would say to visiting cousins. "But I jump off."

And so he did — with the others sliding, rolling and tumbling to the beach behind him.

The Joys of the Outdoors

Theodore Roosevelt loved the outdoor life, and he shared with his children its wonders and its joys. Birds became more than just birds to them. They were indigo buntings or thistle finches, Baltimore orioles that nested in the elms around the house, or orchard orioles in the apple trees near the garden. The children learned to see beauty in the shy mayflower and the trailing arbutus, in laurel bushes and locust trees, and in sunsets flam-

(continued on page 136)

ing over the bay. They had many kinds of pets, from dogs and ponies to guinea pigs and rabbits. And Father taught all the children to swim by dropping them off the dock into deep water.

For the boys, camping out was a yearly adventure. Father had just two rules a boy must obey if he wanted to come along. He must be able to dress himself. And he must not complain about minor hardships like mosquitoes and downpours of rain. Father always tried to pick a day that promised a clear night. But once he was fooled and the campers got an all-night drenching.

As many as eleven boys might go on the trip. Four or five boats would be moored at the water's edge. Into these the campers stowed their food, blankets, axes, frying pans, knives, forks and a kettle. Father would stand nearby, giving orders. You would never have guessed that the man in the slouch hat, flannel shirt and old trousers was the President of the United States.

It was usually a five- or six-mile row to the point that had been chosen for the camp. When they got there, they would unload their supplies and start a fire. Then the boys would plunge into the water while the President himself would cook supper. The sun would be setting before the meal was spread. And Father's fried chicken or beefsteak would taste wonderfully good!

After supper the campers would pile fresh wood on the fire. Sparks leaped into the deepening darkness, and the mystery of the night closed round about them. Then the President would thrill them with his best stories of hunting big game or desperate men, of cattle herding in the West, or the charges of the Rough Riders through Cuba. He never cared if the younger boys stayed up long past their usual bedtime. But at last they all would roll up in their blankets under the stars to sleep — and to dream.

Father's Wild Games

One year Father thought up a new initiation. This was an obstacle course between the house and the beach. You had to go over or through every obstacle, never around it. Once the President's sister saw "an especially unpleasant-looking little bathing house with a very steep roof" on the line of march. She prayed that the leader might choose not to go over it. But she had no such luck. Long afterward she said that she could still see the President of the United States hurling his sturdy body at the obstacle, chinning himself to the top and sliding down the other side. She herself managed to scramble up the roof with the aid of a rusty nail. As she came down the other side, she was greeted with such cheers as she had never heard before.

This wild sport was not as dangerous as it may sound, however. Father had certain rules that he strictly enforced. If you slipped in climbing a tree because you had not used both hands, for instance, you had to go home.

Father also invented a new swimming game called "Stagecoach." Each child on the dock was given the name of a part of the stagecoach — the whip, the old lady passenger, and so on. Then Father would make up a story about the stagecoach. Whenever he mentioned a part for which a child was named, that child had to jump into the water. When finally Father said, "Stagecoach!" everybody left on the dock went overboard together. And the water foamed with all the kicking legs! Father was the last in. For he always took a moment to count the number of heads that came up — and make sure it was the same as the number of children who had gone down.

Sometimes the President landed in the doghouse. One day the family went on a day-long picnic. After lunch Father left Mrs. Roosevelt sewing in the shade while he took the children for a walk. The day was warm, and Father let the children go wading. Soon, of course, they were all swimming in their clothes.

Mrs. Roosevelt was not a bit pleased when she saw the children. She said they would have to take some medicine to keep them from catching colds. When she went to get it, the children flocked around Father, begging him to stop her.

"Children," he said, "I don't dare to. I shall be very fortunate if I don't get some too."

One Fourth of July the President had to make a speech in Pittsburgh. So he did not arrive at Oyster Bay until the next day. The children drove a covered carriage to the station to meet him. Rain had been falling lightly all morning. And it was raining hard by the time the train arrived.

The President was urged to get into the covered carriage with the children, but he refused. He got into an open carriage instead. And little Ethel, Archie and Kermit scrambled in beside him. Just as he put a raincoat over them there was a deafening crash of thunder. It set the spirited horse rearing and plunging. Several men sprang to the horse's head.

"Give him room, please," said the President.

The horse dashed off at a gallop. Away they went — down the muddy Cove Neck Road, up

The Roosevelt family in 1903. Left to right, standing, Ethel, Theodore, Jr., Alice and Kermit; seated, Father, Archie, Mrs. Roosevelt and Quentin

the steep and winding roadway to Sagamore Hill.

Once again Mrs. Roosevelt was waiting for a dripping-wet family. As they trailed in, filling the house with their shouts, she was heard to say: "I really have *five* boys!"

One summer there were special fireworks over the bay. Twenty-one saluting bombs were set off first. Then came beautiful skyrockets sent to the President from China and Japan — and balloons that trailed red, white and blue stars across the sky. Through it all could be heard the President's happy laugh. Later he was to say to Mrs. Roosevelt: "I wonder if you will ever know how I love Sagamore Hill."

Today the Audubon Society has a bird sanctuary near Sagamore Hill. It is named for Theodore Roosevelt. If you are ever driving with your family near Oyster Bay on Long Island, you can wander through this sanctuary. You can also visit the Trailside Museum where many of the wild flowers of the region and other nature exhibits are shown. These are open from May to November. Nearby is Young's Memorial Cemetery where President Roosevelt is buried.

The house where Father lived with his lively family is open to the public all year round, and is furnished just as it used to be. You will see a buffalo head that Father brought from near Little Cannonball Creek in the Dakota Territory, and the antlers of deer and elk from the Bad Lands and the Big Horn Mountains. From the porch you can look out on Long Island Sound. Perhaps, in your mind's eye, you will see the skyrockets bursting over the water on some long-ago Fourth of July — or hear, with your mind's ear, the exciting stories that Father told in the summer darkness.

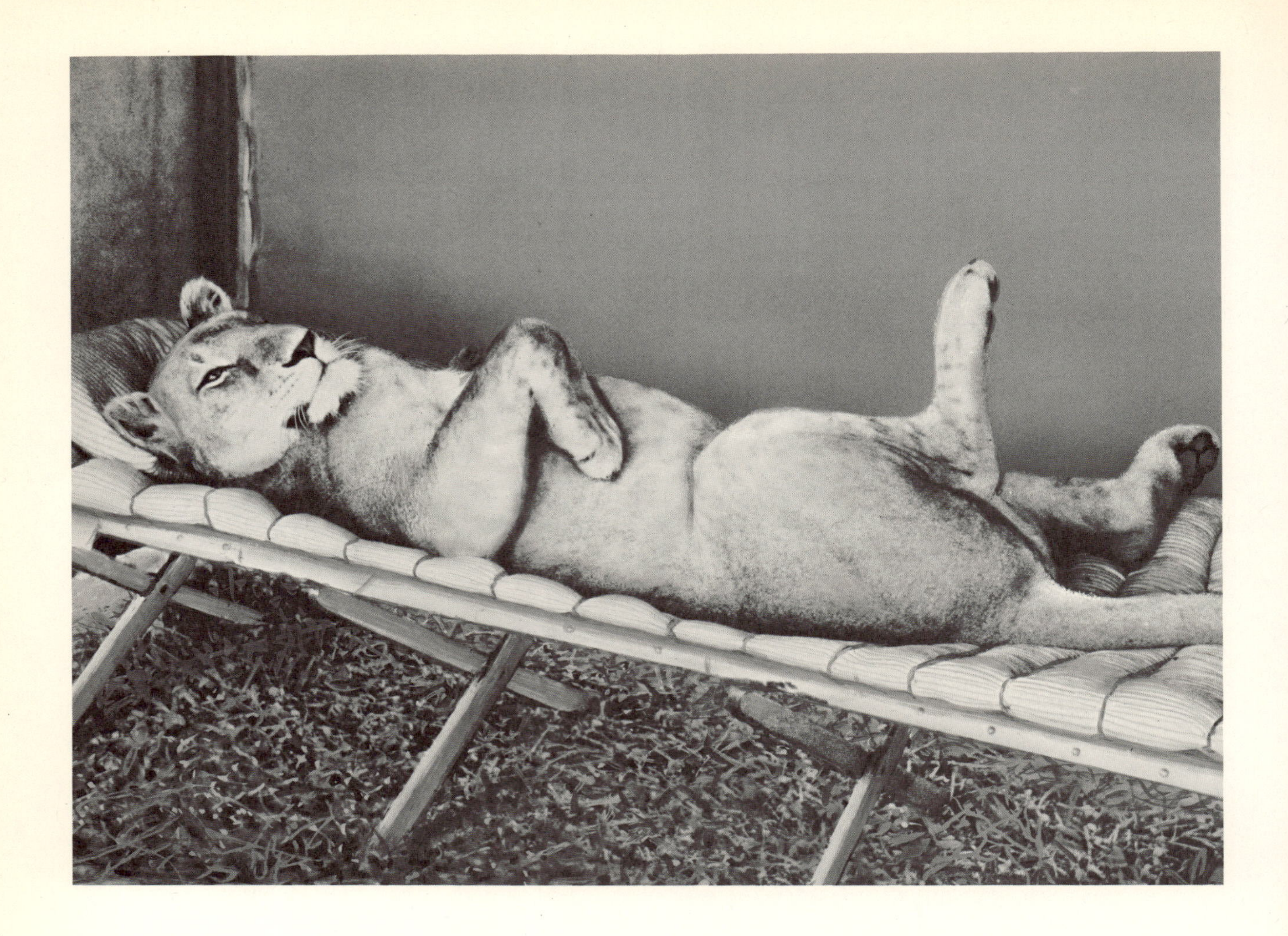

Elsa the Lioness

BY JOY ADAMSON

The true story, told in words and pictures, of a weakling cub who grew up in a human household—and what happened when her "family" decided to return her to a life in the wild

ELSA'S story began one day when my husband, George, and I were out on safari. George (who is senior game warden in the Northern Frontier Province of Kenya, East Africa) had gone off into the bush, where he was suddenly attacked by a wild lioness. He had to kill her. And, while he was looking at the beautiful creature, he realized why she had been so angry — she was defending her cubs.

George and Nuru, our African garden boy, searched until they found three tiny lionesses, not more than a few days old, hidden down a hole in a rock. They brought the babies back to me, and we took them home.

Adapted from Born Free, *copyright © 1960, and* Elsa, *© 1961, by Joy Adamson and published by Pantheon Books Inc.*

A *wonderful game*

Pati-Pati watching "her" cubs

Our rock hyrax, Pati-Pati, who had been with us as a faithful friend for six years, immediately took on the role of nurse. This little animal, who looks like a woodchuck or a large guinea pig but is more closely related to rhinos and elephants, watched over the cubs with great care. Even when they went exploring in search of adventure she kept an eye on them.

For the first two days the cubs only wrinkled their noses at the canned milk I offered them. Once they had accepted it, however, they couldn't get enough of it. And they drank from regular baby bottles with nipples.

The weakling of the three was the pluckiest in spirit, and she became our favorite. We called her Elsa because she reminded me of a friend of that name.

When the cubs' eyes were fully opened we gave them rubber balls and inner tubes to play with. They would try to take an inner tube from one another, pulling with all their might in a tug-of-war. Then, when the battle had been won, the victor would parade the trophy in front of the others.

But their favorite toy was a sack filled with old rubber tubes which we tied to a tree branch so that it dangled invitingly. They loved hanging onto it, while we pulled and they swung high in the air. The more we laughed the better they enjoyed the game.

The cubs go exploring

Elsa asleep with her rubber ball

Elsa dragging tarpaulin

Up she comes!

They stalked one another — and us — from the earliest age, and they knew by instinct how to do it properly. As they grew older, they tested their strength on everything they could find. A tarpaulin, however large, *had* to be dragged about — just as in later life they would drag a kill. The cubs were also great climbers and liked to get up in the branches of trees.

When they were about five months old, we realized that we couldn't possibly keep three fast-growing lions in the house. So we regretfully decided that the two bigger ones should be sent to the zoo in Rotterdam, Holland, and that we would keep Elsa.

When her sisters left, Elsa was very upset. She followed us around constantly as if she were afraid we too would desert her. She even slept in our bed at night. And we were often wakened by her rough tongue licking our faces.

Elsa rubs noses with the author

Comfort in the treetops

Soon, however, she began to meet other wild animals. She was quite fearless and would chase a whole herd of elephants. Giraffes were also great fun. Wriggling her body close to the ground and shivering with excitement, she stalked them, advancing step by step. The giraffes arched their slender necks and took no notice of her. She would look at them as if to say, "Why do you just stand there and spoil my stalking?" But one day, when she thought *we* had spoiled her stalking by standing up and watching, she got so cross she rushed back and knocked us to the ground!

By now Elsa's food was mainly raw meat. She liked to lick out the marrow from the bones while I held them for her. After her supper she would often stretch out on a camp bed for a little nap.

When she was nearly two years old, her voice began to grow much deeper. Often she went away for two or three days, and we knew that sometimes she joined up with other lions. But always she returned to us for food and water — and because we were still her "pride" (as a family of lions is called) and our home was hers.

We had always known, of course, that we could not keep Elsa forever. Now we began to wonder if we could release her back to the wild instead of sending her to join her sisters in Rotterdam. It would be an experiment worth trying. We thought we would take her to a place where there was plenty of game, spend two or three weeks with her, and then — if all went well — leave her.

Giraffes were great fun!

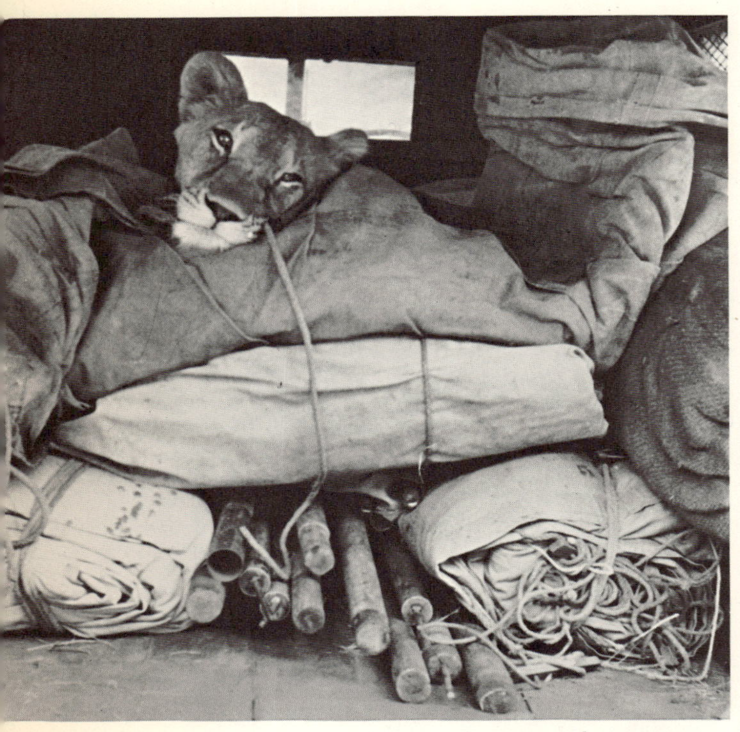

A contented passenger —

— and a surprising perch

Dreaming by the river

Elsa traveled in the back of my truck, and after our arrival we took off her collar to show her she was free.

She hopped right onto the roof of the Land-Rover, and we set out to explore the territory.

One day we came upon a handsome young lion just finishing the carcass of a zebra. The perfect husband for Elsa, we thought. Though he looked surprised to see a lioness on top of a car, he had had his fill of meat and did not mind sharing his kill with her. Elsa jumped greedily from the Land-Rover and onto the carcass. Then we did a sneaky thing. We drove away as fast as we could, leaving her with the lion.

Early next morning we went back, hoping to find a happy pair. But poor Elsa was waiting alone. She was so overjoyed to see us she sucked my thumbs frantically and held me close.

Quite obviously, we could not leave Elsa yet. But after a while we chose a new home for her — a beautiful place with a river running through it where many wild animals came to drink.

Nuru helps Elsa with a kill

Although we had taught Elsa to retrieve game for us, we had always given her her own meat cut up. We were not sure she could cope with a dead animal, as she would have to do if she were to be left alone. To our surprise and delight we discovered that she knew by instinct exactly what part of an animal was eatable and what should be buried. But she had no idea how to kill.

We stayed by the river for several months while Elsa learned the things her own mother would have taught her. At first we did most of the killing for her. But she always helped and soon learned to kill on her own.

After that we watched for a chance to leave her. Then one afternoon she refused to go for a walk with us and disappeared until the morning. We realized she had made friends with a wild lion and that the time had now come.

After this we paid short, frequent visits to see how she was getting along. She was always glad to see us, and her welcoming rubbings and *meaows* touched us deeply. But it was quite clear that she could manage without us.

A joyful sight

Although we missed Elsa, we had always hoped that she would find a mate and that one day she would walk into our camp followed by a family. So you can imagine our great joy when, a few months later, she swam across the river to us with three fine cubs.

Elsa continued to live in the wild, but she brought her cubs often to visit us. They learned to play many of the games she herself had played as a cub. But in January of 1961 Elsa fell ill and died quietly at our camp. After her death, the cubs began to attack the natives' herds of goats and cattle. Rather than shoot Elsa's family, we trapped them in large crates and moved them through eight hundred miles of bush to Serengeti National Park in Tanganyika. There they were set free.

"You're on *Candid Camera!*"

A peek behind the scenes of Allen Funt's popular television show

BY JOHN REDDY

NOT long ago a plump woman with a large bundle under her arm entered a cleaning shop in New York. She found the place deserted. But a loudspeaker near the door said: "Welcome to the Empire Cleaners and our new electronic system. If you have cleaning and/or laundry, please follow these simple instructions."

The woman looked around, startled.

"Take all the dry cleaning and put it in the blue bag you see in front of you," the speaker continued.

The woman seemed puzzled but did as she was told.

"Put shirts with starch in the yellow bag. Shirts with no starch go in the gray bag. Underclothing goes in the green bag and sheets and pillowcases go in the red bag."

The woman scrambled about, wildly trying to do everything right.

"So that there will be no mistake, we will repeat," said the loudspeaker. "Put shirts with starch in the *red* bag, shirts with no starch in the *green* bag, underclothing in the *yellow* bag and sheets and pillowcases in the *gray* bag."

The woman frantically juggled laundry from bag to bag trying to keep up with the garbled instructions. Finally she gave up. Crossly she gathered up her scattered clothing and started for the door.

At this point a stocky man with gray hair burst out of the back room. "I'm Allen Funt," he called, "and you're on 'Candid Camera'!"

This sort of diabolical joke has been making millions of Americans laugh for more than fifteen years, first on radio and then television. The stunts — and the funny ways people react to them — have made "Candid Camera" one of the most popular TV programs. Funt wanders all over the world taking pictures for his show.

He has put REST ROOM signs on closet doors, left a million dollars in cash on a store counter, and demanded a parking ticket from a cop. Once, at a lunch counter, he objected to the man next to him ordering onion on his hamburger. He said the smell of onion made him ill. When the man was nice enough to get his hamburger plain, Funt ordered a hamburger with onion himself. The man looked amazed, and Funt explained that it was only onion on other people's hamburgers that made him sick.

Another time, in a diner, Funt sat down next to a man who was drinking a cup of coffee. Funt ordered a doughnut. "Pardon me," he said to the man, "but do you use sugar?"

The man said that he did. "Good," said Funt, dunking his doughnut in the man's coffee.

"Why don't you order your own coffee?" the surprised man demanded.

"My doctor won't allow me to drink coffee," Funt explained. "But I love to dunk."

The man shoved his coffee in front of Funt and ordered a new cup. No sooner was a fresh cup of coffee set in front of the man than Funt reached over and dunked in it.

"Why don't you dunk in the coffee I gave you?" the man demanded.

"It's cold," complained Funt. He then turned to a helper sitting on the other side of the fuming man. "Have you tried this?" he asked, dunking again in the man's coffee. "It's delicious."

The helper then also dipped his doughnut in the man's coffee. "It needs more sugar," he suggested.

"If you dunk once more," the man told Funt, "it will be the last dunk you ever dunk!"

Funt says the secret of his getting away with the things he does is doing them with authority. Whenever anyone questions Funt and his crew lugging their equipment into some location, he barks, "Exterminators." And he keeps right on going. Funt believes that most people are so good-natured that they will put up with almost anything rather than cause trouble.

He may be right. Once during a rainstorm Tom O'Malley, one of Funt's helpers, waited until a well-dressed young woman came out of a hotel with an umbrella.

"Do you mind if I share your umbrella?" O'Malley asked, seizing it and crowding in under it with the woman. She looked startled but smiled agreeably as he fell in step beside her.

A few steps down the street another "Candid

Adapted from Television Age, *© 1962 by Television Editorial Corp.*

Camera" man sidled up to them. "Excuse me, mister," he said to O'Malley, "but may I share your umbrella?"

"Certainly," replied O'Malley. The two men then both grasped the umbrella handle, crowding the woman farther out in the rain. She, too, clung grimly to the umbrella. A few steps farther on the trio came to a corner.

"I'm turning left here," the woman told the men politely.

"Gosh, I'm going right," said O'Malley.

"I'm going right, too," his companion said. "I guess it's majority rule." With that the two men turned right, dragging the lady behind them like the tail on a kite.

Funt's career developed from an idea that he had in the Army in World War II. At one base he was assigned to help soldiers record spoken messages to their families. He discovered that GIs were more interesting and colorful when they didn't know they were being recorded. When he got out of the Army he hid microphones in public places, hoping to record interesting off-guard conversations for a radio program.

One day he was hiding a tiny microphone in a dentist's office when a patient entered. Assuming he was the dentist, she began to tell Funt about an aching wisdom tooth. He decided to pretend he was the dentist. Asking her to open wide, he looked at her teeth carefully. "I can't find your wisdom teeth," he finally announced.

The woman flounced out of the office in a huff, but Funt had his first funny interview. Today the "Candid Camera" show has fancy offices, with thirty-five employes. It also has two camera crews roving the country. Funt's round, pleasant face is so well known that it gets harder all the time for him not to be recognized.

One thing he has discovered is that people are generally kindly and helpful. "When people want to describe someone stingy they say, 'He wouldn't give you the time of day,' " Funt says. "I've stopped hundreds of people on the street and asked them the time and have never been refused once. Then I've asked them for two nickels for a dime and for a cigarette and a match. Finally I've asked the way to city hall and then for paper and pen to write it down. In most cases they held my armload of packages so I could write. Some even let me use their backs to brace the paper against while I was writing.

"But there have been times," Funt confesses, "when people came within an inch of hitting me in the nose."

Over a parrot cage in a hardware store Funt put a sign saying: DON'T TALK TO THE PARROT ABOUT HARDWARE. Hidden in the cage were a small microphone and speaker, so that a concealed helper could both listen and talk back. This man disobeyed the sign and spoke to the parrot — in Spanish. The helper answered in Spanish, and the amazed man thought he was talking to a Spanish-speaking parrot!

DON'T PEEK IN HERE says this sign on a boarded-up window. In the sign were tiny holes. When these men got so curious they peeked through the holes, they saw someone looking back at them!

This man sat down in a roadside diner and got a spoon that dissolved in his coffee! It had been planted by Funt, of course.

COURTESY OF "CANDID CAMERA" CBS-TV

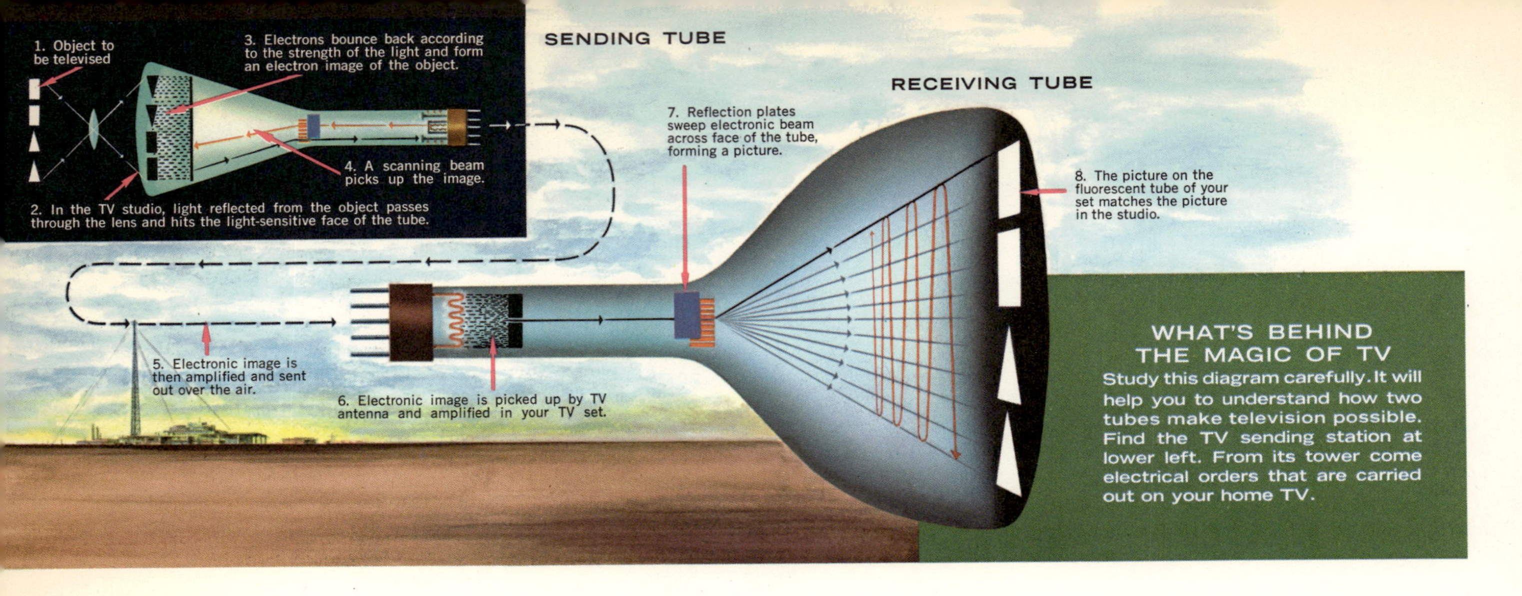
1. Object to be televised
3. Electrons bounce back according to the strength of the light and form an electron image of the object.
SENDING TUBE
RECEIVING TUBE
7. Reflection plates sweep electronic beam across face of the tube, forming a picture.
4. A scanning beam picks up the image.
8. The picture on the fluorescent tube of your set matches the picture in the studio.
2. In the TV studio, light reflected from the object passes through the lens and hits the light-sensitive face of the tube.
5. Electronic image is then amplified and sent out over the air.
6. Electronic image is picked up by TV antenna and amplified in your TV set.
WHAT'S BEHIND THE MAGIC OF TV
Study this diagram carefully. It will help you to understand how two tubes make television possible. Find the TV sending station at lower left. From its tower come electrical orders that are carried out on your home TV.

How Television Works

What goes on behind the screen?

ANYONE can transmit a picture through space. All you need is a pencil, a sheet of square-ruled graph paper, a telephone and a friend with the same equipment. Draw a sampler-type picture by filling in some squares on your paper. Then telephone your friend and report, line by line, which squares are blank and which filled in. By shading the squares you tell him to, your friend will duplicate the picture.

That's all television does. But it does it with a high-speed stream of electrical orders, called signals or pulses. So fast are these signals that if your graph-paper drawing had been televised instead of telephoned, every dark and light square in it would have been reported thirty times in a single second.

Within the television system are two tubes. In the camera tube the picture is taken apart and converted to bits of electrical information. In the picture tube those bits are put together again and become a picture on your TV screen. Just how this happens is not as mysterious as most people think.

The television camera acts like your own eye. Its lens "sees" the picture and focuses it on the "retina" — a miniature screen at the front end of the camera tube. This screen is coated with thousands of particles, or "dots," of material that is sensitive to light. Each dot reacts to the light that hits it by producing a tiny electrical charge — the more light the greater the charge. So, the picture projected on the little camera-tube screen is not just a visible image; it is also a mass of tiny electrical charges, varying according to the light and shadow in the picture. It is an electrical chart of the picture.

From the back of the tube, a pinpoint-thin beam of electrons is shot out by an electron gun. Directed by electromagnets (which can tug a stream of electrons this way or that), the beam scans the picture in a rapid series of lines, from left to right and from top to bottom — just the way your eye scans the page of a book. But the rate of scanning is phenomenal. In 1/60 second it makes a trip of 262½ lines down the picture, then repeats it in another 1/60 second. On the second trip it covers the spaces between the first lines. This "interlacing" minimizes coarse visible lines on the receiving end.

As the scanning beam crosses each dot, it transfers the dot's charge, strong or weak according to how much light the dot received, to a conductive "signal plate" behind the screen, where the electrical image is duplicated. As each charge is transferred, it is carried away in a stream of electrical pulses — each one a lightness or darkness message — to be amplified and broadcast from the transmitter tower at a rate of 5,700,000 messages each second!

In the receiving set in your home, all those electrical signals are converted back into visible light and shadow on the screen of the big picture tube. This screen is coated with a fluorescent material in the same arrangement of dots as those on the camera-tube screen. The electron gun in the back of the tube is triggered by a special broadcast signal which keeps it going in perfect time with its twin in the camera. Known as the "flying spot," the beam darts back and forth across the picture screen, exciting each fluorescent dot with its varying electrical charge, so that the dot glows with the same amount of light that its mate on the camera screen received.

In effect, the electron beam in the picture tube "paints" the picture in a sweeping series of brush strokes that add up to 525 lines across the screen. It does this thirty times every second. Because of the flying spot's fantastic speed, and the human eye's ability to hold an image through a flickering series of pictures, television — like movies — gives you the illusion that you are watching uninterrupted motion.

Adapted from an article by Harland Manchester

Pilot of the Alpine Peaks

The story of a shepherd boy whose dreams of flying led to an amazing rescue service

BY EDWIN MULLER

ONE day a pilot was flying his Piper Cub over the Kander Glacier in the Swiss Alps. Looking down, he saw a lone man precariously balanced at the very edge of a deep black hole in the snow.

The man was a guide. He had been crossing the glacier with two tourists, a man and his wife. The three were roped together. Suddenly the husband and wife had disappeared. Where they had walked was a round, black hole. The guide had been pulled off his feet, but, by jamming his ice axe into the hard snow, he had managed to hold their weight. So there he sat at the edge of the deep crevasse — as these splits in the ice are called — holding on, but quite unable to pull them up.

The pilot circled twice and landed. He and the guide together slowly hauled the couple to the surface, not seriously hurt. The pilot then flew them down the mountain to safety. It was all part of his day's work.

The pilot was Hermann Geiger — the first, and still the greatest, of the men who risk their lives daily in the Alpine Air Rescue Service. A few years ago, people would have thought such a rescue impossible, and the guide and his companions would have died. It was Geiger who started the whole idea.

Adapted from Air Facts, *copyright 1956 by Air Facts, Inc.*

Geiger's Dream

About thirty-five years ago, as a boy guarding his father's sheep, Geiger watched the birds circling above him, and dreamed of the day when he could fly. Especially, he longed to fly among the mountains that he loved.

He thought of those who injure themselves climbing and skiing, or who are trapped by sudden slides of snow. When a climber slips and hurts himself, it is very difficult to rescue him. He may have broken bones, or be so badly injured that it is dangerous to take him down on a toboggan.

In those days it took a long time for a rescue team to climb up the mountains. If only a pilot could land up there on those white fields and take off again, thought Geiger, the patient could be in a hospital in half an hour. But only twice had pilots landed their planes on the Swiss glaciers. They had done it for fun, and had found it impossible to take off again. The wheels had sunk into the soft snow. Geiger was not going to find it easy.

As soon as he had learned to fly, Geiger began carrying building materials to places in the mountains where huts were being built. In his small Piper he carried hundreds of tons of supplies, dropping them by parachute. In an hour he could do a job that would take a team of mules and their drivers two days. In winter he dropped bundles of food for the mountain goats.

But Geiger wanted to save human lives. This meant landing his airplane on the snow. He soon found a way of fixing skis, as well as wheels, to his Piper, but that was only the beginning.

As level fields are rare among the mountains, he had to solve the problem of landing on slopes. Also he would have to land on very small fields, as glaciers are cut by crevasses, often as wide as city streets. The plane might fall into one and disappear.

The Jackdaw Pilot

For years he tried to think of an answer, until he suddenly remembered the big black birds called jackdaws he had watched as a child. When jackdaws alight they use their wings as brakes, rising up again slightly before setting their claws on the ground. If he could copy their flight with his airplane, he would be able to land and stop quickly on the mountain slopes.

On May 10, 1952, Geiger took off from the airstrip at the little town of Sion, where he lives. That day he did the impossible — he landed on a glacier and took off again.

A few years later, Geiger took me with him to show me just how he had managed it. He climbed in circles out of the Rhône Valley, and then turned toward one of the biggest peaks of all — thousands of feet of snow and ice and sheer rock precipice.

At one point on the mighty west wall was a shelf, about fifty yards long and twenty across. (A Piper Cub usually needs about two hundred yards of level ground to land or take off.) On the lower side, the shelf curved over gradually, steeper and steeper until it ended in a precipice.

Geiger, leaning out, studied the surface carefully. Next he headed away from the mountain and flew about half a mile, losing height. Then he turned and started back straight for the wall.

Just before we reached it, he tilted the nose of the plane up. The skis touched down at a point where the slope was about twenty-five degrees. With a swoosh and a swirl of snow, the plane climbed up over the brow. The steep slope cut our speed rapidly, and we came to rest on the level — about ten yards short of the cliff ahead. His jackdaw method had worked.

Taking off was less difficult, but even more exciting. He just picked up the tail of the plane and swung it around. Then he climbed in, headed for the precipice — and dropped right over the edge. It was like one's dreams of falling into space.

Avalanche!

Geiger is no daredevil. He looks just like a Swiss mountain guide. He has broad shoulders, a face tanned brown by the winds, and the clear, steady eyes of a man who spends his life in the high hills.

He knows the dangers he faces, and he is a careful as well as a brave man. He takes great care over each rescue operation, and it is because of this that he has been able to save hundreds of lives. He has now made thousands of landings in the Alps — without a single accident.

When he is not out in the plane, he is seldom far away from his telephone in Sion. One morning in spring the phone rang.

"Avalanche accident on Mont Calme. Come quickly."

Within twenty minutes Geiger was on the spot. He saw below him a long steep slope. At the top, the surface was smooth, but halfway down the slope was a mass of broken blocks of snow. Ski tracks entered one side of the slide, but there were no tracks on the other side.

Geiger circled until he found a small patch of snow level enough for landing. A rescue party was there to meet him. They told him that twelve skiers had been crossing the slope when they had been suddenly swept off their feet and buried by the thundering fall of snow.

After several hours all twelve skiers were found. Five of these were injured, and Geiger took them down one by one.

"You Must Come"

One winter's day Geiger was told that there had been a climbing accident high up on Monte Rosa. He looked out of the window. Down in the valley there was rain and snow. The clouds were low, only five hundred feet from the ground. Geiger said that he could not possibly fly in such weather.

"You must come. The man is in a bad way."

Geiger never takes risks — except when a life is in danger. So he took off in the Piper, and flew to the entrance of the valley that leads to Monte Rosa. He could see nothing but clouds.

He flew this way and that until at last a blue hole appeared in the gray ceiling of cloud. Geiger zoomed up through it. Now he was above the clouds which hid the jagged peaks. At sixteen thousand feet, he flew in wide circles, guessing his position.

At last he recognized a shadow. It was the peak of the Weisshorn. Now that he had fixed his position, he flew to where he knew Monte Rosa must be.

He circled patiently until he found a gap in the clouds, and dived. There, by a hut, a guide was holding an ice axe with a handkerchief tied to it, to give him the direction of the wind. Geiger made his landing.

The flight back with the injured man was even worse. This time Geiger flew under the clouds. All the way down the narrow, twisting valley he was seldom more than fifty feet off the ground. At times it seemed as if his wing tips were brushing the rocks on either side.

Still, once again the risk proved worth while. They got back safely and the man recovered — thanks to an old-fashioned airplane and a man who had the courage to prove that nothing is impossible if you set your heart on it.

What's in a Name?

When Captain Cook discovered Australia, his sailors brought aboard ship a strange animal whose name they did not know. Sent ashore to inquire of the natives, they came back and said, "It is a kangaroo." Many years passed before it was known that when the natives were asked to name the animal and said, "Kangaroo," they meant, "What did you say?"

— *From* Low Man on a Totem Pole, *copyright 1941 by H. Allen Smith and published by Doubleday & Co., Inc.*

Spring Time

A big-game hunter in Africa was on his way back to camp one night when an enormous lion walked out of the jungle not twenty feet away. As the lion was about to spring, the hunter fired his last cartridge and missed. The lion sprang too far and landed fifteen feet beyond the hunter, who then ran for camp and made it safely.

The next day the hunter went back of the camp to practice a little shooting at close range. He heard a strange noise in the brush and investigated. It was the lion—practicing short leaps!

— *Webster cartoon in* New York Herald Tribune

False Scent

A clue for a girl-scout treasure hunt was hidden in the mailbox, but the postman got there before the girls. Mystified, he rang the doorbell. "I've looked under the tree," he told the lady of the house, "and under the big rock, but I still haven't found your letter."

— *Neil Morgan in San Diego (Calif.)* Tribune

JON KOLOMITZ

America's Dancingest Boy Scouts

Famous for their Indian dancing, these young palefaces have set a record hard to match in scouting

BY PAUL FRIGGENS

"THE great chieftains have gone their way. The buffalo have faded into Mother Earth, never to return. So listen to the rhythm of the Great Medicine Drum. See again the life of the Red Man as the Koshares reveal the age-old scenes. . . ."

The voice of the storyteller stopped. A war whoop sounded. *Boom*-thump, *boom*-thump went the thunder drum! And a hundred young "braves" danced into the light of the tepee fires flaring in the night wind. The music of their ankle bells and Indian hand rattles mingled eerily. For an hour and a half they weaved and stomped, their bare backs shining with sweat. They danced a prayer for a successful buffalo hunt and a Pueblo house blessing. They danced the Hopi prayer for rain, with wriggling bull snakes clenched in their teeth.

And there wasn't a real redskin in the outfit!

For these Koshare Indian Dancers were boy scouts from the Colorado prairie town of La Junta. They travel thousands of miles every year giving their dances. And they are so good that they earn five hundred dollars a night.

It all started about thirty years ago, when Scoutmaster "Buck" Burshears fixed up an old chicken

Adapted from The Denver Post, © *1961 by Post Printing & Publishing Co.*

coop for his troop. Buck was an eagle scout himself. But he soon found he needed something special to keep the older boys interested.

"They all loved to take trips," he said. "So I figured we'd build up a troupe of entertainers and pay our way on a lot of trips." The La Junta scoutmaster has done just that. And boys have been beating on his door ever since.

"Funmakers" All

Buck's own interest in Indian lore and dancing gave him the idea for a boy-scout "tribe." He named his tribe Koshare because that is the Pueblo word for "funmaker." The boys soon find that being a funmaker is no idle play. Indian dancing is more strenuous than many sports. And the Koshares do more than just dance.

"I want these boys to know how much we owe the Indian," Buck says. Together they study Indian lore. And they have worked up a hundred dances based on what they have learned about tribal life from books and visits to real Indians.

Buck himself has studied tribal dancing from the Montana Blackfeet to the Florida Seminoles. For a time he lived with a Southwest tribe, and he has helped to write a book on Indian beadwork. Each year he takes his scouts to the great Indian ceremonial dances at Gallup, New Mexico. There he takes pictures of the finest dancing and costumes, and records the Indian chants. His home — which is almost like an Indian museum — is often full of boys running his movies, reading his books or practicing new dance steps.

"The Indian dances," Buck says, "were mostly ceremonies in which they worshiped their gods. They worshiped the sun and moon, the wind and rain, thunder and lightning, birds and animals." Other dances celebrated such events as marriage, death or the harvest. Many Southwest dances, like the Hopi Snake Dance, were prayers for rain.

One of the Koshares' most exciting performances is the Sioux Ghost Dance. In the late 1880s a Paiute Indian named Wovoka claimed he had power to crush all white men and raise the buffalo out of the earth again. Wovoka roused the Plains Indians with a religious dance, in which they wore "ghost shirts." These shirts supposedly protected them from the White Man's bullets. The dancing craze spread like prairie fire and terrified the whites. United States Army troops finally put an end to it at Wounded Knee, South Dakota, in 1890.

Buck and his boys tramped the battlefield at Wounded Knee. They listened to firsthand accounts of what happened from surviving Sioux. Later, seeing the Koshares dance, an old chieftain said to Buck: "Come, teach our young people, too!"

Their Own Kiva

It takes time and hard work to be one of Buck's Indians. A junior-high boy starts on trial as a "papoose." Right away he starts to get together his Indian costume. This includes such items as owl claws, horsetails and eagle feathers. It may take him six months to bead his breechclout and vest. He must spend several hours a week learning the basic toe-heel and stomp steps. He must also earn fifteen merit badges and read five books on Indians. He must attend at least seventy-five percent of the scout meetings, and have no less than a "C" average in school.

Some years ago Buck decided to build a scout headquarters modeled after the underground kiva — the sacred meeting place of the ancient Pueblo. The Koshares put up ten thousand dollars from their earnings, and the people of the town put up another ten thousand dollars. Everyone thought Buck was planning something modest. But one day astonished La Juntans found that he was pouring the foundation for a building with recreation rooms, a trading post, a little theater, an Indian museum, an art museum and a ceremonial kiva that would seat five hundred people.

"He'll never finish it!" said one businessman.

But Buck put everyone in town to work. The boys helped tear down an abandoned Army mess hall for lumber. Old telephone poles were used to make the huge dome-shaped kiva ceiling. A famous Pueblo artist, Valleno Herrera, painted pictures of Indian dancers on the walls. In 1949 the building was finished. And it has had nearly a million visitors since.

An Exciting Life

Today the Koshares travel in their own air-conditioned bus, mostly during summer vacations. A faithful team of dads — businessmen, electricians, plumbers, doctors — help the scoutmaster. One father gives up his vacation every year to drive the bus. He has driven it more than two hundred thousand miles.

The road show sets a rugged pace for the Koshares. They put on an evening performance. Then they clean up, reload their equipment and bunk down in sleeping bags. They may sleep in armories, in gyms or under the stars. After a few hours' sleep they drive maybe four hundred miles. But the boys love it. Every third or fourth day they take time off to do some sight-seeing or go to a ball game. On Sundays they go to church.

Buck's scouts have toured America's national parks and visited famous art galleries. They have flown to Canada, had lunch with Congress and have even been received at the White House. One summer they spent five days off San Diego on a Navy aircraft carrier.

It's an exciting life. But the boys gain much more than excitement from being Koshares. One of them who is now in college says, "As a brave I learned hard work and sportsmanship. As head chief I learned public speaking and leadership. I owe everything to the Koshares."

By now Buck Burshears has seen more than two hundred and fifty boys attain eagle rank — a record probably no other troop can match. And, for more than eight hundred, he has opened up a whole new world — where discipline and romance go hand in hand.

NEW HORIZONS IN SCOUTING

by Albert Q. Maisel

Today more and more boys from fourteen to seventeen are going on from cubbing and regular scouting to become "explorers." Like the "funmakers" of La Junta, explorers have many interests that are exciting for them and useful to others.

Post 501 in Van Nuys, California, for instance, specializes in science. The boys have designed and built their own rocket engines, wind tunnels, and even a model nuclear power plant. Post 8 in Tucson, Arizona, explores caves and climbs mountains. They help the Sheriff's Mountain Rescue Team bring down climbers trapped on the slopes. Post 686 in Portland, Oregon, trains and takes care of the Portland Council's string of horses. They repair saddles and bridles, build corrals, teach younger scouts to ride. Every summer they trek the horses a hundred and ten miles across the Cascade Range to pasture. In winter they work on show riding and jumping. Post 50 in Runnemede, New Jersey, turns on the firehouse lights and warms up the fire engines for the volunteer firemen when an alarm is sounded. And in Phoenix, Arizona, explorers ride the ambulances, carry stretchers, and help in the hospital on Saturday nights.

Adapted from The Denver Post,
© 1960 by Post Printing & Publishing Co.

Make Yourself an Indian War Bonnet

TAKE the crown of a worn-out felt hat that is—as nearly as possible—the same size as your head. Cut the hat to the shape shown in Fig. 1. The small curved flaps on each side should cover your ears. Make thirty pairs of slits around the rim and a hole in each earflap, as shown in Fig. 1.

Get thirty long goose or turkey feathers.* For a more interesting effect, dye the tips of the feathers whatever color you like, or paint them with indelible ink. Scrape the end of each quill clean (Fig. 2). Soak it in hot water to soften it. Then cut a small piece out of it (Fig. 3). Daub a bit of glue on the tip. Bend the tip double and push it up inside, making a small loop (Fig. 4). Leave it that way until it dries.

Now, at the lower end of the quill, fasten lightweight white chicken feathers* with adhesive tape (Figs. 5 and 6). Cover the adhesive tape with colored ribbon, wired into place (Fig. 7).

To assemble the war bonnet, weave light string or waxed thread in and out through the slits of the hat and through the loops you made in the feathers (Figs. 8 and 9). Fasten it with a tight knot. Seen from above, your war bonnet should look as shown in Fig. 10.

The next step is to straighten the feathers up firmly against the hat. Then pass another length of light string or waxed thread around on the inner side, partway up the feathers (Fig. 11). You can slip it through the feather quills by using a needle as shown in Fig. 12. But you should leave enough free play to keep the feathers from being too tightly pressed together.

The front part of your bonnet can be decorated with a beaded band like the one in Fig. 13. Sew the band to the hat at several points and fasten it to the two holes in the earflaps.

Finally, hang feathers ornamented with beads, or with strips of soft leather, from the earflap holes (Fig. 14).

**Feathers can be obtained from a butcher shop, a millinery-supply shop, or by writing to The Plume Trading and Sales Company, Monroe, New York.*

FIG. 1
FIG. 2
FIG. 3
FIG. 4
FIG. 5
FIG. 6
FIG. 7
FIG. 8
FIG. 9
FIG. 10
FIG. 11
FIG. 12
FIG. 13
FIG. 14

Gertie the scatterbrained duck

The amazing mother mallard who became a legend in Milwaukee

BY GORDON GASKILL

THIS is a story full of heart and hoopla, funny but tender, wacky but wonderful. It happened in Milwaukee in 1945, but it is as old as the coming of spring. And its heroine is a mallard duck named Gertie.

Normally a mallard is among the wariest and shiest of creatures. Yet this duck chose to nest in the noisy heart of downtown Milwaukee. She picked one of the pilings of a bridge that carried the main street, Wisconsin Avenue, across the foul, greasy Milwaukee River. Just four steps away, clanging streetcars and thousands of people crossed the bridge every day. The bridge itself roared open from time to time to let ships through.

In this unlikely spot the duck made a shallow bowl in the rotting top of the upended white-oak log. She lined it with down plucked from her breast, and settled in to lay eggs.

Ray Clemens, a city electrician, was among the first to notice the mallard. He phoned Gordon MacQuarrie, *The Milwaukee Journal's* nature editor. But MacQuarrie wouldn't believe him. "I tell you it's a *duck!*" Clemens said crossly. "A mallard with three eggs already."

MacQuarrie sent a photographer to Wisconsin Avenue to see. For the next five weeks Gertie the Great, as the *Journal* named her, was headline news. So many people flocked to see her that they often blocked bridge traffic. At times Milwaukee radio stations flashed hourly bulletins.

But Gertie needed help. Where the river crosses the heart of the city, it is bound tightly between concrete walls and oil-soaked timbers. There is no greenery, no natural place for a hungry duck to forage. Just across the river, below the other

Adapted from The Rotarian, © *1961 by Rotary International*

end of the bridge, a little mud had collected around some debris. Gertie got in the habit of flying to this mud patch to peck out what she could. Soon the crowds began dropping food there: corn, bread, cookies, lettuce leaves.

Gertie seemed to respond to this kindness. And on April 28 she produced more news for press and radio: GERTIE LAYS FOURTH EGG. She went on laying until at last she had nine. (Three later disappeared, nobody knows how.)

Crisis After Crisis

On May 2 there was a crisis. The bridge had to be opened to pass two ships. Larger crowds than ever came to watch. The bridgetenders set the great lift machinery going to raise the two cantilevers. They worked as gently as they could. The two ships eased by as quietly as possible. When Gertie didn't bat an eye, the bridgetenders and the ships' captains sighed with relief. The crowds cheered wildly.

On May 4 it was announced that workmen were supposed to start replacing the forty pilings near Gertie's nest. City authorities decided to put it off, saying, "It might bother her."

The next day press and radio flashed the news: GERTIE STARTS INCUBATING. Gertie began to get all sorts of presents. They were sent to the shanty of the bridgetenders, who became her guardians. Hundreds of people sent "Get Well Soon" and "Greetings to the New Arrival" cards.

Then there was another crisis. Lawrence Hautz, state president of the Izaak Walton League for conservation, told a newspaper reporter: "This whole thing is headed for tragedy. What's going to happen when those ducklings are hatched? If they try to swim, the oil in that river will mat their little wings and they'll sink."

The mayor read about this, frowning. So did everybody else. Soon the public-works department announced that no oil would mat the wings of the ducklings-to-be. When the hatching date drew near, great pumps would send two and a half million gallons of clean lake water every hour into the river. This would flush away the oil, and never mind the cost. "Anything for Gertie!"

May 13 was Mother's Day. Gimbels department store, at the end of the bridge, had decorated one window as "Gertie's Window." There were stuffed ducks and ducklings in it. By now everyone in Milwaukee knew about Gertie. Streetcar motormen often stopped their cars in the middle of the bridge and dashed out to peer over the railing. Then they came back to shout to their passengers, "Gertie's okay!" Schoolteachers took their classes to watch her. Boy scouts organized a Gertie patrol to protect her from harm.

Tension mounted as the hatching day neared. Scores of people stopped to ask, "Is there anything we can do to help?" Hautz was still uneasy. He got two long-handled dip nets, a huge roll of absorbent cotton and five pounds of cornmeal. He placed these in the bridgetenders' shanty with a sign: FOR EMERGENCY USE FOR GERTIE ONLY. He added his name and all possible telephone numbers, asking that he be called at any hour of the day or night if something went wrong.

On May 29, the city's pumps began forcing lake water down the Milwaukee River. The superintendent of bridges ordered rowboats to be ready in case of emergency.

May 30, the predicted hatching day, was also Memorial Day. And a great parade was to go down Wisconsin Avenue. As it neared the bridge, the crowds whispered a great "S-s-sshhhhhh!" The bands stopped their music. The marching thousands almost tiptoed across the bridge. Gertie didn't seem to notice.

At five thirty that afternoon the news was flashed: GERTIE'S FIRST DUCKLING BORN. The newspapers named it "Black Bill." Thousands rushed to the bridge. In the next twenty-four hours one egg after another hatched out. By the evening of May 31 Gertie had five ducklings.

Gertie's Family

That night a terrible storm struck Milwaukee, bringing high winds and rain. Shortly after midnight, Hautz's phone rang. It was Bridgetender Alex Rehorst. "Things are in a terrible mess down here," he said. "The little ducks keep falling out of the nest into the river. And Gertie's gone!"

"Dip out all the ducklings you can and take them into your shanty," Hautz said. "I'll be right there." Within a few minutes he was rocketing down Lincoln Memorial Drive.

At the bridge, he found the night tenders with four ducklings. "There's still one egg left in the nest not hatched," one tender said.

"Get it!" Hautz said. He was almost certain the cold rain had destroyed any life in the egg. Still . . . He looked it over closely and found a quarter-inch hole. Every embryonic duckling has a hard "egg tooth" on its bill, with which it cuts its way through the shell. Hautz could see a tiny bill inside still moving feebly.

He decided to peel the shell away from the egg membrane and save the duckling. It had to be done with great care. For often the duckling's yellow "life sac" (on which it lives for the first few hours of life) is attached inside to the membrane. If it is ruptured, the duckling dies. Absorbed, dripping with perspiration, Hautz barely noticed the people crowding into the shanty. A news flash had alerted the city to the drama.

At last he peeled off the final bit of shell. The membrane and life sac were still intact. The duckling seemed dead, but very gently Hautz fluffed up the tiny feathers. He dusted them with cornmeal flour to dry them. Then he placed the duckling inside his hat, which he had filled with soft cotton. He set this on a chair near the open stove door. Soon the duckling began to move. Before long it could be put in the cardboard box with the other four. Carefully Hautz fed them. He dipped their beaks first in milk, then in the crumbled-up yolk of a hard-boiled egg.

Not until about three a.m. did Hautz have time to worry about Gertie. Taking a long-handled net, he climbed into a rowboat. Then he shoved off, with the bridgetenders at the oars. They spotted her about a half block away, and gently herded her downriver to the mud patch where she usually fed. There they caught her in a net that had already been rigged up. Gertie was soon back with her ducklings in the warm shanty.

By five a.m. Hautz was tired out, but still not satisfied. Gertie and her brood had to have a better home. Then he thought of "Gertie's Window" in Gimbels store. Just the thing!

He dialed the store manager, who snapped wide awake when Hautz asked, "How would you like to have the *real* Gertie in your window, with all her family?" The manager thought this was a wonderful idea. So Hautz listed the things he wanted: clean sand on the floor, plenty of fresh water, infrared lamps for heating, a humidifier, a thermometer, no drafts, and an attendant to make sure the temperature was always between seventy and seventy-two degrees.

By six thirty a.m. the window was alive with workmen. By nine thirty lines were forming to see Gertie and her family. So great were the crowds that a barricade had to be put up to keep the window from being broken.

But mallards are made for freedom. On the third of June, with policemen to control the crowds, Gertie and her family were taken to a lagoon outside the city. The five ducklings were released first. They huddled together on the grass, not knowing what to do. Then Gertie was freed. She made an eager flight straight toward the lagoon, until she remembered that she was a mother. She came back and put herself at the head of her family. Then with great dignity she led them into the water. They swam off briskly, as pictures were taken and people cheered.

Nobody can know where Gertie and her family went. Probably off into the vast freedom of the skies — winging along the mysterious, unmarked aerial highways that migratory birds follow.

Could Gertie still be alive now? "Hardly possible," Hautz says. "With a lot of luck, a mallard can live maybe twenty years. And she was about four years old in 1945. But, anyway, she's a legend now. And legends never die."

THE PRAYER OF THE LITTLE DUCKS

By Carmen Bernos de Gasztold

Dear God,
give us a flood of water.
Let it rain tomorrow and always.
Give us plenty of little slugs
and other luscious things to eat.
Protect all folk who quack
and everyone who knows how to swim.

Amen

From Prayers from the Ark, *translated from the French by Rumer Godden, copyright © 1962 by Rumer Godden and published by The Viking Press, Inc.*

TRICK QUESTIONS

Watch your step as you try these teasers (Answers on page 200)

1 How much earth is there in a hole measuring one foot by one foot by one foot?

2 Would a marble fall faster through water at 60° F. or at 10° F.?

3 Two fathers and two sons each shot a duck. None of them shot the same duck, but only three ducks were shot. Why?

4 A deep-sea fishing boat is lying in harbor. Over the side hangs a rope ladder, with its end just touching the water. The rungs of the ladder are one foot apart, and the tide is rising at the rate of eight inches an hour. At the end of six hours, how many of the rungs will be covered?

5 How is it possible for Jim to stand behind George and George to stand behind Jim—at the same time?

6 There are five apples in a basket and five people besides yourself in the room. How can you give an apple to each of the five people, and yet leave one apple in the basket?

7 A farmer has five half-size haystacks in the corner of a field, and two three-quarter-size haystacks in another corner. If he puts them all together, how many haystacks will he have?

8 If you were given the height and radius of a spool of thread, and the thickness of the thread on the spool, what would be the quickest way of finding out the length of the thread?

9 All the other teachers ended their classes as soon as they heard the first stroke of twelve o'clock. Mr. Jones never let his children out until the school clock sounded the twelfth stroke. "It's a shame," groaned Peter. "Each stroke takes six seconds; so we do seventy-two seconds' more work than any of the others." "It's not as bad as all that," said Sally. "I counted the first six strokes today, and they only took thirty seconds. So we are only a minute late." How much longer did Mr. Jones's class work each day?

10 What five-letter word sounds the same even when you take away four of its letters?

11 A notebook and a pencil cost a total of $1.20. The notebook costs $1 more than the pencil. What is the cost of each?

12 How far can a dog run into the woods?

13 What is the closest relation your mother's brother's brother-in-law could be to you?

1, 4, 11 adapted from "Campfire Quiz" by Andrew G. Ross in Outdoor Life. *5, 13, copyright 1954 by Lee Segall, Creator-Owner, Dr. I.Q. 6, 7, 12 adapted from* Collection of Brain Twisters *by Peter Storme and Paul Stryfe, copyright 1941 by Simon and Schuster, Inc. 10, Matt Weinstock in Los Angeles* Daily News.

Don Vesuvio and the House of the Urchin

A young Italian priest walked into a den of thieves and came out with a houseful of friends

BY FREDERIC SONDERN, JR.

THE Archbishop of Naples was shocked. "You wish to masquerade as a *scugnizzo* — a pickpocket, a thief?" he said. "This is unheard of. Impossible! The urchins would find you out at once."

Father Mario Borrelli drew himself up. "It is the only way we can save these poor children," he said firmly. "I have learned to speak as they do and to look like them. Let me explain, your Eminence."

The ancient Italian city of Naples has been plagued for centuries by dangerous young hoodlums known as *scugnizzi*. The *scugnizzi* are orphans and outcasts. From the age of six, or even younger, they live on the streets, begging and stealing. Naples is a busy port, and their biggest racket is robbing tourists and sailors.

"I have tried to reach them by ordinary means and I have failed," Father Borrelli pleaded. "If I could become one of them, I might be able to help them."

The Archbishop listened. He remembered what fine work this twenty-five-year-old priest had done with the young workers in the city's factories.

Adapted from The Catholic World, © *1956 by The Missionary Society of St. Paul the Apostle in the State of New York*

"Very well," he said at last. "The Church must sometimes work in strange ways. But be careful."

Vesuvio Is Born

Some days later the *scugnizzi* who hang around the Naples railroad station found they had a new member. This short young man with fair hair and keen blue eyes knew how to beg, and he was very tough. When the leader of the gang swaggered up and demanded half his money, Borrelli exploded like a volcano. He gave the boy an expert beating. The *scugnizzi* were amazed.

"We should call him Vesuvio," said one boy. "He sounds just like Mount Vesuvius."

And Vesuvio the priest became — an important *scugnizzo*.

That was in 1950. For the next six months Father Borrelli was a teacher of religion by day. By night he was Vesuvio. After his classes, he changed into scuffed shoes, ragged trousers, a dirty shirt and a shapeless woolen cap. He made his face and hands grimy.

Most *scugnizzi* sleep in the streets. In winter they use newspapers for blankets, and make their beds over gratings that give out some heat. Vesuvio did the same.

He talked with his new friends over meals of scraps heated in old tin cans. He learned a great deal about them. Most important, he made these outcasts feel that he was one of them.

Still, Father Borrelli was always in danger. The hoodlums of Naples are rough with police spies. If they suspected him of working with the police, he would be in real trouble. Somehow he came through without a slip. And he was encouraged to find that, in their hearts, most *scugnizzi* longed for a home and for love.

A Home at Last

One winter evening Vesuvio told the gang that he had found a place where they could live. He led them to the little church of Saint Gennaro. It had been bombed during World War II and was not being used.

"The police will never think of looking for us in a church," said Vesuvio.

There were gaping holes in the roof of the church, and rubble on the floor. At first the boys did not like the idea of cleaning and patching. But they soon found that building was fun. With crude tools and homemade barrows the church was repaired.

One night Vesuvio arrived with a straw mattress and a blanket. The boys had always believed such things were sissy. But, one by one, they followed his example. Then Vesuvio brought in a cooking stove and some fresh groceries. The boys thought this nourishing food had been stolen, and they began to eat it.

Soon the boys were calling their new home *la Casa* — the House. Father Borrelli noticed that they came in earlier from the streets. There were changes in their manner toward each other. They were still tough, but not quite as tough as before. He decided the time had come to tell them who he really was.

The next night he went to the house dressed in his priest's robes. The *scugnizzi* were silent for a moment. Then they roared with laughter.

"Look at Vesuvio," they shouted. "He has become a priest!"

One boy said, "You cannot do this, Vesuvio. I am not religious, but I know it is not right."

Father Borrelli smiled. "I *am* a priest, my son," he said. "Here is a snapshot of me with other priests to prove it."

As the boys passed the picture around, Father Borrelli held his breath. Then one especially hard *scugnizzo* stepped forward. He took the priest's hand. "We will call you *Don* Vesuvio," he said, grinning. "But you will stay with us here, won't you?" The others crowded around.

With tears in his eyes, Father Borrelli said, "Yes, I will stay. We will make this into a *casa dello scugnizzo.*" And thus the House of the Urchin was started.

School for the Urchins

On a borrowed donkey cart Father Borrelli and some of his boys went through the city begging furniture. The people of Naples gave freely, and the *Casa* became a real house. But one thing worried the good priest. How long would the *scugnizzi* be willing to stay here?

He knew that his urchins needed kindness and love as well as food, clothing and beds. He also knew that he could not close them in and teach them in the *Casa*. So he suggested that they go to school or get jobs.

The boys were horrified by this idea. But the priest explained that an education would help them to do whatever they wanted to do in life. Slowly, they came to understand that Don Vesuvio was right.

Slowly, too, they began to change in other ways. They washed in the morning, and shaved when necessary. What pleased Don Vesuvio most was their new and truly happy laughter.

Then one day thirteen-year-old Pietro led a revolt. "I'm going back to the streets," he said angrily. "In school they dislike me."

"Very well," the priest said. "We shall close the *Casa,* and Don Vesuvio will be no more. For I shall have lost faith in the friendship we *scugnizzi* have for each other." He turned and left. And within a few minutes the revolt was over.

Some months later, Pietro came to the priest again. "I've made good marks," he said. "They *don't* dislike me." Pietro had been called "The Hand" because of his skill as a pickpocket. Today he has a good job in a machine shop.

At first Father Borrelli had trouble getting jobs for the older boys. The businessmen he talked to were afraid to trust a *scugnizzo*.

"I'll give you money, Father," said one store owner. "But one of those little devils in my shop? Oh, no!"

Don Vesuvio erupted when he heard this, and finally the store owner gave in. He hired a boy named Mario as a messenger.

One day Mario said to Borrelli, "Father, may I steal just a little something at the store? No one would notice."

Don Vesuvio took the boy by the shoulders and looked into his eyes. "Mario, if you take so much as a pin, I will find you out. I shall have to tell. I will have to close the *Casa,* and there will be no more jobs for the other boys. Do you want that to happen?"

"No, Father," said the boy. "I will not steal."

Today Mario is a clerk in the same store.

Only One Rule

Soon Don Vesuvio had an assistant, a fellow priest named Father Spada. Together they have helped hundreds of boys to "graduate" from the *Casa* as decent youngsters.

Up to the age of fourteen, the boys in the *Casa* must go to school. After that Father Borrelli finds jobs for them in stores, factories and hotels. The businessmen of Naples are now eager to get Don Vesuvio's boys.

"They are more honest than most," said one store owner. "Amazing, isn't it?"

In the *Casa* itself there is only one firm rule. Every boy must be in off the streets before nine in the evening. He is warned once. If he breaks the rule a second time, he is asked to leave.

Father Borrelli finds he doesn't have to punish or demand much more than that. He likes to join in the football games of the older boys in the play yard of the *Casa,* and to play leapfrog with the little ones.

The boys learn by themselves to prefer shoes to bare feet, clean clothes to dirty ones, and good food to slops. They could be out on the streets if they wanted to. But they like it in the *Casa* — with a houseful of friends.

The Power of Punctuation

This may look very odd, but it makes good sense if you can put in the correct punctuation:

John where James had had had had had had had had had had had the teacher's approval.

(Answer on page 164)

BILL RAY/BLACK STAR

The Farm Horse That Became a CHAMPION

The amazing story of Snow Man—
and the young Dutchman who saved his life and rode him to glory

BY PHILIP B. KUNHARDT

Adapted from Farmer's Advocate, *© 1960 by The William Weld Co., Ltd., with editorial additions*

If you had been at the National Horse Show in November 1959, you would have seen something truly thrilling. Thirteen thousand people had come to New York City's Madison Square Garden to see the show. The seats that ringed the great arena were filled.

In the middle of the evening the arena was cleared. The lights were dimmed and the band struck up a triumphal march. All eyes followed a spotlight toward the entrance gate at the west end of the ring.

There a big gray horse — obviously not a thoroughbred — appeared. Ahead of him walked five small children. As a fair-haired young man and his wife led the horse to the center of the huge ring, the crowd rose to its feet and began clapping. In a moment the applause was deafening. The young couple and their children beamed and bowed their thanks. The horse stomped his feet, and the clapping and cheering went on and on like thunder.

The horse was Snow Man, champion in the open jumping — one of the highest show honors a horse can win. The handsome de Leyer family were his owners. And the wild cheers that greeted them were enough to make you believe in fairy tales.

For, less than four years before, Snow Man had been on his way to the slaughterhouse. He was then a tired farm horse that nobody seemed to want or care about. Luckily Harry de Leyer *did* care — and this is the story of that caring.

A Boy in Holland

Harry was born in Holland in 1928. He was brought up on a farm, and he always loved horses. He dreamed of riding a champion. But World War II came, and for four years Holland was held by the German army. Then, when Harry was sixteen, a unit of American airborne troops arrived in his hometown to set it free.

The slim blond Dutch boy listened with wide eyes to the soldiers' stories about the wonders of their homeland. When the town hospital was bombed, he fought with the Yankees all one night to put out the blaze. The mayor gave him a medal for his heroism. But, more important, he became a kind of mascot to the troops — and another dream was born. Someday he would go to America.

When the war was over, the soldiers went home. Harry couldn't follow them yet. But he did become an expert rider—so good that for three years he rode with Holland's Junior Olympic Team.

BILL RAY/BLACK STAR

The children love Snow Man

Harry had a childhood sweetheart named Joanna. In 1950 the two were married and came to the United States.

First they worked on a farm in North Carolina. Harry was put in charge of the cows, but he longed to be back with horses. Before long he got a job in Pennsylvania, training show horses. He saved the money he earned to buy a few horses of his own. And within five years he had become riding master at the Knox School for Girls on Long Island. By then he and Joanna had their first three children. (They now have seven.)

A Crazy Decision

One wintry morning in 1956 Harry set out to buy some horses for the school at an auction in New Holland, Pennsylvania. He arrived so late that most of the horses had been sold. But he saw several sorry-looking animals being loaded into a van that was destined for the dog-food factory. These were the "killers" — worn-out workhorses that only the meat dealer wanted. The sight made Harry sad. He wished that all horses could live out their last years in green pastures.

Suddenly he spotted a big gray gelding plodding up the ramp into the van. The horse was chunky, but lighter than the others. There was a spirited tilt to his ears, a brightness in his eyes. On a hunch, Harry called to the loader to bring the horse back.

"You crazy?" said the meat dealer. "He's just an old farm horse."

The man is probably right, Harry thought. The animal's ribs showed. His coat was matted with dirt. There were sores on his legs. Still, there was something about him. . . .

"How much do you want for him?" Harry asked.

That's how it all started. Harry de Leyer saved an old plug for just eighty dollars.

Snow Man Learns Fast

The whole de Leyer family was out to greet the horse the next day. Down the ramp of the van he came, stumbling over his big feet. He looked slowly about, blinking in the bright winter sun. Then, ankle-deep in snow, with snowflakes in his shaggy hair, he stood still as a statue.

One of the children said, "He looks just like a snowman." And from then on Snow Man was his name.

They all set about turning Snow Man into a horse again. First they clipped him lightly. Then they washed him — three times. In a while the horseshoer came. Finally, cleaned and curried and shod, Snow Man was ready for his first lesson as a riding horse.

Harry laid a dozen thick wooden poles on the ground, spacing them a few feet apart. To walk across the network of poles a horse had to lift his feet high and space his steps. When Snow Man tried it, poles flew every which way. He stumbled and wove.

But Snow Man learned fast. By spring he was carrying the beginning riders at Knox. He was so gentle that any child felt safe on his back. Some of the girls asked for him instead of the better-looking horses.

When school closed that summer, Harry made what might have been the biggest mistake of his life. He sold Snow Man to a neighborhood doctor for double the money he had paid for him. After all, Harry told himself, he *was* in the horse business.

Now Snow Man began showing a new side of his character. He jumped the doctor's fences no matter how high they were raised. And he came home — across country, over fields and lawns, through back yards and gardens. Angry citizens called the police. The doctor was glad to sell Snow Man back to Harry.

Harry was glad too. For, in some strange way, he had come to believe that he and Snow Man belonged together. He promised himself never again to part with the horse.

Now that he knew Snow Man liked to jump, Harry began giving him special schooling as a jumper. With kindness and hard work, he helped Snow Man over tougher and tougher obstacles. Finally, in the spring of 1958, he decided to put the big gray horse to his first test—at the Sands Point Horse Show on Long Island.

As Snow Man stood at the gate, waiting to go out on the jump course, no one gave him a second look. He stood with his head down and his eyes half closed, looking sleepy and bored. But once out on the course the big gray horse could do no wrong. Again and again people held their breath, expecting the clumsy-looking animal to come crashing down on the bars. He never did! By nightfall of the second day of the three-day show, he was tied for lead in the Open Jumper Division with the great old champion Andante. Then, with success so close, on his final jump of the day Snow Man landed with his feet too close together. And a back hoof slashed his right foreleg.

By morning it would be stiff and swollen. But Harry isn't one to give up easily. He cut out a section of a tire tube, and slipped it over Snow Man's wounded leg like a sock. Then he tied up the bottom and filled the top with ice. All night long he kept the "sock" full of fresh ice. He told Snow Man over and over how they would win the next day.

When morning came, the leg was neither stiff nor swollen. And on the final round of that day Snow Man beat the mighty Andante!

Harry Has a Scare

Harry now saw that Snow Man had the makings of a champion. But giving the horse a chance to prove it meant traveling to a new horse show each weekend. It meant paying big entry fees and riding his heart out—a long, tiring summer that *could* end in little reward.

Harry takes Snow Man over a jump

FREUDY PHOTOS

At the same time, a spot on Harry's tongue had begun to hurt and to worry him. It would be easy to forget about championships. Still, after talking it over, Harry and Joanna decided that Snow Man deserved a try.

So to Connecticut they went. Snow Man won at the Fairfield Horse Show and at Lakeville. Then to Branchville, New Jersey—but Harry was too sick by then to ride a winner. His tongue had begun to bother him badly, and he had scarcely eaten for a week. Snow Man had a bad day. Harry blamed himself for the big jumper's first loss. He drove home that night, gritting his teeth against the pain.

On Monday Harry went to a doctor. On Tuesday he entered a Long Island hospital to have a tumor removed from his tongue. On Saturday he got the laboratory report: the tumor was malignant. It was the end of the life he had known, the end of Snow Man's quest for glory.

Harry drove to the Smithtown Horse Show, a few miles from his home. He was planning to sell his horses. But somehow he would keep Snow Man. The big gray horse would be turned out to pasture. Sitting at the show, Harry heard his name announced over the loudspeaker. He was to go home at once. His first thought was: the children! His second: a fire! He sped home, wondering how much more a man could take.

But when he turned into the driveway the children were playing in the yard and there stood the house. Joanna was crying with happiness. A report had come from the hospital that there had been a mistake. Harry did not have cancer, after all!

"All of a sudden," Harry says, "my life was handed back to me."

From then on, the summer and early fall became one happy rush of championships at important horse shows. Finally it was November, time for the biggest show of all — the National, at Madison Square Garden.

The Big Night

The National Horse Show lasts eight days. After seven days Snow Man was tied in the Open Jumper Division with a chestnut mare named First Chance. For their jump-off on the eighth day the course was long and complicated. It wove around the Garden oval in four overlapping loops. It included quick turns and changes of direction—combinations which call for perfect timing and coördination.

First Chance went first. Was it the tenseness of the moment? The wear and tear of so many days of jumping? Or the difficulties of the course? No one can be sure. At any rate, First Chance "knocked" several barriers.

Now it was up to Snow Man to run a cleaner course. Slowly he headed for the first jump. Harry nudged him with his knees, and the big gray horse exploded over the jump. Now up and over Snow Man went, and up and over again. Over the brush jump, over the chicken coop, the hog's-back, the bull's-eye, the striped panel. There were some touches, but far fewer than First Chance had made. Finally Harry and Snow Man approached the last jump.

Now Harry sat up in the saddle and threw the reins over the horse's neck. He was showing everyone that it was not he who was giving this great performance. It was the horse. Snow Man rumbled up to the final jump, and he thrust and he sailed and it was done! An old farm horse had won it all—the Open Jumper Championship, the Professional Horsemen's Association Trophy and the American Horse Shows Association high-score award. He was named "Horse of the Year" for 1958 in open jumping.

Then, in 1959, Harry took Snow Man and all his family back to Holland for a visit. News of Snow Man had gone before them, and they were given a royal welcome. While they were there, Snow Man jumped a seven-foot-two-inch wall to become the Dutch champion. Later that year he won at many more shows and was named American "Horse of the Year" again.

Snow Man went on to win more blue ribbons as well as the affection of millions. But if you had been one of the vast crowd that filled Madison Square Garden for the National Horse Show in 1962, you would have seen the big gray horse competing for the last time. Harry de Leyer — a man who cared — knew the time had come for America's most valiant and beloved horse to enjoy a quiet old age in the green pastures near his home.

ANSWER to question on page 160: *John, where James had had "had," had had "had had." "Had had" had had the teacher's approval.*

The Romance of Maps

For centuries maps have been man's keys to adventure and treasure

BY DONALD CULROSS PEATTIE

A MAP is the beginning of adventure. Travels and treasure hunts, wars and explorations all open with its unrolling. It is a magic carpet, taking the mind in a flash just where you want to go.

Road maps are given freely these days, but once maps were closely guarded secrets. Men who revealed them might be put to torture or death. To the privateer a captured chart could be booty richer than bullion. For, in the little-known world of long ago, it could point the way to fortune. The mariners of Tyre had their Mediterranean trade routes to hide — the Arab sailors their sources of ginger, camphor, lacquer and silk. The Spanish had their plundered New World gold, the Dutch their East Indian spices.

The charts that Columbus and Magellan made on their immortal voyages were kept hidden in the archives of Seville. But so many men wanted them that most of them mysteriously vanished. In the seventeenth century the Dutch East India Company printed one hundred and eighty maps showing sailing routes to India, the Malay Straits, China and Japan (where all maps were long forbidden to any foreigner). This *Secret Atlas* could be used by the company's captains only.

Today people all over the world use the same maps. There are maps of the bottom of the ocean, and of caves; maps for the flier and the hiker. But for you and me there is nothing like a good atlas. With it we can travel to all the places we may never see: the ancient cities of Samarkand, Istanbul and Phnom Penh. We can sail down storied rivers like the Niger, the Indus and the Tigris. We can visit Ghana (once known as the Gold Coast), the Ivory Coast, the Windward and Leeward Islands — all the names that ring in the mind like music.

Turn to the pages that picture the United States. There you can read the country's history. Tallahassee, Kennebec, Okefenokee — they are moccasin prints. Hoboken and Harlem are Dutch as wooden shoes. Dubuque and La Salle tell of the French cavaliers passing this way like wind through grass. Spaniards marked the Southwest forever with Albuquerque, Pueblo, Los Angeles and Las Vegas. And the westward course of the pioneers is written in names like Grand Detour, Wagon Mound and Death Valley.

The great historic trails are there, too — the Natchez Trace, the National Road, the Wilderness Road — in the modern disguise of numbered highways. Here is the run of the Pony Express, beginning at St. Joseph, Missouri, and ending at Sacramento, California. Here are marked great finds of dinosaur bones, the site of a frontier fort, of a long-ago battle, of an Indian massacre.

The ancient Greeks were among the first to wonder what the world as a whole looked like, and to picture it as a sphere. Claudius Ptolemy, Greco-Egyptian astronomer and geographer, completed his great atlas about 150 A.D. In it he showed that Greece was *not* the center of the world, as earlier Greeks had supposed. Conquests and voyages enabled Ptolemy to map Europe as far north as Denmark and the Shetland Islands. To the south he could sketch a large part of Africa and to the east a large area he called India. From the camel caravans bringing silks out of the unknown Orient, and from black slaves and ivory arriving from the Dark Continent, these ancients guessed at lands beyond the known.

In the Dark Ages much that had been learned was forgotten. Medieval monks who never left their cloisters drew maps of the world based on their reading of the Bible. Jerusalem was usually in the center. East, not north, was put at the top, since there the Garden of Paradise was supposed to lie.

Because the Bible spoke of "the four corners of the earth," some map makers took this to mean that the earth was square or oblong. And they drew it this way, decorating it with the grotesque monsters which they thought dwelt in those far corners.

But pilgrimages, the Crusades, the journey of Marco Polo to China, and the voyages of the Portuguese explorers all pushed out the borders of the known world.

The first map (1500) of the new discoveries in the "western sea" was crudely painted on oxhide by Juan de la Cosa, a captain with Columbus. In 1506 the first printed map of the New World appeared. The single surviving copy is in the British Museum, which has one of the world's finest map collections.

It is fascinating to watch man's knowledge of North America grow by lining up maps from the year 1500 onward. Slowly our continent takes shape as the result of the explorations of Cabot and Cartier along the northeast coast, of La Salle on the Mississippi, and the Spanish in Florida, Texas and Mexico.

Map after map clears up the complex New England and Canadian coasts, gives form to Chesapeake Bay, to Long Island Sound and Cape Cod.

Open on my desk is one printed in Holland sometime before 1682, picturing "Nieue Amsterdam" (New York) as a cluster of houses at the southern tip of the island, with windmills, a church, a gibbet for pirates and a pillory for Sabbath breakers — the whole ending at a stockaded wall (Wall Street) beyond which dwelt the war-whooping Manhattoes. Offshore are pictured Indian canoes, upstate are Mohican villages, and enlivening the wilderness are elk, deer, bear and beaver. It is charmingly inaccurate.

Because the world is round, the only really correct map of it — even today — is a globe. Globes are usually too small to show detail or too large to use easily, so we have to spread out flat what is really round by means of a projection such as Mercator's. This results in a distortion which increases the farther one moves from the equator, until Greenland looks larger than South America, which is really eight times as big.

Since a globe cannot be flattened accurately, only small areas *can* be mapped with exactness. Wars change the boundaries of nations. Vast areas of jungle and wilderness are still unexplored. In spite of all these difficulties, about half the earth's surface has already been accurately mapped.

How well do you know our good neighbors?

THE people of South America are our good neighbors. Their great continent stretches from the warm waters of the Caribbean Sea to the icy wastes of the Antarctic. Within its borders are rich tropical rain forests, mighty rivers such as the Amazon, and the towering snow-capped ranges of the Andes Mountains. Cowboys, called gauchos, herd beef cattle in the vast grassy pampas (or prairies) of Argentina. Spanish is the language of most South American countries, but the people of Brazil speak Portuguese, and in some areas ancient Indian dialects are still spoken. Now let's see how many of these countries you know. In the space before the name of each country write the number shown on the map which you think belongs to that country. For example, before French Guiana you would write 1. You will find the right answers for the rest on page 200.

The House at the Crossroads

An eerie tale of an accident on a dark and lonely country road

A MAN and his wife are driving along a strange country road in New England. They are going to dinner with friends, and have gotten lost twice. Now they are late, so the husband is driving at top speed. In spite of this, he notices a large frame house at a crossroads. It is in bad repair, and has a sign saying that a doctor lives there. The man stores this in his mind as a landmark for the trip home.

Half a mile farther on something goes wrong with the steering gear. The car crashes against a tree. The driver is unhurt, but his wife is unconscious and seriously injured. The road is a lonely one. The husband has seen no other car and few houses.

Desperately, he remembers the doctor's sign half a mile back. He takes his wife's limp figure in his arms and half walks, half runs back to the tumbledown dwelling.

He tugs at the bell. A tall, gaunt, gray-haired and unkempt man opens the door, and says he is the doctor. There is no one else in the house.

Together the two men carry the woman into a dusty, cluttered room, and lay her down upon an operating table. She is still unconscious. The doctor examines her with evident skill, and says that her skull is fractured. The only chance — a slim one — of saving her life is to operate at once. The husband glances around the messy room. The bottles and instruments look as if they had not been used for a long time. He hesitates, but he has no choice.

"You'll have to give her the ether," the doctor says. "There's no one else here."

The husband feels weak, ill and shocked, but he obeys. When his wife has been given enough ether, he is ready to collapse.

The surgeon has his knife in his hand. "You'd better wait outside," he says. "I can get along alone now."

The husband paces up and down the porch, now and then peering from the darkness into the lighted room. Then, suddenly, he sees three men lurking in the shadows. Two are armed and the third carries a rope. Now they are moving slowly toward the door!

"Wait! Wait!" the husband begs. He can see that the operation has begun. Any delay now must mean his wife's certain death.

One of the men whispers, "What do you take us for?"

"Thieves," the husband answers.

"No," the man says. "We are from the madhouse. The man operating on your wife is a dangerous lunatic. He escaped only two hours ago."

Still whispering, the three men agree to wait until the operation is over. The lunatic was once a famous surgeon, they say. But he has been odd for some time, and recently violent. Several years ago he came from one of the larger cities, and bought and furnished this house. He worked there as a doctor until he had to be put in the madhouse.

"When he escaped, he must have found his way back to this house from force of habit," the head guard says. "And from force of habit he might be able to do this operation. In any event, we have no choice. If we stop him now, your wife certainly must die."

They stare through the window, until they see that the operation is finished at last. Then the three guards spring upon the lunatic. He fights and screams, but they take him away. The head guard promises to bring back doctors and nurses, which he does. The wife gets well enough to be taken to New York. There she is placed under the care of a well-known doctor. He examines her skull carefully.

"Your wife will get well and be perfectly normal again," he says to the husband. "But I cannot understand it. Only one operation I know could have saved her. And only one surgeon ever did that operation successfully. There is the mystery! For that particular surgeon went crazy years ago. He is now in a madhouse somewhere in New England."

Adapted by Channing Pollock from a story by Robert Adger Bowen, reprinted by permission of Redbook

A PRESENT FOR ALICE

BY MARGARET REARDON

A story that has delighted millions was first told for one little girl

ONE summer day a century ago, three little English girls set out on a picnic. They were Lorina, Alice and Edith Liddell, daughters of Dean Liddell of Christ Church College, Oxford. All three wore white cotton dresses with hoopskirts, open-lace socks and black slippers. Broad-brimmed hats tied under their chins were to shield them from the blazing sun. For this was to be a three-mile trip up the River Thames to Godstow.

The day was July 4, 1862, during summer vacation when — in the words of one Englishman — "Oxford was a city of dreams . . . of bells . . . of fragrant air." The laughter of the little girls on the path through Christ Church meadow to the river was in harmony with this setting.

There were five in the picnic party that day — the Liddell sisters and two young teachers from

Adapted from The Horn Book Magazine, *copyright © 1962 by The Horn Book, Incorporated, with editorial additions*

Alice Liddell in 1858

Christ Church College. Two of these five were to become famous. The tall young man who carried a large picnic basket was Charles Lutwidge Dodgson, clergyman and teacher of mathematics. On that summer day he was still unknown, but he was to become Lewis Carroll, author of the immortal story *Alice's Adventures in Wonderland*. The other member of the party who was to become famous was just ten years old. She was Alice Liddell, for whom the story was written.

On that memorable trip to Godstow, Charles Dodgson had brought his friend Robinson Duckworth. Several times before, Mr. Duckworth had helped with the rowing on these river picnics. Next to Mr. Dodgson, he was a great favorite with the Liddell sisters. He had pleasing manners, a sense of humor, and a very fine voice. On the homeward trip in the long English twilight he always led the girls in singing such old songs as "Star of the Evening, Beautiful Star."

Mr. Dodgson's students would have been astonished if they had seen him on the path to the river that day. Instead of the black clothes he always wore in the classroom, he had put on white flannel trousers and a hard straw hat tilted at a careless angle. And as he walked with rapid strides toward the river, followed by the three girls, anyone could see that he was happy — something the students had never seen him look. They thought of him as a lonely young man who made few friends, yet he was obviously enjoying the company of the little girls a great deal.

At the river, Mr. Dodgson selected a boat that would be safe enough and large enough for the three girls in hoopskirts. He seated them in the stern. Then he placed the large picnic basket in the bow. In it was a kettle to boil water for tea when they arrived at Godstow—also a generous supply of cakes.

Soon they were off, with Mr. Dodgson and Robinson Duckworth manning the oars. Alice was a little afraid of a swan who thrust his long neck and big bill into the boat, but the joys of the trip more than made up for this. Sometimes they rowed in midstream. Sometimes they passed close to lovely banks and under willow trees that bent over the river. But the best part of the trip for Alice came when Mr. Dodgson told a story. It started like this:

> *Alice was beginning to get very tired of sitting by her sister on the bank, and of having nothing to do. . . . So she was considering in her own mind (as well as she could, for the hot day made her feel very sleepy and stupid) whether the pleasure of making a daisy-chain was worth the trouble of getting up and picking the daisies, when a white rabbit with pink eyes ran close by her.*

The story went on to tell how Alice followed the white rabbit down a rabbit hole, and about the strange people she met there, and the wonderful things that happened to her. As the real Alice listened she must have looked very much as she does in the picture on this page, which was taken by Charles Dodgson himself.

The white rabbit, drawn by Sir John Tenniel

The little party had tea in the shade of a haystack in a field near Godstow, and returned to Oxford in the early evening. When the two men left the children at the door of the Deanery, Alice Liddell said:

"Oh, Mr. Dodgson, I wish you would write out Alice's adventures for me."

Until that day, none of the many stories that Charles Dodgson told on the river had ever been written down. Years later he recalled that these fairy tales "lived and died, like summer midges, each in its own golden afternoon." But on that day he told Alice he would try to do as she had asked.

The little girls went upstairs to bed, tired but happy. However, they were not too tired to play a bedtime game that Alice had invented. On the posts of the stairway, and along the hall that led to their bedroom, there were carved wooden lions. Every night the children pretended that the lions jumped down from the posts and chased them. So the girls would race down the dark hall as fast as they could.

By nine o'clock, the sisters were asleep. But a light burned in Charles Dodgson's window as he began to write out in his finest script the story that he had told that day on the river. Only the scratch of a pen could be heard in the quiet room as he sketched those first crude pictures that illustrated the story. Dawn was creeping into the town before he put aside his work. It took him many, many nights to finish his task.

The book was small, about six by four and a half inches. It was ninety pages long and had thirty-seven pen-and-ink drawings. At the bottom of the last page Charles Dodgson pasted the photograph of Alice that he had taken when she was seven years old. On the title page were these words:

A Christmas Gift to a Dear Child in Memory of a Summer Day

This handwritten book has the title *Alice's Adventures Under Ground*. It was given to the little daughter of Dean Liddell on Christmas Day, 1864.

Friends urged Charles Dodgson to publish it, but he was shy about doing so. It wasn't until a famous artist, Sir John Tenniel, said he would draw new illustrations for it that Mr. Dodgson agreed.

The Mad Hatter's tea party, drawn by Sir John Tenniel

In 1865 *Alice* was published, under the pen name of Lewis Carroll. It won the hearts of everyone who read it, and Lewis Carroll became famous. But plain Mr. Dodgson did not want fame. He tried his best to keep the peaceful life he had always lived at Oxford.

The years passed, bringing with them many changes. And in 1880, when she was twenty-eight years old, Alice was married in London's Westminster Abbey to Reginald Hargreaves. She left Oxford, taking with her the precious little handwritten book. It was in her possession for almost fifty years.

Very rarely in the long years did Lewis Carroll see the real Alice. As Mrs. Reginald Hargreaves, she was busy raising three sons. She lived in a world apart from Oxford and the friend of her childhood.

Fame brought many important people into the life of Charles Dodgson. But he kept the memory of the child Alice — and of "the golden afternoon" when he had told her a story that will live forever. At the end of *Through the Looking-Glass,* which was written later, he recalls the little picnic party that went up the River Thames on July 4, 1862:

Long has paled that sunny sky;
Echoes fade and memories die;
Autumn frosts have slain July.
Still she haunts me, phantomwise,
Alice moving under skies
Never seen by waking eyes.

A Strange Wild Song

by LEWIS CARROLL

He thought he saw a Buffalo
Upon the chimney-piece;
He looked again, and found it was
His Sister's Husband's Niece.
"Unless you leave this house," he said,
"I'll send for the Police."

He thought he saw a Rattlesnake
That questioned him in Greek;
He looked again, and found it was
The Middle of Next Week.
"The one thing I regret," he said,
"Is that it cannot speak!"

He thought he saw a Banker's Clerk
Descending from the 'bus;
He looked again, and found it was
A Hippopotamus.
"If this should stay to dine," he said,
"There won't be much for us!"

He thought he saw a Kangaroo
That worked a coffee-mill;
He looked again, and found it was
A Vegetable-Pill.
"Were I to swallow this," he said,
"I should be very ill."

He thought he saw a Coach and Four
That stood beside his bed;
He looked again, and found it was
A Bear without a Head.
"Poor thing," he said, "poor silly thing!
It's waiting to be fed!"

He thought he saw an Albatross
That fluttered round the Lamp;
He looked again, and found it was
A Penny Postage-Stamp.
"You'd best be getting home," he said:
"The nights are very damp!"

He thought he saw a Garden Door
That opened with a key;
He looked again, and found it was
A Double-Rule-of-Three.
"And all its mystery," he said,
"Is clear as day to me!"

Reprinted from Sylvie and Bruno
by permission of The Macmillan Co.

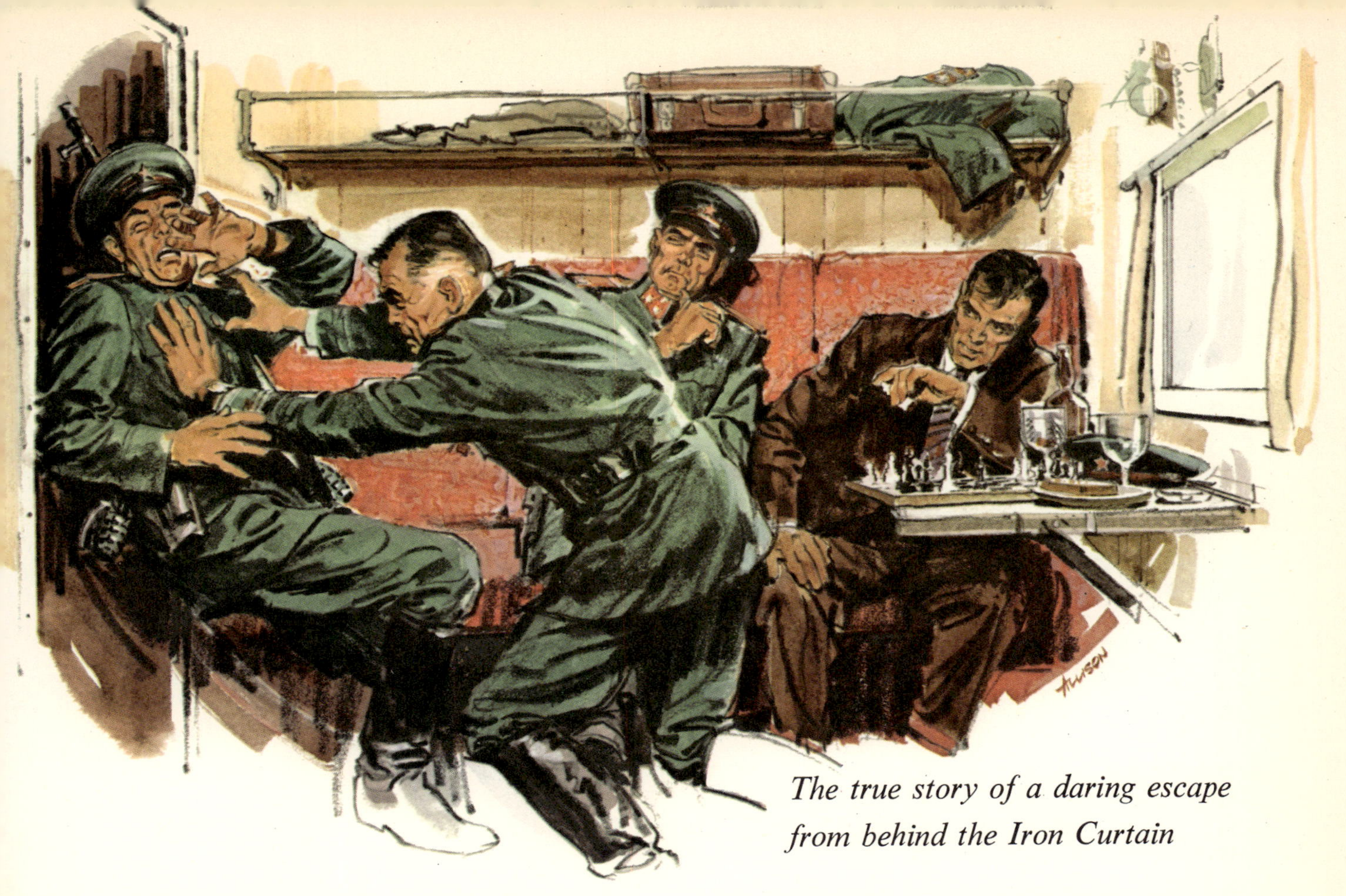

The true story of a daring escape from behind the Iron Curtain

"YOUR MOVE, HUNGARIAN!"

BY FERENC LASZLO

"THERE's a chance," said my friend, "that you could escape from Hungary by pretending to be an Austrian. Would you care to take the risk?"

Would I! It was vital that I should flee from my country as soon as possible. During the Second World War, I had worked for the Allies as an intelligence agent in Budapest. But now the Russians, who had occupied Hungary after the war, suspected me of spying against them. At any moment I might be arrested.

My friend had come secretly to the house where I was hiding. He had information about a train that was to leave Budapest in ten days' time, taking Austrian refugees home to Vienna.

"One person on the passenger list," he said, "hasn't replied to the letters telling him about the train. He may even be dead. This man is a portrait painter named Oscar Zinner. You would have to pretend to be him."

I agreed eagerly. In changing my name from Ferenc Laszlo to Oscar Zinner, I shouldn't have to worry about a passport. In 1946 very few people in Budapest had such things. Hungarians weren't allowed to travel out of the country.

My friend handed me some typewritten pages, giving details of Zinner's life. "You are now the painter Oscar Zinner," he said. "Sit down and learn. You must become Zinner in every action, in every thought."

He tapped the papers. "At each stop, Russian officers will board the train to check the passengers. They will have copies of this, and will question you closely. Another copy will be held by the supervisor of your group. He does not know Zinner. But when the name is called at the station, *wait* before replying."

"Wait?" I asked.

"There's a chance that Zinner might turn up at the last minute," he explained. "If two of you should answer, it would be embarrassing for the one who wasn't Zinner."

For the next few days I studied Oscar Zinner's life story until I knew almost as much about him as I did about myself. I could describe the house where he was born in the town of Graz. I knew where he had been to school. I knew his habits, his likes and dislikes, even his style of painting.

Late on the night before my departure, I walked to the Franz Josef Bridge in Budapest. The notes my friend had given me must not be found. I tore them into shreds and watched them flutter down into the Danube.

Terrible Moments

Next morning I stood at the railway station waiting for the name of Oscar Zinner to be called. I tried hard not to seem anxious. Panic, I knew, could ruin everything.

A sudden crackle came from the station loudspeaker. Then a rasping voice began to call out a list of names, in alphabetical order.

My stomach seemed tied in knots. Why did my new name have to begin with the last letter of the alphabet? I shoved my hands deep into my pockets to hide their trembling.

At last, "Oscar Zinner!" the voice barked.

I wanted to shout. But instead I waited, my heart pounding, my ears straining, my mind praying that there would be no answer from the real Oscar Zinner.

"Zinner!" the voice called again, this time with annoyance.

I stepped forward. "Here!" I said timidly.

There was no challenge from the real Zinner. So far, all was well. We were divided into groups of ten and herded into compartments on the train. Over and over again I went through the story in my head. "I am a portrait painter. I was born in Graz. My father was an architect. . . ."

A shrill whistle sounded from the station platform, signaling the train to start. It didn't move. Suddenly, voices speaking in Russian could be heard at the end of our coach. Four Russian officers marched past the door of our compartment. They stopped at the next compartment, and ordered the people there out into the corridor. The Russians took over the seats. Soon they were laughing and shouting and clinking glasses. The whistle blew again and the train jerked into movement.

As we picked up speed, I gazed out of the window and wondered when I should see my country again. Then I realized that I must not look sad. I was now Oscar Zinner, going home to Vienna.

The train groaned to a halt at a place called Kelenföld. This was the first checkpoint. The Russian inspecting officer and his interpreter soon arrived in our compartment. Behind them, heavily armed Russian soldiers stood in the corridor and watched.

The Russian officer started with the woman sitting opposite me. Looking at his notes about her, he barked questions in Russian, which the interpreter translated into German so that the Austrian woman could understand.

Next he came to the man sitting by the window on my side of the compartment. Once again I began rehearsing what I would say: "I am a painter. I was born in Graz. My name is . . . My name is . . ."

Sweat broke out on my forehead, and my heart seemed to miss a beat. I could remember everything about the man I was pretending to be, except his name.

As if from a distance, I heard the sharp voices of the officer and the interpreter as they moved toward the woman beside me.

"Please, God," I prayed, "what is my name? I am a portrait painter. I was born in Graz. My name is . . ." It was no use. The name would not come.

The Russian General

Just then I heard the door of the compartment slide open. There was a sound of voices in the corridor, and then a Russian colonel poked his head into our compartment.

"Wer spielt Schach?" — Who plays chess? — he asked gruffly in bad German.

Our examining officer turned and glared at the interruption, then stepped back respectfully when he saw the colonel. As I was sitting next to the door, the colonel put his next question to me.

"Spielen Sie Schach?" — Do you play chess? — he asked.

I hadn't played chess for ten years, but it didn't matter. This was the breathing spell I needed. No one else in the compartment spoke.

"Ja, ich spiele Schach" — Yes, I play chess — I said.

The colonel beckoned me to follow him.

In the Russians' compartment were two other colonels and one general, a giant of a man whose powerful chest was covered with medals. It was the general who wanted to play chess. He muttered his thanks to the officer who had brought me, and waved me to a seat opposite him.

On the small table under the window were sandwiches, candy and vodka. Gruffly, he offered me some. I ate and drank in tortured suspense.

At any moment one of the Russians might ask my name; or, worse, the examining officer might come into the compartment.

The Game of My Life

As the train started, the general produced a chessboard and began arranging the men.

"This is the game of my life," I thought. "I must make it good, and yet I mustn't win." Russians hate to be beaten at chess. But no chess player can play for long unless his opponent can make it interesting.

As we played, some of the tricks of the game slowly came back to me. The other officers watched the game in respectful silence. They seemed to think that the general was a wizard at it. As a matter of fact, he was quite a good player, but I was able to make him work for every advantage.

Time flew, as it does in every good battle of chess. Suddenly I realized that the train was slowing down at the next checkpoint. Once again my mind began to race. Now the door of the compartment slid open, and in stepped the supervisor of our group. "This man has not yet been questioned," he said firmly.

I need not have worried. Without a word, the general rose. He spread his huge bear's paw of a hand against the supervisor's chest and thrust him into the corridor. Then he slammed the door and pointed to the chessboard.

"Davai, Magyar!" — Your move, Hungarian! — he thundered as he sat down.

Hungarian! I *was* coming from Hungary, of course. Was it a slip of the tongue, or did he suspect that I was really a Hungarian and not an Austrian? Whatever the answer was, my scalp started tingling. Once or twice after that I thought I caught him looking at me strangely, but each time his eyes went back to the board.

The general won the first game. When we had finished playing, he said something to the colonel who had first spoken to me in German.

"The general enjoys your style," the colonel interpreted. "He will play another game."

I became so interested in this game that I suddenly found myself on the brink of winning. We were playing the last vital moves as the train slowed down at the Austrian frontier. Here I would win or lose — not just a game of chess, but my precious freedom too.

This time the train was boarded by a procession of frontier guards. With them were dozens of Russian soldiers, rifles slung from their shoulders, grenades hanging from their belts. The guards merely glanced into our compartment and went on to the next. There, the angry supervisor must have told them about the "Austrian" who was sitting with the officers, for one guard came back. He stepped smartly in at the door, saluted, and spoke rapidly in Russian, at the same time pointing at me.

Once again my brain froze in fear. Surely the general would let them question me this time. Desperately, I began saying to myself, "I am a portrait painter and my name is . . ." But I could not remember.

As the guard spoke, the general's face slowly turned purple. I had no idea what the guard was telling him, but it made him terribly angry. He looked at me, his eyes blazing. Then he stood up.

This is the end for me, I thought. To come so close and then to be caught —

"What Is Your Name?"

But again it was only the interruption that had made the general so angry. He thrust the guard away with such force that the man reeled backward and struck the corridor wall. The general slammed the door and returned to his seat, muttering angrily. He looked at the chessboard.

"Davai, Magyar!" he said.

My heart was bursting with relief. No one would dare come in again — I was sure of that. As the train gathered speed, taking us safely into Austria, I felt so happy that, for the first time, I smiled. The general looked up from the board and smiled back. He said something to the colonel, who translated for me: "The general wonders if you would enjoy playing him again in Vienna. Where can he reach you?"

Automatically I mentioned a well-known hotel in Vienna.

"And what is your name?" asked the colonel.

Now, without the awful terror, I hesitated only a moment. How could I ever have forgotten those two simple words?

"My name is Oscar Zinner," I said.

The true identity of "Ferenc Laszlo" and certain details surrounding his escape from Hungary must, for obvious reasons, remain concealed. Under his right name he received special commendation from the highest Allied authorities for his intelligence activities in World War II.

How to Play "HEXAPAWN"

BY MARTIN GARDNER

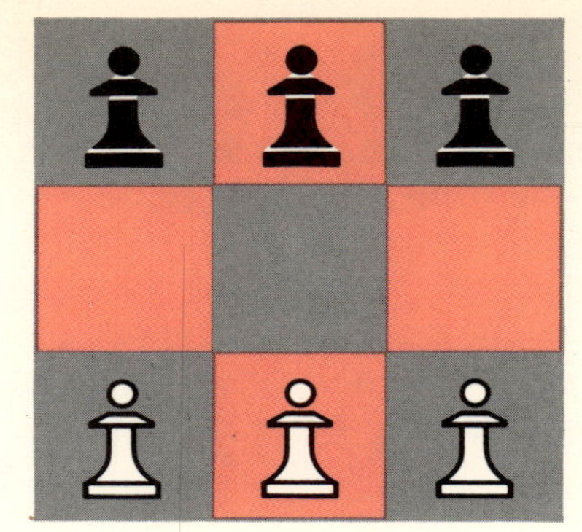

Ill. 1

"Hexapawn" is a simplified form of chess that you can play with HER (Hexapawn Educational Robot). Knowing that today's giant electronic computers have been "taught" to play chess with men, Martin Gardner invented a simple game-playing machine that will operate on the same principles. You feed HER instructions and information, just as men must feed instructions and information into a computer. And, like a computer, your "robot" can "learn" from experience. The great computers flash lights, spin tapes, and function with the speed of light. They can guide missiles to pinpoint targets in space, translate books from one language to another, and even help in the diagnosis of illness. Some of them cost millions of dollars. HER neither flashes nor spins, and costs only a few cents to make. Its one function is to play Hexapawn with you. But it too can "learn"—and you can have a lot of fun being "teacher."

HEXAPAWN is played on a board of nine squares, with three chess pawns on each side, as shown in Illustration 1. Coins can be used instead of actual chess pieces.

Only two types of move are allowed: (1) a pawn may advance straight forward one square to an empty square; (2) a pawn may *capture* an enemy pawn by moving one square diagonally, left or right, to a square occupied by the enemy. The captured piece is removed from the board. These are the same as pawn moves in chess.

The game is won in any one of three ways: (1) by advancing a pawn to the third row; (2) by capturing all enemy pieces; (3) by achieving a position in which the enemy cannot move.

Players take turns, moving one piece at a time. A draw clearly is impossible, but it is not immediately apparent whether the first or second player has the advantage.

To construct HER you need twenty-four empty matchboxes and a supply of colored beads or buttons. Small candies that come in different colors work nicely. (I used five five-cent boxes of jujubes.) Each matchbox bears one of the diagrams shown in Illustration 2, so you will have to copy the twenty-four labels and paste them on the boxes.

Inside each box place a bead to match the color of each arrow on the pattern. The robot is now ready for play. Every legal move is represented by an arrow; the robot can therefore make all possible moves and only legal moves. The robot has no strategy. In fact, it is an idiot.

The robot always makes the second move. Patterns marked "2" represent the two positions open to HER on the second move. You have a choice between a center or an end opening, but only the left end is considered because an opening on the right would obviously lead to identical (although mirror-reflected) lines of play. Patterns marked "4" show the eleven positions that can confront HER on the fourth (its second) move. Patterns marked "6" are the eleven positions that can face HER on the sixth (its last) move.

The teaching procedure is as follows: Make your first move. Pick up the matchbox that shows the position on the board. Shake the matchbox, close your eyes, open the drawer, remove one bead. Close the drawer, put down the box, place the bead on top of the box. Open your eyes, note the color of the bead, find the matching arrow and move accordingly. Now it is your turn to move again. Continue this procedure until the game ends. If the robot wins, replace all the beads and play again. If it loses, "punish" it by

Adapted from Scientific American, *copyright © 1962 by Scientific American, Inc.*

taking away only the bead that represents its *last* move. Replace the other beads and play again. If you should find an empty box (this rarely happens), it means the machine has no move that is not fatal, and it loses. In this case take away the bead of the preceding move.

Keep a record of wins and losses so you can chart the first fifty games. Illustration 3 shows the results of a typical fifty-game tournament. After thirty-six games (including eleven defeats for the robot) it has learned to play a perfect game. The system of punishment is designed to cut down the time required to learn a perfect game, but the time varies with your own skill. The better you are, the faster the machine learns.

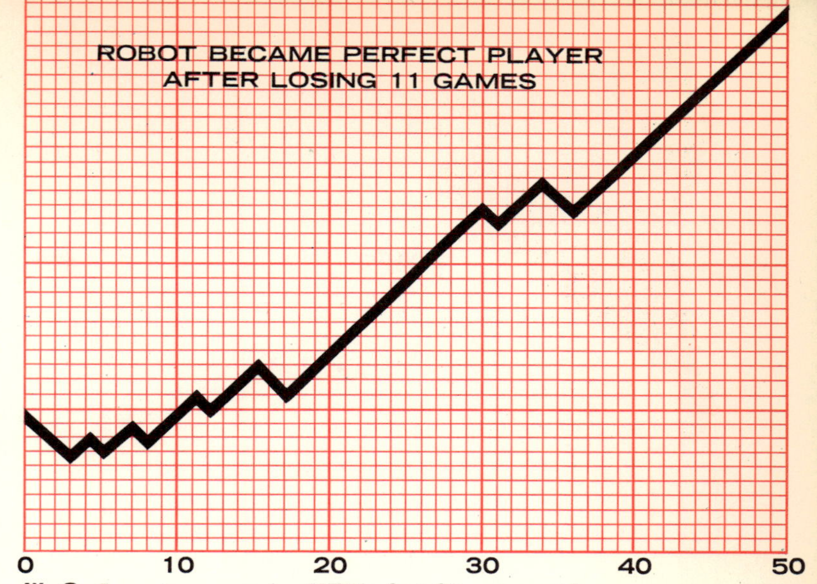

Ill. 3 *Learning curve for HER's first fifty games (downslant shows loss, upslant a win)*

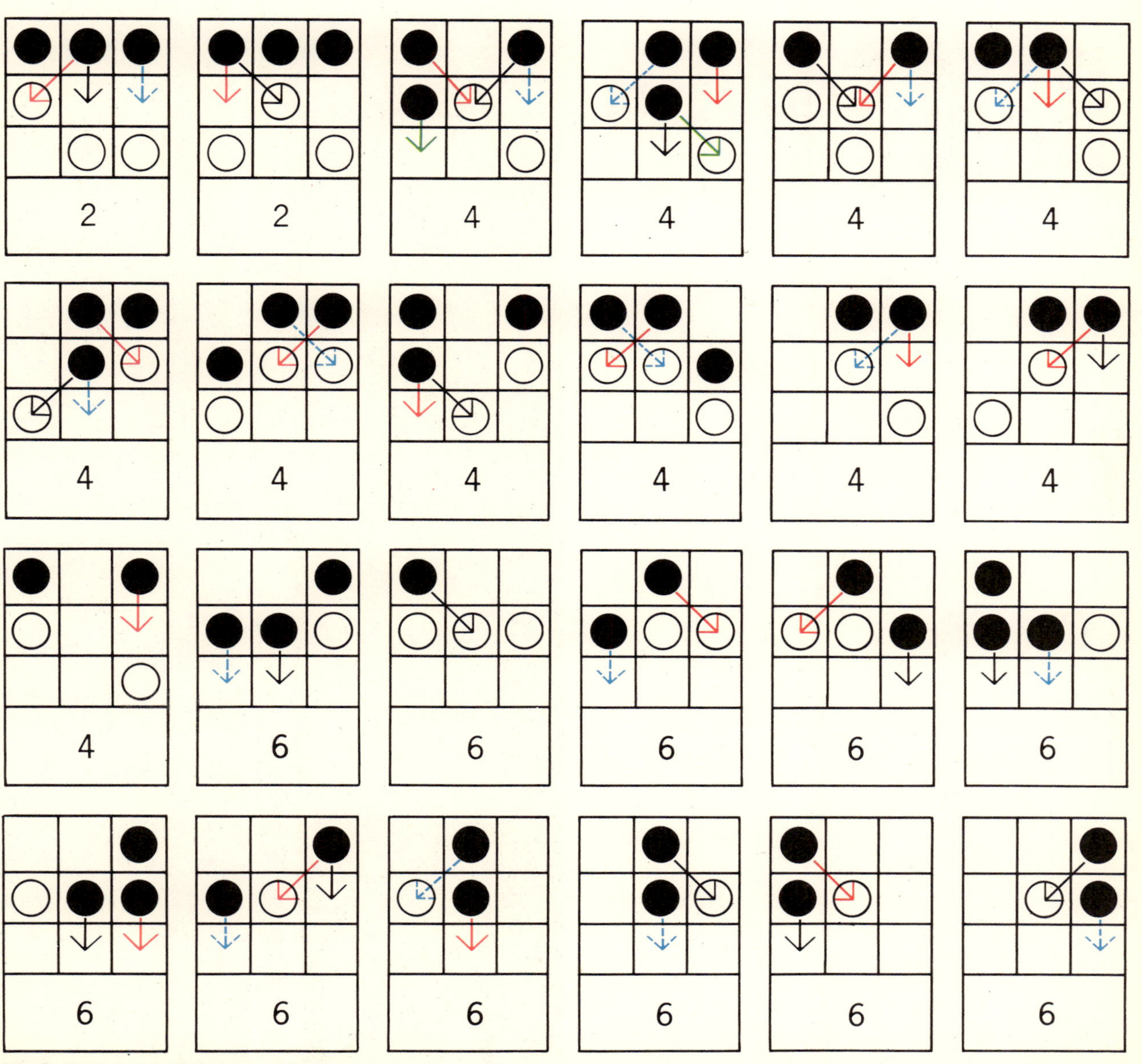

Ill. 2 *Labels for HER matchboxes*

Strange Creatures of the

Rain Forest

BY LINCOLN BARNETT

MILLIONS of years ago — even before the ice ages — the earth basked in a long, long summer that lasted all the year round. From the equator almost to the poles, the land lay covered by a forest of everlasting green. But unlike pines and fir trees — the evergreens with cones and needles that we know in the temperate climates of today — those ancient trees had broad leaves and brilliantly colored blooms.

On the equator that old forest still stands. Though smaller than it once was, it covers more than a tenth of the earth's land surface and nearly half its total forest area. Still everlastingly green, it is richer in plant and animal life than any other of Nature's domains except perhaps the sea. It is called the rain forest.

The largest and richest of today's rain forests is in South America. Stretching northward from the Mato Grosso Plateau and the Amazon River Valley to the Caribbean Sea, it covers a million square miles. What does this forest look like?

(continued on page 180)

Adapted from Life, *copyright 1954 by Time Inc.*

Over 120 feet in height, the tallest trees lift their tops into sunny skies patrolled by fierce birds of prey.

At 60 to 120 feet the leaves of less towering trees mingle to form a green forest roof. Here bright-colored birds sing and monkeys leap from branch to branch.

Below 60 feet the forest gets no sunlight, and young trees struggle for life. Here live the "basement dwellers," creatures of the shade.

The tops of the trees form three or more layers, one upon another. First there are the sparse young trees up to sixty feet high; overshadowed by their larger neighbors, they have to struggle for life in perpetual gloom. Above them, at heights between sixty and a hundred twenty feet, the treetops are so thickly woven together that they make a green roof which covers the whole forest. Higher still soar the giant trees whose crowns — sometimes two hundred or more feet high — have burst through the roof into the sunny upper air, like tropical islands above a green sea.

Each of these layers receives a different amount of sunlight and has its own strange plants and animals. At noontime the forest is silent and seems empty of life. Only at dawn and dusk, when the hunters of night and day are out together, do many voices betray the numerous living things.

Animals of the Forest

Furtive, seldom seen, are the animals in the lower part of the forest. They are the basement dwellers, the creatures of the shade.

The most ancient of all forest mammals are the opossums, small furry creatures with pouches like kangaroos', and long tails by which they swing from the branches. Scarcely less old are the lumbering anteater, whose swift tongue is the terror of insects, the giant armadillo with its plated sides, and two sturdy relatives of the guinea pig, the paca and the agouti. The largest animals of the forest are of less ancient descent. They are the shy tapir, a long-nosed cousin of the rhinoceros, and his only dangerous enemies, the puma and the jaguar. The jaguar prowls the branches as surefootedly as he does the forest floor.

Older even than the forest itself are the cold-blooded reptiles and amphibians: turtles, tortoises, toads and lizards. Here are some of the world's most dangerous snakes: the twenty-foot anaconda, a water snake; and the boa constrictor, which lives on dry land.

In the rain forest live the greatest acrobats on earth. The star gymnast is the skinny, intelligent spider monkey. Hanging by his tail from the loop of a liana (climbing plant), he may suddenly give a short swing and throw himself a distance of fifty feet, lightly catching the branch of a tree on which he spied a shining berry. The marmosets, smallest of the monkey tribe, are tough, noisy hooligans that travel in gangs. They, too, are capable of great leaps into space, but their landings are not very graceful — they go smack

against a tree trunk with their arms and legs spread wide!

The most noticeable of all the high-perch artists is the red howler monkey. He has a hideous, almost human face with a pointed beard, and he produces the most earsplitting and bloodcurdling animal sounds on earth. A hollow bone at the base of his tongue acts as a sound box and makes his cries unbelievably loud.

Among the treetops even the reptiles perform feats of grace and daring. The tiny ho-ko-bee lizard not only leaps great distances but can land upside down on the underside of a branch far above his head, clinging by sticky pads on his feet. The iguana lizard is a specialist in high diving, and will plunge as much as eighty feet from an overhanging branch into a shallow pool below.

Two-toed and three-toed sloths hang upside down by their clawed hands, moving slowly among the branches, munching leaves. As the sluggish, stupid sloth cannot fight or flee his enemies, his only safety lies in camouflage. His long hair is encrusted with a mossy green scum, and when he is asleep among the leaves with his head tucked between his legs he is almost invisible.

Strange Birds and Insects

To fit in with this circus scene, the birds provide bright color and loud music: brilliantly feathered parrots and macaws, and the toucans with their thick bills. These birds seldom venture into the shadows below, or into what is to them the dangerous upper air above the forest. Fierce birds of prey patrol the open sky: owls, eagles, falcons and hawks. The fiercest of all is the harpy eagle with his cruel talons. When he dives down from above, he seldom misses his victim, whether it is a stupid sloth or a leaping monkey which he bears off screaming into the air.

Outnumbering all other creatures are the insects and spiders found everywhere from the forest floor to the tallest treetop. Of the hundreds of thousands of different kinds, the most amazing are the army ants which march in legions, clearing the ground of all living things that cannot escape. There are huge butterflies with shining wings that span five inches; and a caterpillar six inches long whose poisonous spines, if you touched them, would make you ill for days.

So, from top to bottom, the rain forest is full of strange, exciting creatures. Keep your eyes open next time you visit the zoo, and see if you can recognize some of them.

QUIZZLES-FOUR

(*Answers and explanations on page 199*)

FIND THE FLOWER

Each of these groups of mixed-up letters spells the name of a flower when put in the right order. For instance, YSNAP would be PANSY. Can you find the other flowers?

1. NTUAPIE . . . .
2. ORMIDLAG . . . .
3. LEVOTI . . . .
4. WFURONELS . . . .
5. FDOLADIF . . . .
6. YHMRTUHCAMESN . . . . . .
7. PLUIT . . . .
8. PRUSKALR . . . .
9. NCIHAHYT . . . .
10. BOLCNIEMU . . . .

CAN YOU COUNT?

Of course, but can you count *all* the squares shown here? Sixteen? No — almost twice that number.

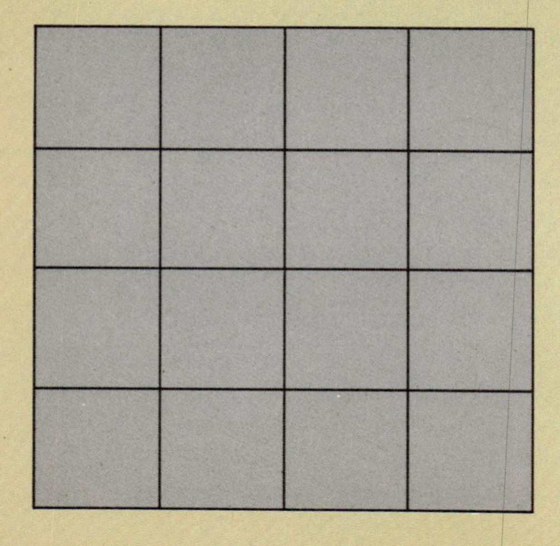

TEST OF GENIUS

Ask your friends to read this sentence slowly: "Finished files are the result of years of scientific study combined with the experience of years." Then tell them to count aloud, only once, the number of *f*s in the sentence. How many?

"Test of Genius" is adapted from The Correspondent.

THE TANGLED THREADS

The names of the objects shown here are your clues to the word that belongs in the 11 squares below. Follow the tangled thread (or line) that connects each object with an empty square. Then put the first letter of the object's name in the square. If you don't get all tangled up, you'll spell a familiar word.

FOR YOU TO FINISH

Each of these sequences is arranged in an order that makes good sense, if you can find the key. For example, you would add a 3 to this sequence: 13, 11, 9, 7, 5. ...See if you can find the number, letter or design to finish each of the others.

1. 20, 17, 14, 11 . . . .

2. 16, 15, 13, 12, 10, 9 . . . .

3. H g F e D c . . . .

4. A A C B B D . . . .

5. 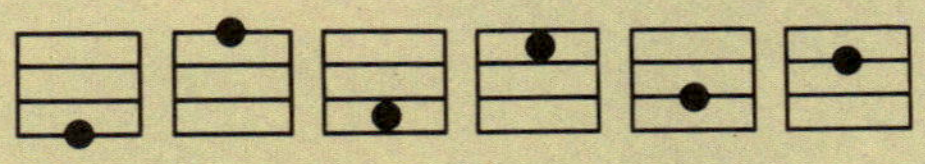

6. a C B d F E g . . . .

7. 

8. ★ ★★ ★★★ ★★★★ ★★★ ★★

9. 30, 15, 45, 15, 60 . . . .

10. A B D G K P . . . .

11. 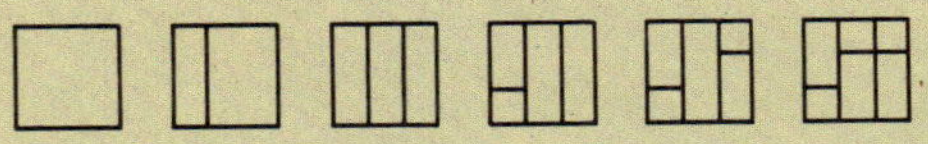

12. 

13. 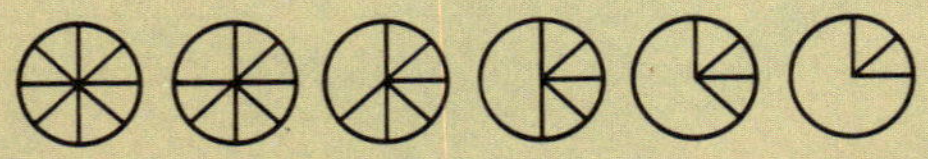

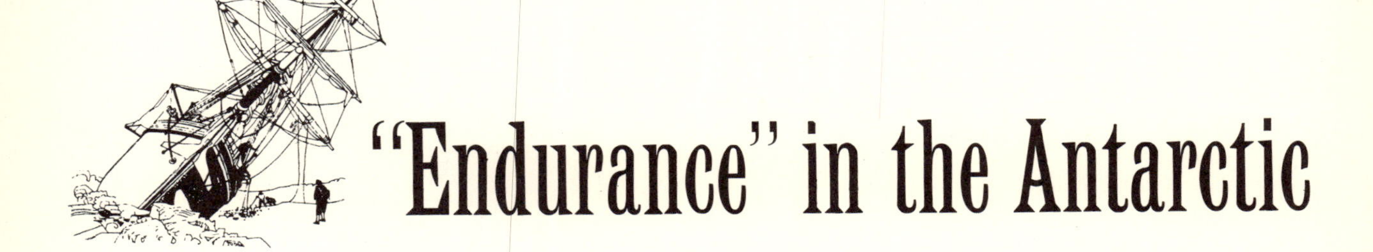

"Endurance" in the Antarctic

WHEN the order to abandon ship was given — at five p.m. on October 27, 1915 — the twenty-seven members of Shackleton's Trans-Antarctic Expedition were almost glad to hear it. After days of exhausting work at the ship's pumps, they hardly had the strength to care. By then every man aboard knew that the ship was doomed.

The *Endurance,* a 144-foot auxiliary-powered barkentine, was probably the strongest wooden ship ever built. Her hull planking, of oak and mountain fir, was in places two and a half feet thick. And the *Endurance* lived up to her name.

For months she had stood up with magnificent staunchness to the ice that was squeezing her from every side. Her great timbers creaked and groaned as the terrible pressure mounted. At last, when they could no longer stand the strain, they broke with a report like artillery fire. The decks buckled; the stern was thrown upward twenty feet; and the rudder and sternpost were torn out of her.

Frank Wild, the second-in-command, passed Shackleton's order on to the crew: "Time to get off!"

Within two hours, all essential equipment had been unloaded onto the ice. It included three boats — two cutters and one whaler — and the expedition's forty-nine dogs. A camp was pitched on a solid floe close by.

Sir Ernest Shackleton could not share his men's feeling of relief. As leader of the expedition, he knew that their plight could hardly be more desperate. They were alone in the Antarctic, marooned on the icy wastes of the Weddell Sea, midway between the South Pole and the nearest outpost of humanity — and that was about twelve hundred miles to the north.

The closest known land, the Palmer Peninsula, was two hundred and ten miles away and uninhabited. They had no radio transmitter, and nobody in the outside world knew they were in trouble. It is unlikely that rescuers could have reached them in any case.

Thus their plight was frighteningly simple. If they were to get out, they had to get themselves out.

The Men and Their Leader

Shackleton had already decided that they would march over the frozen ocean toward Paulet Island, a tiny spot of land three hundred and forty-six miles to the northeast, where stores of food were known to be cached. He felt certain that, sooner or later, they would come to open water, so they would have to drag the three lifeboats with them on sledges.

The men who faced this tremendous task could hardly have been a more varied collection of people. They included university professors, Yorkshire fishermen, and one stowaway who had slipped aboard at Buenos Aires. But sharing the long polar night aboard the *Endurance* had turned them into a cheerful, close-knit team.

Shackleton, too, managed to seem cheerful and resolute, for he was a true explorer — tough, romantic, a little swashbuckling. He was now forty years old, a stocky, iron-jawed man who thoroughly believed in the motto of his Irish family: *By endurance we conquer.*

This was Shackleton's third Antarctic expedition. He had been with Robert Falcon Scott, the noted British polar explorer, in 1901. And in 1907 he had led his own expedition to within

Adapted from Endurance: Shackleton's Incredible Voyage,
© 1959 by Alfred Lansing and published by McGraw-Hill Book Co.

a hundred and thirteen miles of the Pole — a feat for which he received a knighthood, and honors from many foreign countries. His aim this time had been to cross Antarctica on foot.

Shackleton's Example

After they had spent thirty-six hours on the ice, Shackleton called all hands together and talked about the journey that lay ahead. It was vital, he explained gravely, that they should take only what was absolutely necessary. Each man would be allowed the clothes he was wearing, plus two pairs of mittens, six pairs of socks, two pairs of boots, a sleeping bag, a pound of tobacco — and two pounds of personal gear.

When he had finished speaking, he reached under his jacket and took out a gold cigarette case and several gold sovereigns. These he threw into the snow. Then he opened the Bible that Queen Alexandra, the Queen Mother, had given the expedition. From it he tore the flyleaf containing her message: "May the Lord help you to do your duty & guide you through all the dangers by land and sea." He also took out the page containing the Twenty-third Psalm. Then he laid the Bible in the snow and walked away.

Shackleton had shown that he meant what he said. And, as the day wore on, it was clear that his example had been followed by the men. The pile of things dumped in the center of the tents grew steadily. It was an extraordinary collection: clocks, saws, socks, sweaters, chisels, books, pictures, and all sorts of private keepsakes.

That night, on the eve of their starting the journey to Paulet Island, Shackleton wrote in his diary:

"I pray God I can manage to get the whole party safe to civilization."

Hard Going

Next day they started off, with Shackleton and an advance party leading the way to search for the most level route. The dog teams came next, pulling heavily laden sledges. Then, under the command of Frank Worsley, who had been captain of the *Endurance,* came the last and most difficult operation — moving the boats.

This was dreadful toil. The boats, weighing over a ton each, were drawn one at a time by fifteen men harnessed to ropes. They sank deep into the soft snow, and to move them the men had to strain forward until they were leaning almost parallel with the ground. Every few hundred yards they had to chop a miniature mountain pass through ridges of ice. On particularly high ridges, a ramp of ice and snow had to be built up one side and down the other.

COURTESY OF THE AMERICAN MUSEUM OF NATURAL HISTORY

Sir Ernest Henry Shackleton was born in Kilkee, Ireland, in 1874. He died on South Georgia Island in 1922 while on his third expedition to the Antarctic

During the first day they covered no more than one mile. It snowed heavily that night, and the next day progress was even less. Shackleton decided that it was not worthwhile going on. They were then camped on a strong ice floe, ten feet thick and a third of a mile across. Shackleton announced that they would stay there until the drift of the ice carried them closer to land.

On November 21 the *Endurance* sank. Shackleton noticed her unusual movements and shouted, "She's going!" A moment later all the men were out of the tents and scrambling to places from which they could see. They watched without speaking as the *Endurance's* stern rose into the air and hung there with her motionless propeller held aloft. Then she disappeared beneath the ice. For a few moments there was a gap of black, open water to mark where she had been. After that, there was nothing but endless ice.

Everything now depended on the drift of the ice. It might continue to go roughly northwest, carrying them toward Paulet Island. Or the drift might stop for some reason, and they would remain more or less in the same spot. Finally, there was the chance that the ice pack might veer east, carrying them *away* from land, but nobody cared to think about that.

Ocean Camp

They stayed at Ocean Camp, as they called it, for almost two months. Crammed together in their tiny tents, with little between their sleeping bags and the bare ice, they soon got used to the cold and wet. At mealtimes they ate out of aluminum mugs, into which everything was dumped at once. To eat with, they each had a spoon, a knife — and their fingers.

As one day turned into the next, they waited in vain for the ice to open up. When it did not, they cheered themselves with the thought that at least the ice pack was moving north at about two miles a day. But in mid-December even this changed, and the drift became definitely to the east. Moreover, since the men had little to do, they began to get restless and impatient.

Shackleton was worried. Of all the enemies they had against them — the cold, the ice, the sea — he feared none more than sinking spirits. These could be bolstered only by action.

He called all hands together and told them that they would start off across the ice again in two days' time. They intended to travel mostly at night, when temperatures would be lower and the ice surface firmer. He also said that, since they would be on the trail over Christmas, they would celebrate before leaving. All hands could now eat everything they wanted. A great deal of food would have to be left behind anyway.

The Christmas "feast" began at once, and lasted almost all the next day.

At five thirty the next morning they started over the ice. After making slow progress all day, Shackleton handed Frank Worsley a corked jar containing a note. Worsley was told to take it back to Ocean Camp and leave it there.

The note said that the *Endurance* had been abandoned, and that the members of the expedition were making their way westward across the ice, in the hope of reaching land. It was a message to those who might come after, explaining what had happened to the expedition in 1915.

Shackleton had purposely not left the note until after the party had gone from the camp. He didn't want the men to find it and think that their leader feared they might not live.

Patience Camp

On Christmas Day Shackleton wrote in his diary: "Curious Christmas. Home thoughts."

It was curious indeed, for now they were on the march again, and many of the ice floes were melting and waterlogged. The frozen, snow-covered surface looked firm enough. But every few steps a man would break through the crust and sink knee-deep in water. The shock was jarring and the water numbingly cold. The men pulling the boats could take only about two hundred yards of this punishment at a time.

After five days, during which they advanced nine miles, Shackleton decided that it was hopeless to continue. Many of the men had reached a point of complete exhaustion.

Their position, if anything, was worse than it had been. They had had to leave a lot of food behind at Ocean Camp, and now they were simply camping again — this time on waterlogged, untrustworthy ice. If the pack ice let them, they might manage to escape. Otherwise there was nothing to do except keep themselves alive.

For three and a half months, with starvation threatening, they were doomed to stay on this bit of ice — aptly named Patience Camp. As the long wait dragged on, the supply of blubber for cooking dwindled alarmingly. Shackleton ordered the ration cut to one warm drink a day — a helping of hot powdered milk at breakfast.

The Sea Leopard

But Fortune never failed them altogether. They always managed to kill enough seals to keep themselves from starving. And one day thousands of Adélie penguins suddenly appeared on the ice, frolicking in the water and making a great deal of noise. During the next three days, the men were able to kill some six hundred of them for the camp larder.

The search for food sometimes led to strange dangers. One day the storekeeper, Orde-Lees, was skiing across an ice floe on his way back from a seal hunt. Suddenly an evil, knoblike head burst out of the water just in front of him. He turned and fled, pushing as hard as he could with his ski sticks, and shouting to Frank Wild to bring his rifle.

The huge animal — a sea leopard — sprang out of the water and came bounding after him. The beast looked like a dinosaur, with a long, thin neck. After half a dozen leaps it had almost caught up with Orde-Lees when, for some reason, it wheeled around and plunged into the water.

By then, Orde-Lees had nearly reached the opposite side of the ice floe. He was about to cross to safe ice when the sea leopard's head

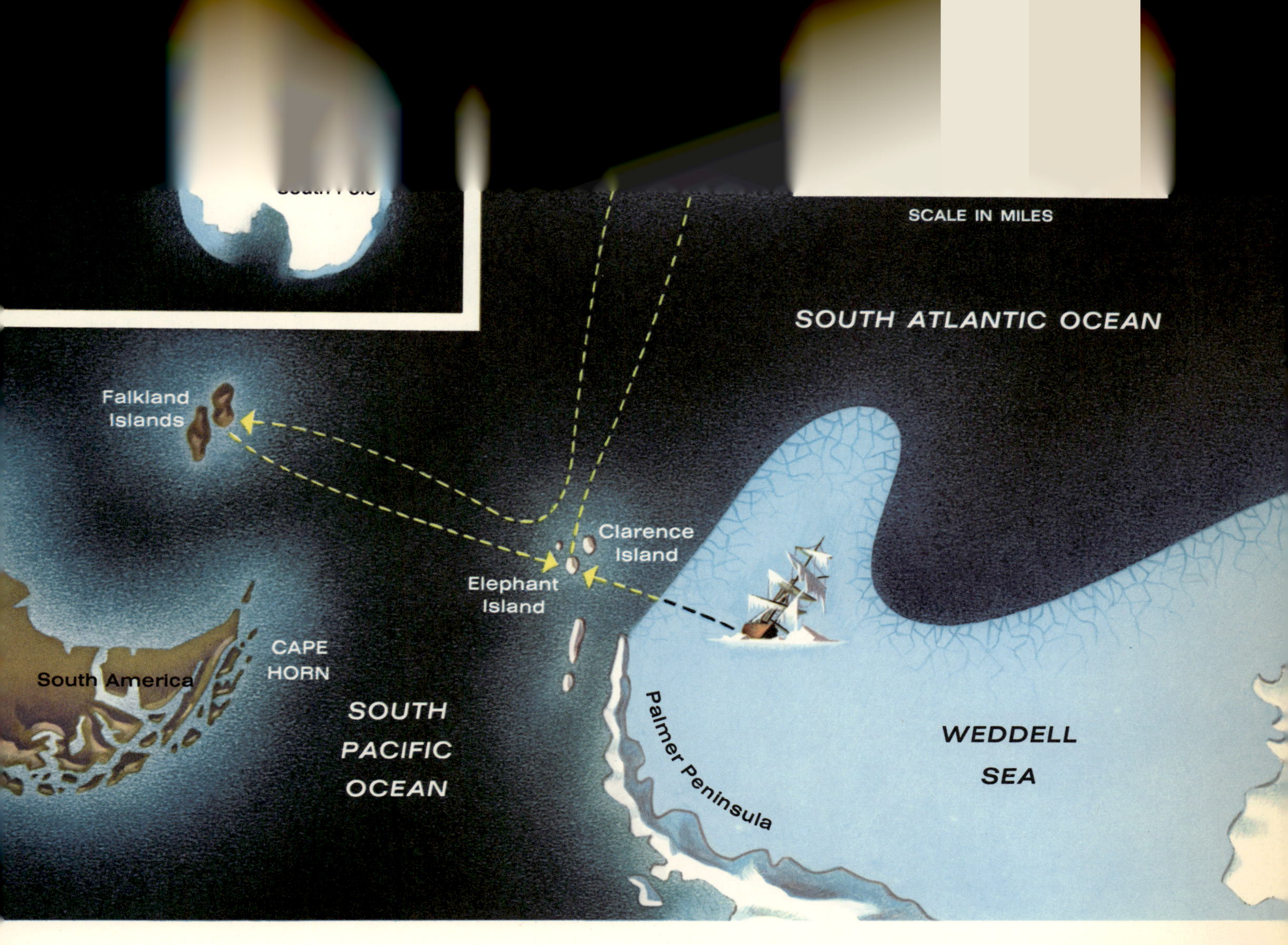

exploded out of the water directly in front of him. Obviously, it had tracked his shadow from under the ice. It made a savage lunge for him, opening its mouth and revealing an enormous number of teeth.

Orde-Lees' shouts for help rose to screams as he turned and raced away from his attacker. The animal leaped out of the water again just as Frank Wild arrived with his rifle. The sea leopard spotted Wild, and turned to attack him. Wild dropped to one knee and fired again and again at the onrushing beast. It was less than thirty yards away when it finally fell.

Two dog teams were needed to bring the sea leopard — a kind of large seal — into the camp. It was twelve feet long and weighed half a ton.

A New Danger

Late in January, a gale blew up from the south. It was so violent that it almost swept them out of the camp. But they bore it gladly, since it carried them the way they wanted to go. It took them eighty-four miles in six days, and the men began to look northward with new hope.

It was on March 9 that they first felt the swell — the unmistakable rise and fall of the open ocean. They gathered in little groups, excitedly pointing to the gentle, lazy movement across the surface of the ice. But how far away was the open water? After long discussions, they decided that it could not be more than thirty miles at the most.

Shackleton alone seemed to sense that the swell was actually a far more dangerous threat than any they had faced until then. The one peril from which he knew there could be no escape was for the swells to grow while the pack remained closed. The movement of the sea would then crack and break the floes, and at last grind the ice to bits. They would not be able to camp, and the boats would be crushed as soon as they were launched.

To make matters worse, the food store was

now desperately low. More than two weeks had passed since they had killed a seal, and the blubber provided by the penguins was nearly gone. On March 16, the last of their flour was used up.

Land, Ho!

One morning Shackleton, who was up early, saw a black object far in the distance. He watched it for a few minutes, then hurried from tent to tent shouting, "Land in sight! Land in sight!"

Some of the men at once bounded out of their tents to see for themselves. Others, however, refused to stir from their sleeping bags. They were tired of distant icebergs being mistaken for land.

But this was not a distant iceberg or a mirage. It was one of the tiny Danger Islets near the tip of the Palmer Peninsula. They could tell by its flat-topped cliffs, rising steeply out of the water. It lay exactly forty-two miles away in a westerly direction.

"If the ice opens," one member of the expedition wrote in his diary, "we could land in a day."

But the ice showed no sign of opening, so they could not launch the boats. The sight of land, so near and yet so far, was just another reminder of their helplessness.

They had drifted to the very tip of the Palmer Peninsula, and hope of reaching land there was now gone. All that remained between them and the terrifying open seas — the most storm-tossed ocean in the world — were two small islands. These lonely outposts of the Antarctic Continent, known as Clarence Island and Elephant Island, lay about a hundred and twenty miles to the north. Beyond them there was nothing.

Every day, almost every hour, their plight became more desperate. By April 3, their ice floe, which had once measured nearly six hundred yards across, was less than a third of that. It was constantly threatened by swells and collisions with other floes. Their position showed that Elephant Island now lay sixty-eight miles due north of them. Though they seemed to be making roughly toward it, they were always worried about the gradual westerly drift which might sweep them past it and out to the open sea.

The Ice Breaks

At about six forty-five on the evening of April 8, Harry McNeish, the carpenter, was writing in his diary: "There has been a large swell since yesterday, but it is doing us no harm now [since] our floe is broken up so small. It rises and falls with . . ."

He never finished the sentence. There was a heavy thump, and the floe split.

Worsley was on watch, and he shouted for help. All hands dashed from their tents. Two of the boats and some of the stores were on the other half of the floe. They were quickly dragged back across the widening crack.

The floe was now a triangle of ice, each side measuring roughly a hundred yards.

Toward midmorning, lanes and pools of water spread through the ice pack and widened out.

At ten thirty, Shackleton's booming voice rang out: "Strike the tents and clear the boats!"

The men jumped to their tasks.

Crack!

Again the floe had split in two, this time exactly through the spot where Shackleton's tent had stood a few minutes before. The two halves of the floe drew rapidly apart, separating one of the boats and a large amount of provisions from the party. At once almost everyone leaped over the widening gap, shoved the boat across and managed to save the stores.

Then they waited, longing to launch the boats, but knowing that, once they did so, there could be no turning back. Small as it was, theirs was the only decent floe in sight. If they abandoned it, and the pack closed up before they reached another campsite, there could be no escape.

The men looked at Shackleton. For the moment the ice pack was open — but how long would it remain open? And yet, how long could they stay where they were? The immense floe that had once been Patience Camp was now just an irregular rectangle of ice, hardly fifty yards across.

At twelve forty Shackleton gave the order.

"Launch the boats," he said in a quiet voice.

In the Boats

The floe came alive with action as they hurried the three boats into the water and loaded them. Then they scrambled aboard, put out every oar they had, and pulled with all their strength for open water. But even as they drew away from Patience Camp, the ice began to close.

The first few minutes were vital — and they were maddening. The oarsmen did their best to pull together, but they were clumsy and out of practice, and hampered by their own anxiety.

The surrounding ice fouled the oars, and the boats collided with one another. And yet, to their surprise, they made headway.

In fifteen minutes Patience Camp was lost in the jumble of ice astern. But, like the *Endurance* and Ocean Camp, Patience Camp belonged now to the past. They were in the boats, and that was all that mattered . . . row . . . get away . . . escape.

Throughout the afternoon they made excellent progress. There were places where the ice was thick, but not dense enough to block their way. At about five thirty the light began to fail, and Shackleton decided that they would camp for the night. Luckily, they found a flat, heavy floe which seemed quite firm.

The boats were hauled up, and tents were pitched. It had been a tiring but rewarding day. By Worsley's estimate, they had made seven miles to the northwest. They were thus seven miles closer to Clarence or Elephant Island — whichever they might happen to reach.

Everyone except the night watchman turned in immediately after supper. But toward eleven o'clock Shackleton became strangely uneasy. Dressing, he went outside, and noticed that the swell had increased. A moment later there was a deep-sounding thud as the floe split in two beneath his feet — and directly under the tent in which eight of the men were sleeping.

The Missing Man

Almost instantly, the two pieces of the floe drew apart. The tent collapsed and there was a splash. Seven of the men scrambled quickly out from under the limp canvas.

"Somebody's missing!" one of them shouted.

Shackleton rushed forward and began to tear the tent away. In the dark, he could hear muffled, gasping noises coming from below. When at last he got the tent out of the way, he saw a shapeless form wriggling in the water. It was a man in his sleeping bag.

Shackleton reached down and got hold of the bag. Then, with one tremendous heave, he pulled it out of the water. A moment later, the two halves of the broken floe came back together with a violent shock.

The man in the sleeping bag turned out to be Ernie Holness, one of the ship's stokers. He was soaked through, but there simply weren't enough dry clothes to give him. In order to prevent him from freezing, Shackleton ordered that he should be kept moving until his clothes dried. For the rest of the night the men took turns walking up and down with him. His companions could hear the crackling of his frozen garments, and the soft tinkle of the ice as it fell from him.

They took to the boats again at eight o'clock the next morning. Three hours later they came to a long, dense belt of pack ice. After hours of searching they finally found a passage through it. On the other side, they suddenly saw that at last they were in the open sea.

A Fight with the Sea

This was the moment they had dreamed of ever since the days of Ocean Camp. But, as so often happens, the dream came true in a way they had not bargained for. As soon as the boats left the shelter of the ice pack, they were struck by the full force of the wind and a high-breaking sea. Freezing spray burst over the men, and the boats shipped water perilously.

Shackleton kept the three boats pounding head on into the seas until about two o'clock. Then he ordered a retreat behind the sheltering barrier of ice. The exhausted men scrambled onto an ice floe and pulled the boats up after them. They had not slept for thirty-six hours and, as they lay down that night, one thought was uppermost in all their minds — that their floe would hold together until morning.

By some miracle it did. But a northeast wind arose, and great quantities of pack ice were blown in all around them. By dawn, the ice reached to the horizon in every direction, and waves thirty feet high swept through it at half-mile intervals. Thus their floe was pounded from every direction, and the swell was steadily destroying it.

Finally, some trick of the current cleared a passage through the ice. Anxious hands seized the boats and pushed them into the water. Warned by their narrow escape, the men did not try to pitch camp on the ice again. In fact, they never left the boats once during the next four days.

Elephant Island

Often drenched by freezing spray, the men sat crowded together in the little boats. The days were just bearable, for then at least they were making progress. But the nights, which they spent hove to, lest the boats should become separated, seemed endless. Their equipment and stores left no room for the men to stretch out, and sitting still all night in that freezing temperature brought

dire results. Not a man escaped frostbite, and at least three had frozen feet.

On the fifth day they sighted the peaks of Elephant Island off the starboard bow — the promised land, no more than thirty miles away! In the joy of that moment, Shackleton called to Worsley to congratulate him on his navigation. With secret pride, Worsley looked awkwardly away.

They would land by nightfall — provided not a moment was lost. Hour after hour they rowed, and the outline of Elephant Island slowly grew larger. Much of their strength had gone, but they leaned on their oars with the desperation of men rowing for their lives.

By early afternoon the snowy peaks of Elephant Island rose steeply out of the water, probably no more than ten miles off. But an hour later the island was still in the same position. It seemed to hang there, no closer and yet no farther away. Row as they might, they were obviously standing still, caught in a strong offshore current. In addition, the wind now shifted to the north, and increased to gale force.

They fought the gale all through still another night and into the next day. Afterward they could never understand how they did it; but, exhausted as they were, they held their own. And finally the storm dropped.

With the last remains of their strength, they drove the boats onto the bleak shore of Elephant Island. For the first time in four hundred and ninety-seven days they were on land. Solid, unsinkable, blessed land.

Six Go for Help

Elephant Island turned out to be a very unfriendly place. There were plenty of seals and penguins for food, but they were almost all the life there was. All along the coast, hostile cliffs rose like an enormous wall thrown up against the sea.

The cliffs at the head of the beach where they had landed bore the marks of high tides, showing that the whole beach was often covered by the sea. Obviously it was safe only when the tide was low.

After nine hours of scouting around the island, a boat came back with the news that there was only one safe beach. This was a fairly sheltered stretch, a hundred and fifty yards long and thirty yards wide, seven miles to the west.

Shackleton lost no time in moving the whole party there; but he realized that, if they were to be rescued, someone would have to go for help at once.

After their third day on the island, Shackleton announced that he would take a party of five men and set sail for South Georgia, eight hundred miles away, to bring help from one of the whaling stations there. He would leave as soon as their whaler — a twenty-two-foot boat named the *Caird* — could be made ready for the trip. The crew would be: Worsley; McNeish, the carpenter; Second Officer Crean; and two sturdy seamen, Vincent and McCarthy.

Worsley, of course, was an obvious choice. Their goal was an island no more than twenty-five miles wide at its widest point. To guide an open boat eight hundred miles to a place that was just a pinpoint on the chart would tax even Worsley's skill as a navigator.

McNeish went to work at once to make a canvas decking over the *Caird*. Hundreds of pounds of rocks were gathered for ballast, and Orde-Lees melted ice to fill two casks with drinking water. A month's supply of food was collected, together with all the spare clothing possible. Nine days after they first came to Elephant Island, arrangements for the trip were complete.

On April 24 a farewell breakfast was prepared, for which Shackleton permitted every man an extra two biscuits and a quarter pound of jam. Jokes were cracked, and everyone tried to seem lighthearted. But at twelve thirty, when the *Caird* cast off, both groups knew they might very well never see one another again.

Life in the "Caird"

As Elephant Island dropped astern, and the waving figures on the shore faded from sight, Shackleton was very uneasy. He was a land explorer, and he felt somewhat out of place at sea. But the twenty-two men he was leaving behind were as helpless and alone as if they had been on another planet. Their plight was known only to the six men in this tiny boat; and the sea was the only road to rescue.

Within two days, the sea had shown the boat's crew what miseries they were to suffer in their life aboard the *Caird*. First there was the water — impossible to keep out, getting into everything. It came partly from the spray flung astern by the wind. And every time the boat dipped into a wave more water came pouring across the decking and into the cockpit.

Sleeping was almost the worst part. The sleeping bags were kept in the bow, which was the driest place in the whole boat. To reach them, the men had to crawl painfully over the rock ballast, going first on their hands and knees, and then on their stomachs. Sometimes, as they tried to sleep, they would be heaved into the air by the movement of the boat, only to fall down on the sharp rocks again.

Running before almost gale winds, they logged a hundred and twenty-eight miles in two days. They were in the Drake Passage, where it seems that Nature likes to test her mightiest powers.

Here, where there is no land to interrupt it, the sea has been blown clockwise around the world since the beginning of time. The gigantic waves thus produced have become famous among seafaring men. They are sometimes more than ninety feet high, and their speed reaches as much as thirty knots.

Cape Horn Rollers

From the tiny *Caird,* these Cape Horn rollers seemed terrifying. Once every ninety seconds or so, the boat's sail would go slack as one of the huge waves loomed astern, shutting out the wind. Towering perhaps fifty feet above her, each wave threatened to bury her under countless tons of water. But somehow the boat would be lifted higher and higher up the onrushing swell, until she found herself hurtling forward on the foaming crest. Over and over again, a thousand times a day, this was repeated.

Nine days out from Elephant Island, they were granted a short breathing spell. The wind dropped to a breeze, and glorious patches of blue sky appeared above their heads.

Worsley took their position at noon, and announced that they were four hundred and three miles out — about midway to South Georgia. The long battle was half won.

They started to dry their gear. Soon the rigging was covered with their tattered clothing and dripping sleeping bags. And the off-duty watch, no longer huddled miserably under the decking, relaxed and even became quite cheerful.

After two days of warm skies and gentle winds, however, the weather turned its fury on them once more.

Search for an Island

The task of navigation was almost impossible. Often the movement of the boat was so violent that Worsley was not able to support himself while taking sights. So he knelt in the stern while McCarthy and Vincent held him tightly around the waist.

The navigation books had been soaked by the sea, and their pages had to be peeled carefully apart. If Worsley made a mistake they would certainly miss the island. And beyond South Georgia the South Atlantic Ocean is empty for three thousand miles.

They thought that they were now getting close. Their last position showed that the western tip of South Georgia lay only ninety-one miles away. Soon there should be signs of land — seaweed or a piece of driftwood. But there were none that night, or the following day.

By the evening of May 7, they were becoming anxious. They should have been only a few miles off the coast, though Worsley's calculations were admittedly rough. The men peered into the darkness with salt-rimmed eyes, looking for the shadowy outline of a cliff, straining their ears for the sound of pounding surf. They saw only foggy mists, heard only the sea, and the wind moaning through the stays.

Dawn came, and still no trace of land. At eight o'clock, Shackleton's watch was due to take over. But nobody thought about keeping watches. Instead they all crowded into the cockpit, searching, hoping, fearing.

At ten thirty Vincent spotted a clump of seaweed, and at twelve thirty, when the fog began to lift, McCarthy called out, "Land!"

And there it was. A black, frowning cliff ahead, with patches of snow clinging to its sides. They could just see it between the clouds, about ten miles away.

Shackleton was the only one who spoke. "We've done it," he said, and his voice was unsteady.

A Bitter Blow

By two thirty the *Caird* was only three miles off the coast. They could see patches of green lichen and grass on the headlands — the first growing things they had seen for over sixteen months. As they drew closer, however, the deep rumbling sound of breakers reached them. Presently they could see great, seething waves hurtling against uncharted reefs.

Although the shore lay so near, they could not possibly land there. The boat would not have lived for ten seconds in such breakers.

At three ten Shackleton gave the order to turn about. They headed out to sea again. They would lay off until morning, hoping that then they might be able to find a way through the reefs. Hardly a man spoke as each one fought down his disappointment.

Their plight was soon to become far worse, however. A violent storm arose, which lasted all night, all day, and all the next night. Winds blew at eighty miles an hour.

To prepare food was impossible, but they didn't want it anyway. They had used up all but about a pint of their fresh water. Their tongues were swollen with thirst, their lips were cracked and bleeding.

At last the gale ceased. South Georgia came into view again, and they began seeking a place to land. The wind died away so completely that they had to row themselves closer to find a safe passage through the reefs. Once inside, they spotted a small cove with a beach.

It was five o'clock in the afternoon of May 10, 1916, when the *Caird's* keel finally ground against the shore.

Overland

Unluckily, they were on the wrong side of the island. The four whaling stations, and the only human beings, were on the opposite coast. By sea, it was a hundred and fifty miles away. And the *Caird* was now hardly fit for the journey.

That left only one thing to do; they must cross the island. The distance overland was only twenty-nine miles, but the interior of South Georgia is a mass of jagged mountains and glaciers. Nobody had ever crossed it.

But Shackleton told the party that he and Worsley and Tom Crean would make the attempt. For eight days they rested, while they waited for a full moon and the best possible weather. Then, in the early hours of May 19, the three of them set out.

First came an exhausting climb that ended in a range of four small mountains — like the knuckles of a tightly clenched fist. It took the men seven hours to reach the first of these summits, only to discover that on the other side of it there was a sheer drop of at least fifteen hundred feet.

For five hours they worked their way along the sides of the ridges, looking for a way down. Darkness began to fall; and a thick fog was creeping in, threatening to blot out everything. It looked as if they would be trapped, blinded and helpless, on top of the razorback. Furthermore, for the sake of speed, they had brought neither sleeping bags nor tents. They would have to get lower, or freeze to death.

A Mad Idea

Working furiously, Shackleton began to cut steps down the face of the cliff with an axe. But after thirty minutes he stopped short, realizing that it was useless. He called the others and said it was vital that they get lower — and with all possible haste.

So he suggested that they slide. Worsley and Crean were stunned — especially at such a mad idea coming from Shackleton, who never took an unnecessary risk. But he wasn't joking; he wasn't even smiling.

"What if we hit a rock?" Crean asked. "Or if there's another precipice?"

But Shackleton's mind was made up. "Can we stay where we are?" he asked impatiently.

Obviously they could not, and so the decision was made. Shackleton said they would slide as one man, holding onto each other.

Quickly they sat down and untied the rope that held them together. Each of them coiled up his share to form a mat. Worsley locked his legs around Shackleton's waist and put his arms around Shackleton's neck. Crean did the same with Worsley.

Shackleton allowed no time for second thoughts. And just as soon as they were ready he kicked off.

Down ... Down ...

In the next instant their hearts stopped beating. They seemed to hang poised for a split second; then the wind was shrieking in their ears, and a white blur of snow tore past. Down . . . down . . . faster and faster!

A hundred seconds later they shot forward onto the level. Their speed slackened, and then they came to a sudden halt in a snowbank. They'd done it!

The three men picked themselves up. They were breathless and their hearts were beating wildly. But they found themselves laughing till they couldn't stop. What had been a terrifying thought only two minutes before had now become an exciting adventure.

They looked up toward the darkening sky, and saw the fog curling over the edge of the ridges far above them. Then they felt that special kind of pride, of a person who takes an impossible dare — and pulls it off beautifully.

But the journey was far from over. They had covered only nine of the twenty-nine miles they had to go.

In front of them was a weary four-thousand-foot climb, and another range of ridges. Next they went down a snowy cliff almost as steep as a church steeple. Finally they had to drop through an icy waterfall — through which they lowered themselves with their rope.

Never once were they sure that they would make it. But they were kept going by the hope that they would soon be among friends. The *Endurance* had spent a month at South Georgia on her way to the Antarctic. Shackleton and the others had come to know the men at the whaling stations well.

At seven in the morning, when they had been on the trail for twenty-seven hours, they heard a sound which sent their spirits soaring. It was the first sound from the outside world that they had heard for seventeen months. Shackleton had just climbed a small summit to look ahead, when he was startled to hear what he thought was a steam whistle. He gathered the others around him to listen anxiously.

Then through the thin, cold air, the second hoot of the factory whistle at Stromness Whaling Station reached their ears. They looked at one another and smiled. Then, without speaking, they all shook hands.

Three Strangers

At four o'clock that afternoon, the station foreman at Stromness was helping some men to unload boats at the dock. Something caused him to look up, and he was surprised to see the figures of three men walking slowly toward him. They were strangers, and obviously bowed down with weariness. He was puzzled because they were not coming from the docks, where a ship might have put in. They were coming from the mountains, from the interior of the island.

As they drew closer he saw that they were heavily bearded. Their hair was long and matted. And their clothing was peculiar, too. It was not the sweaters and boots worn by seamen. The three men seemed to have on the loose parkas that explorers wore. But it was hard to tell because the clothes were so filthy and torn.

As he stepped forward to meet the strangers, one of them spoke to him softly in English.

"Would you please take us to Anton Andersen?" he said.

The foreman shook his head. Anton Andersen was no longer station manager at Stromness, he explained. He had been replaced more than a year before by Thoralf Sørlie.

The Englishman smiled. "Good," he said. "I know Sørlie well."

The foreman then led the way to Sørlie's house and knocked at the door. It was opened by Sørlie himself.

When he saw the three men, he stepped back. A look of disbelief came over his face. For a moment he seemed too shocked to speak.

"Who on earth are you?" he said at last.

"My name is Shackleton," replied a quiet voice.

Rescue

That night, after a hearty dinner, Worsley boarded a whaling ship and set out for the other side of the island. There he picked up the three men they had left behind on the beach.

Nor did Shackleton waste a moment. He managed to borrow a large wooden whaling ship, the *Southern Sky,* in which to return to Elephant Island and rescue the twenty-two castaways there. She set sail forty-eight hours later.

Three days out, however, the *Southern Sky* ran into ice. Although Shackleton tried desperately hard to find a way through, they never got closer than seventy miles to Elephant Island. A shortage of fuel forced them to put in to the Falkland Islands.

After two more unsuccessful attempts, Shackleton set out in the *Yelcho,* an old seagoing tug lent by the government of Chile. This time the ice let them through.

On August 30 Worsley wrote in his log:

"11.10 . . . land faintly visible.

"1.10 p.m. Sighted the Camp to SW.

"1.20 Stopped & sent boat in. 3 cheers from shore to Sir E. . . .

"2.10 All our 22 men aboard, once more we are complete."

The rescued men, who had been waiting four months and five days since the *Caird* set out, were surprisingly well. They had made themselves a hut by turning the two boats upside down. Most of their food supplies had run out, and they had lived mainly on penguins. But their spirits had remained high.

Shackleton's feat in saving every man in his expedition is the most extraordinary in polar history. He had set out to cross the Antarctic Continent on foot. What he did instead was far braver and more remarkable.

ANSWERS TO QUIZZLES

ONE

(*See pages 8 and 9*)

THE LAZY ARTIST

(A) Two people arguing **(B)** Mexican frying an egg **(C)** Snake going upstairs **(D)** Bubblegum champion **(E)** Fat lady scrubbing the floor.

PUZZLING PARAGRAPH

The most common letter in the English language is the letter *e*. There is not a single *e* in the Puzzling Paragraph.

COPY THE DRAWINGS

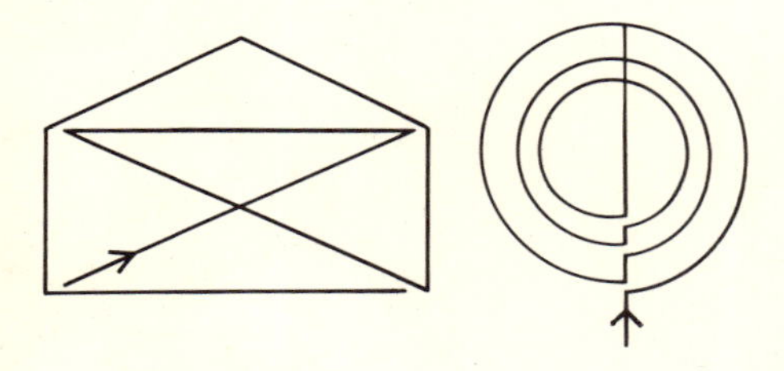

HOW MANY EYES?

Twelve. Each jack has two heads!

HOW IS IT DONE?

The second time you drop the penny, pick it up with your left hand and only pretend to pass it over to your right. Your audience will by now be used to your dropping the coin and picking it up again.

BAFFLING CIRCLES

2 and **3**

TWO

(*See pages 86 and 87*)

CAN YOU SEE STRAIGHT?

They are *all* parallel.

THE MAGIC SQUARE

2	9	4
7	5	3
6	1	8

WORDS WITHIN WORDS

2. Custard
3. Feather
4. Mislead
5. Neatest
6. Menaced

LEAP-SHEEP

When the black leader had jumped over the white leader, the second black sheep moved into his space, and the first and second white sheep jumped forward. Then the third white sheep moved into the new gap and the first three black sheep jumped forward. Then the fourth black sheep moved forward and all the white sheep could jump forward to freedom.

AUNT EMILY LIKES—

Aunt Emily dislikes anything that contains the letter *t*.

HOW FIRM ARE YOUR FISTS?

When you place your fists one on top of the other, grip the thumb of the lower hand in the hand that is on top. It will take a lot more than two fingers to shift your fists.